GINETTE ASHKI

Thracian Princess

PORTRAIT OF A YOUNG WOMAN IN EXTRAORDINARY TIMES

Ж

Studio 12 Books
Queens Park
London

First Published December 2009
by Studio 12 Books

A CIP record of this title is available
from the British Library
ISBN 978-0-9564063-0-9

Ж

Studio12 Books
Queens Park
London NW6 6TS
UK
www.thracianprincess.com

*Printed and bound in England by CPI Antony Rowe,
Chippenham, Wiltshire*

ABOUT THE AUTHOR

GINETTE ASHKENAZY lives and works in Queens Park, London. She is an artist and sculptor as well as a writer. She was born in Bulgaria in 1932. In 1950 she emigrated with her parents to Israel. In 1967 she moved to London. Her life story is the armature on which **Thracian Princess** is sculpted.

DEDICATION

This book is dedicated, with my heartfelt thanks,
to Elizabeth Spillius who understood immediately;
to Dr. Elinor Wedeles who not only understood,
but spent many hours helping me through the maze
of my emotional problems and didn't give up until
I came out safely at the other end of my tunnel.
To my husband, Josh Kutchinsky, who gave me,
and still does, his unreserved love and support,
both with this book and my art,
and last but by no means least to my friend
M. Patrice Guiffray without whose enthusiasm and
encouragement, the manuscript of this book would
still be in the loft, on 600 pages
typed on my old Olivetti portable.

The late E.A. Markham wrote about Ginette Ashkenazy

'Her early life, like that of so many others was disrupted by the turmoil of war and took place under the shadow of terrifying world events. For a variety of reasons, she has been exposed to a number of cultural influences. She has studied in Bulgaria, Israel, England and France.

Her artistic drive has found various means of expression - textile design, batik work, acting, writing, painting and sculpture. She is a keen Chinese martial arts practitioner.

Naturally left handed she was forced, as a child, to use her right hand, as was the custom at the time. However, much later, in adult life, she accidentally broke her right wrist, forcing her – for a while – to use only her left hand. This enforced engagement with her dormant, but naturally dominant left side, released a flow of focussed artistic creativity. In her paintings, and increasingly with her sculpture, she expresses her life experiences with a deceptive simplicity. Her use of colour and texture in her painting is exciting and masterful. Her sculptures explore convincingly and with great inventiveness the potential of different materials with which she works.

It has been a delight to observe this development and growth.'

Prof. E.A Markham,
Hallam Sheffield University, Faculty of Creative writing

BOOK ONE

Chapter One

The Culture Day Parade

The dainty brush ran along the eye-lashes expertly guided by the hand. The swift, sharp movements started at the roots and ran up towards the ends. One eye was half shut whilst the other looked intently in the mirror. I was fascinated.

'Don't look at me like that!'

My mother's voice startled me. I tried to look away, my head turning round, but my eyes still lingering behind. She was such an extraordinary woman, my mother and so beautiful.

The sun, coming in through the window-pane, made a luminous patch on the plush table cloth. In its rays I could see thousands of dust specks performing a wild dance. I made a vague gesture and watched all the specks suddenly changing direction as though attempting to run away. I wondered where they thought they were going. I knew they weren't going anywhere; they were trapped in this room.

'Stop jumping around,' my mother's eyes were still on the mirror, 'You will mess up your dress.'

I was aware of my father struggling with his tie, his face closed and distant. I was not allowed to talk to him in the morning; it irritated him and although today was different, I felt I still shouldn't talk to him.

I was wearing new shoes. They were black patent leather with a strap and a button across the front. I looked at them lovingly. How shiny they were! I knew they were perfectly clean but I rubbed them one after the other against the back of my white knee-length socks, just in case.

'Stop this nonsense,' said my mother, taking me once again by surprise. How could she possibly see me, when she had one eye closed and the other busy with her make-up? She always knew what I was doing. Even when she wasn't in the same room. She would come in and say: 'You have touched the books again' or 'You have been sitting on the settee, and you know you mustn't, before you have changed.' I never quite understood how she managed it. I loved my mother very much. She was so beautiful! But sometimes I felt I just wanted to be left alone, not to be followed and 'found out'. Well, she didn't follow me, not really, but she could read me. She took one look at me, and there it was, she knew. But today none of this mattered. We were getting ready to go out. My father hadn't gone to his office and the maid had the day off.

It was a holiday. The 24th of May is Culture Day celebrating the birth of the twin brothers, Cyril and Methody, who had given us our alphabet; the Cyrillic Alphabet. I knew all this although I wasn't yet at school.

This morning, for the first time, my parents were taking me to see the parade. All school children, dressed in navy and white uniforms and waving the national white, green and red flag, were to parade through the main streets of Sofia and outside the Tzar's Palace where He and His Family would smile and wave back at them. The older children would be playing national songs and marches and the younger children would be singing.

This was the first 24th of May parade I would see and next year I was to be part of it! I would wear the uniform of the French School with a black velvet beret with a golden fleur-de-lys in the front. How I longed for that day to come!

'You are not to ask for anything!' said my father.

But surely he knew that I was a good girl. I would never hang onto his arm begging for sweets and chewing gum or lollipops, like my cousins Mira and Yani who were really unbearable and got smacked ever so often. Not me, I always walked straight and didn't ask annoying questions or interrupt my mother when she was talking. All I wanted was to feel her hand gripping mine.

Soon we were ready. My mother took my hand and we walked down the stairs. We lived in a first floor flat on a street where the trams went zooming by, always clanging their bells as they approached the crossroads. There was a newspaper stand on one corner. I knew it because this was the only place I was allowed to go to on my own – to fetch my father's paper.

'Stop pulling me back,' my mother said and I had to look ahead and try to keep up with her.

We didn't have far to walk to arrive at the street where the parade was scheduled to pass. As we walked, we could hear in the distance the sound of the schools' orchestras, children's voices and, most of all, the cheering of the public. As we passed open windows we could hear the radios of those who chose to stay at home.

' ... and now, in their crisp uniforms, here come the lovely girls of the 1st Girls' Gymnasium ... '

I was terribly impatient to get there and see for myself, so I tried to run ahead, but my father's voice made me freeze.

'Stop this nonsense and don't get so excited!'

Finally we reached Maria Louisa Avenue and found a slight

clearing in the crowd where we could squeeze in. We stood there for quite a while before we heard the music and then, finally, I saw them. All girls, neatly dressed, singing and waving small flags. Oh, how I wanted to be there with them, to be one of them! I started to cheer at the top of my voice. I clapped my hands and jumped up and down. But not for long. My father's fingers gripped my shoulder and hurt me. I froze, and tears pushed through, but a large lump in my throat didn't allow them to stream off my hurting eyes.

'Stop it! Do you hear me!'

I stopped it, quite unable to speak because of the lump in my throat. The stream of school children continued. They sang and played their instruments beautifully. The people around us went out of their way to cheer. Some of the cheers were personal: 'Bravo Annie!' or 'Well done Maria!' and 'Bravo Vanya!' We watched quietly.

Multicoloured confetti flew in the warm spring air and many people joined in the singing. The older children looked so smart in their navy skirts. I looked at them with envy in my heart. I didn't really know what I envied. Maybe it was just the fact that they were older. There were so many things I was told I couldn't do because I was a mere child. To be grown up would mean to be free from the chains of childhood.

Chapter Two

My Friend Misho

Misho was a small boy with whom I was allowed to play. His hair, almost white at the roots, turned yellow at the ends.

I remember his slender face and blue eyes. I also recall that the fact that he was a boy made no difference. I could play with him a lot better than with my cousin,Yani. As for Mira, she was a girl, but she was also just a baby and didn't really count. But Yani who was my age, always wanted to go to war, and I had to get the meals ready for when he returned. So we ended up, him 'at war' in one corner of the room and me 'at home' in the other.

With Misho, it was different. We pretended we went places together and he was always showing me around. Misho's family lived on the same landing and his father was a doctor. His mother wasn't 'sophisticated' at all. She always wore an apron and I remember her brown hair gathered on her neck, some of it hanging untidily down. She was plump and always held her hand in a fist with the thumb tucked in. I was fascinated by this fist, which was not aggressive, and I quite liked sitting on her lap. Her name was Nora. I called her Auntie Nora. She was soft and smiled often. She didn't mind it when Misho and I got a little turbulent and made a mess. My mother used to say that she wasn't much of a housewife. When we played at our place, my mother expected me not to allow any mess, let alone partake in making it.

Life on the whole wouldn't have been so miserable if only I could eat. If only I could once feel what it was like to be hungry and eat everything that was on my plate like others did. Like Yani and Misho did, even little Mira did. But no, I couldn't eat; I couldn't swallow anything, and my mother had to sit by me and feed me for hours and hours on end. She was marvellous about it. She never lost her temper and I tried so hard to swallow. Only occasionally she would pinch my thigh in desperation – it was always bruised on the side where she sat.

Occasionally we played over at Misho's and Auntie Nora gave us lunch. I simply forgot about not being able to swallow and when Auntie Nora told my mother that I had had my meal, my mother reproached me for being so cruel and breaking her heart and never pleasing her by eating as I seemed to be able to do for others. Time and again I promised myself that I would eat because really I didn't want my mother's heart broken. On occasions like this I actually 'saw' in anticipation, the lovely approving smile my mother would give me.

Auntie Amelia, Yani's mother, was short – I could tell even from my height because she was so much shorter than my mother – and she was plump. But she had the largest green eyes possible and they had lights in them. She didn't smile, she laughed. What a laugh she had, like little bells! And I wanted so much to be her friend. I wanted to look at her, the way she talked waving her hand with her long manicured nails, and to listen to her voice. But this was impossible because she didn't like children and whenever we went there, or they came over to us, she would say: 'The children – in the kitchen!', but even that sounded like a song.

Uncle Dori, her husband, was the one all the kids were afraid of. He was a huge man. He was taller than anyone I had ever seen and he had to bend down to come in through the doorway. He used to beat Yani very cruelly with a stick. Uncle Dori made me shudder.

Mira's mother was Auntie Amelia's sister and also my mother's first cousin. She had a strange way of walking, a sort of waddle. Mira's father was the fattest man in the world. He had a good round face and he liked children. He didn't make us leave the room when we were at their place and he found us playing. He would say something to each one of us. His phrase for me was always: 'Aaaaaaahhh, when are you going to learn how to eat your dinner eh?' to which I had nothing to reply and just smiled.

The families would visit each other usually in the evenings and almost always on Sundays for lunch. In the summer we would all go to the country for the day and that meant journeys on trams which I enjoyed very much.

Chapter Three

Where has Misho Gone?

I was looking out through the window one morning. My mother had just finished feeding me. Breakfast, as usual, had been painfully long. I was going to play with Misho that morning but until he came over, I just looked out at the rain. I was looking at the shiny cobble stones as I heard my mother say to me:

'Misho is not coming round today.'

'Why?' I asked

'He is not very well.'

I slipped down from the chair, went over to where my doll was and began preparing her for her bath. I remembered how I once overheard my mother saying to auntie Amelia: 'She is ever so good at keeping herself occupied.' This had sounded to me as though she was describing a virtue, and I had wondered whether my being a 'bad eater' was not redeemed by this virtue. But somehow I could never bring myself to ask.

Misho didn't come to play the next day either. In the night, I woke up and saw my mother coming in. I slept in the same room as my parents and I obviously had not heard her leave the room. She had her dressing gown wrapped around her and I heard her whisper to my father:

' ... been taken to hospital.'

There was something very frightening about these words. I sat up and asked who had been taken to hospital.

'Shhhh', said my mother, 'go to sleep.'

What was a hospital? Why wouldn't they tell me? How would I ever learn anything? I lay on my bed, the bedclothes to my chin. My father switched the light off and all went quiet. Both my parents were here. Then who could it be that had been taken to hospital? I must have fallen asleep, because loud screams woke me up. My mother was at the door. She saw I was awake and said:

'Stay where you are! Don't move!'

I recognised auntie Nora's voice outside, crying, and I knew that it had to do with Misho. She wouldn't just cry like this in the middle of the night. Misho must have fallen or hurt himself badly. My heart was pounding as I listened; my mother came in and told my father:

'He's gone. It was croup and he suffocated on the way to hospital.'

I remember crying, alarmed by all these unknown threatening words. I wanted to get up and run to my mother. I wanted her to hold me.

'For goodness' sake you stay where you are,' my mother said.

'Please, please!' I was crying. 'Who has gone? Where? Is it Misho? It is Misho, isn't it? Where is he?'

My mother sat on my bed and took me in her arms.

'Stop crying now. Misho has ... gone away ... for a while ... ' and she was crying too.

For a day or two everybody seemed to be talking quietly and walking on tip-toes. I was not allowed out of the flat, alone or otherwise. Not even to get my father's paper. I looked at my mother's face, which remained closed to me, and asked no questions, probably knowing that I would not get an answer.

One day suddenly I found myself face to face with Auntie

Nora. She picked me up and held me tight. She wasn't crying but I could feel her shaking. Then, she held me away from her and said:

'No more Misho, my child, no more Misho.'

'Why?' I asked the burning question: 'Why? Where has he gone?'

'He has gone my love,' she said quietly, 'He has left us for good. He died.'

I was put down bewildered and frightened, not daring to ask further. That night I heard my parents talking in the darkness of the bedroom.

'It's impossible … ' my mother was saying and my father seemed to agree.

Soon afterwards, we moved flats, and I never saw Auntie Nora again.

Chapter Four

Birth of a Prince – Kira's Confidences

Our new flat was situated on the third floor of a very large block of flats called Moskovitch Mansions. There was an enclosed, paved space which was a safe playground for the children. It had a little round green in the middle with some benches where, in the afternoon, mothers often sat, watching the children playing and waiting for their husbands to come home. Strict rules were rigidly enforced by the caretakers – a German couple by the strange name of Mr. and Mrs. Tseck. We were all afraid of Mrs. Tseck who, if anybody dared linger in the yard after 12.30pm or show up before 4pm would shout and run after them on her short wobbly legs. In fact, in all the years we lived there Mrs. Tseck never actually caught anybody.

Here too, we had interesting neighbours on the landing. It was my mother's childhood friend from Shoumen, where they were both born, and her family. Aunt Rachel had two daughters. The eldest, Elise, was my senior by a year. She went to the French school and I respected her for it. Aunt Rachel was a very thin woman with short, curly hair. She chain-smoked in a very strange manner, like a man perhaps. They always had visitors and, not used to this, I was drawn to their flat, where things were not so meticulously kept in their places and where meals seemed to be a casual affair.

One night, soon alter we moved in, a terrific noise woke me up. I sat up in bed, frightened, and saw my mother standing by the window counting what seemed to be gun-shots. Suddenly she shouted:

'It's a boy! It's a boy! We have an heir!'

'What is an heir?' I asked.

'A prince! Our Queen has given birth to a baby boy who is a prince and will be king when he grows up. His name will be King Simeon, but he is Prince Simeon now.'

I wondered for a long time how can a baby be a Prince. A prince to me, was a handsome young man who kisses princesses out of eternal sleep.

Our maid's name was Kira. The kitchen was her domain. The kitchen was used during the day as a sitting room; at night it was Kira's bedroom. She would get up early and light the fire in the large stove, filling it with coal which she brought up from the cellar where it was stored. By the time we got up, the kitchen would be warm and the milk boiled. Kira was a peasant girl and her father came occasionally to the city to visit her. I still remember the smell he spread around him. My mother explained that this was the smell of stables, manure and generally, the farm.

One Sunday night, my parents were out and I had gone to bed when Kira came into the bedroom. I remember sitting up in my pyjamas, my legs folded under me, expecting Kira to tell me a story but instead, she sat on my parents' bed, which faced mine, and asked:

'Do you know what men do to women?'

'Nnno,' I said not knowing what she meant.

'Well, haven't you ever heard your parents? You sleep in the same room!'

'What's that got to do with it? What do they do? Tell me!'

'I was with Stephen this afternoon ... ' she said dreamily.

'Who is that? I thought you went out with a girl from your village?'

'Stephen is a man … a soldier. He is also from my village.'

'And your girlfriend?'

'She sometimes comes with her boyfriend.'

'And?'

'What 'And?'. We fuck, don't you know?'

'What?'

'Oh, you know nothing then,' she said quite disappointed by my ignorance.

'Tell me, please!' I pleaded, my curiosity aroused, my heart pounding.

'We … make love … we screw … oh, well, men … they have something there … and they lie on you … and they put it … in there … ' She was pointing out where it all happened. I looked at her, speechless.

'Tell me more!'

'I was with him … he did it to me this afternoon … in the cellar.'

'The cellar?'

'Yes, here, under the flats. It's the safest place. I lie down and he comes on top of me and … oh, it's lovely!' She was staring at some point on the ceiling, 'At first my friend and her boyfriend kept watch while we were doing it, then we watched out for them, in case anybody should come down. But they don't, not on Sunday.'

'*My* mother doesn't do things like THAT!' I shouted.

'Sure she does. Everybody does,' she said with conviction, 'Stephen told me. He knows a lot, he does. Everybody does it, but they don't like to talk about it.'

'Why not?'

'Because it's forbidden, that's why.'

'Is that why you tell my mother you are with a girl friend?'

'Yes. You won't tell her, will you? Oh, it was so good today,

I just had to tell you.'

'My father does not do things like that to my mother!' I cried and my throat went tight with fear, disgust and anxiety.

'He does. He does,' Kira insisted.

I felt sick, sick and disgusted with her.

'Go to sleep now and promise not to tell,' she said.

'I promise.'

I slipped under the bedclothes and she left the room.

From that night on, I became somehow estranged from my beautiful mother. I couldn't believe that she could secretly do forbidden, shameful things. And at my father I looked with disgust that he might do 'things like that' to her. Also, I was looking 'there' to find out whether I could see anything 'long' that might confirm Kira's statement. I saw nothing. I found it difficult to sleep at night and lay for long hours listening to hear any signs of aggressive activity. I did hear some movement at some point, but they appeared to be talking about 'something' that could or should not be done without 'something'.

'You know it's dangerous,' my mother was saying and my father mumbled something in reply. My stomach tightened. I felt sick and on the following morning declared that I wanted to sleep in the other room.

My mother's reaction was one of incredulity. She said I didn't know what I was talking about. That children are afraid of the dark and whereas other parents force their children to sleep in separate rooms, I should consider myself lucky that they still kept me in their room. Eventually I won the argument and was transferred to the lounge where I slept on the divan. Once on my own, I couldn't stop thinking about 'that' and one day spoke about it to my playmates.

'Of course!' said Yani, 'didn't you know?'

'No.'

'Haven't you seen?'

'What?'

'Them – your folks?'

'SEEN THEM?' I was appalled. 'Of course not!' and then: 'Well, I have tried to hear something at night, when I used to sleep in their bedroom, but ... nothing. I think they don't do it at all.'

'Rubbish. Of course they do. Have you seen your old man?'

'How do you mean 'seen'?'

'Seen his thing?'

'NO!'

'Do you want me to show you?'

Of course, I had forgotten that Yani was a boy.

'Yes, please.'

'OK, come here so we can't be seen from the door, in case my old woman peeps in.' We were at their flat. He unbuttoned his trousers quickly. I was looking fascinated. Before I could see anything, the door opened and my mother walked in. She stopped, took one look at me and she knew.

This is how clever she was. I felt I would gladly let myself be swallowed by the ground, if only it would be merciful enough and open up for me!

'Come here,' she ordered in an icy voice. She took me by the hand, her lips tight. She was pale and distant. She made me put my coat on and we went home. As soon as we got there, she ordered me to my room. I went in, shaking. I heard the front door open and shut, then some voices, then my father walked in. His hair looked blacker than usual, his moustache thicker and bigger, and his eyes were flaring terrible lights at me.

'Go to the wall!' he ordered. I obeyed.

'On your knees! Face the wall!' I obeyed again and he left the room. Not a word was spoken,. I don't remember how long I stayed there, my legs numb, my eyes stinging with tears that didn't come.

Chapter Five

Did We Kill Jesus?

As the time was nearing for me to go to school, I overheard my parents talking about not sending me to the French School. I didn't dare say anything for a while. I thought I might be mistaken and decided to wait.

It was at this time that a strange incident occurred. I was playing with a girl who lived in the same block and whom I had known ever since we moved there. She behaved in a strange way, throwing the ball away rather than passing it on to me. Then she suddenly said:

'I don't like Jews.' and walked away. I was puzzled and worried. I felt that this statement was aggressive and that it should hurt me, but I didn't know what it meant. I felt more puzzled than hurt. I ran home and asked my mother:

'Mummy, what are Jews?' and then, 'Are we Jews?'

'Yes' my mother said. Now I felt hurt. The girl had told me she disliked Jews. I was a Jew therefore she disliked me too. I felt rejected and humiliated. What had I done wrong to be disliked?

'Mummy, what does it mean? What does it mean?'

'Go and wash your hands now, daddy will be home soon.'

'But tell me, what does it mean to be Jews?'

'Stop pestering me and do as you are told!'

At dinner I asked my father but was told I shouldn't talk while eating and my question remained unanswered. That same afternoon, Kira, our maid, took me to the park and as we turned a corner on our way there, we came to a small garden square where a lot of people were gathered and a man, standing on something which made him stand high above the others, was shouting into a microphone. Kira took hold of my hand firmly and we turned back, but as we were walking away, the words the man was shouting followed us:

' ... our enemies, the Jews!'

I felt the same painful humiliation and wondered whether Kira was a Jew too.

We were nearly running now. When we slowed down a little I asked:

'Kira, please tell me, what is it to be a Jew?'

'The Jews killed Jesus,' was her brief answer.

'Who is Jesus?'

'Our God.'

I was terrified. Had my father killed God then?

'Kira, who killed God?' I insisted.

'The Jews,' she said, 'They killed the son of God. Jesus was the son of God.'

We returned home. My mother had gone out and I sat in the kitchen with Kira. It seemed to me that a man can only be killed by one man. I was afraid to talk further, because then Kira might also hate me if she felt that my father was responsible for that murder. All the same I had to know more.

'Are you a Jew, Kira?' I asked. She shook her head.

'Do you hate me?' She shrugged her shoulders and said:

'I don't know any more.' She was drying some washing-up

and a glass slipped through her fingers and fell on the floor and broke …

'Oh, my God!' cried Kira, 'Madame will be angry now and she will tell my father! I will never find another job if she writes it in my reference book!'

Kira was on all fours gathering the pieces of glass, when my mother came in. True to her knack of always coming in at the crucial moment. I remember Kira's frightened face. I looked up at my mother and without thinking said:

'I broke a glass, mummy.' Surprisingly she didn't scold me too much and Kira gave me a long warm look.

The question about the Jews was still bothering me, so later at table I ventured to ask again.

'What is it to be Jews?'

'We are not Christians. That's what it is,' my mother said.

'I told you to teach the child about that ages ago,' my father reproached her, 'but being a pagan yourself, obviously you haven't bothered.' He then turned to me:

'You must be proud that you are Jewish. We are the chosen people. What made you ask anyway?

'This morning Helen said she hated Jews.'

'You see,' my father turned to my mother again,' we have to send her to the Jewish school. At that Catholic school she will be even more discriminated against.'

'Yes,' said my mother, 'you are right. God knows what the future holds for us.'

These words frightened me very much.

'I don't want to go to the Jewish school,' I said, 'Why should I? Elise goes to the French school! So should I.'

My mother turned to me:

'We don't know what is going to happen, but it is safer for Jewish children to go to a Jewish school. You won't feel the discrimination there.'

'What is discrimination?'

'Remember what Helen said to you this morning? That is discrimination.'

'But I haven't done anything! Dad hasn't done anything! You haven't done anything either!'

'This is it. We haven't done anything but they hate us. This is discrimination.'

It was one of the longest conversations my parents had had with me. I didn't dare continue asking questions, for fear of being sent away.

I asked Elise when I saw her.

'What is Catholic?'

'The nuns at my school are Catholic,' she said, 'They believe in God, in Christ the Divine Creation.'

'And we have killed their God, is that it?'

'No. It's worse than that. We didn't kill him, we gave him away. At least one of 'us' did. He was hiding and we told where. So he was caught and crucified.'

This sounded so horrible. I was dumbfounded and at the same time full of admiration for Elise. She knew so much! She looked at me suddenly and said:

'Are you in love with Michael?'

'Yes,' I said not really knowing why.

'So am I,' she whispered, 'But let's not tell him. OK?'

'OK.'

I felt flattered at being taken into a secret of hers. From that time on, I observed that when we played in the yard, she would always tease him, pull his clothes and generally treat him badly. I questioned her about this and she said:

'You don't want to show a boy that you are in love with him. You try and hide it the best you can.'

Chapter Six

Why Didn't My Mother Come To Fetch Me?

For a long while, Kira had been the only person who would talk to me, really sit and talk, and when she suddenly left, I felt I had lost my only companion. I wasn't told the actual reason for her leaving, but I understood that Bulgarians were not supposed to be servants to Jews. What surprised me was the fact that Kira had been our servant. I felt hurt that she should be called that and protested to my mother:

'Surely Kira is not a servant?'

'No. She was our 'help',' my mother answered.

I couldn't see the difference.

The great event of that year was to have been my starting school. This was turned instead into a miserable experience, since I had to go to the Jewish school which I just couldn't take seriously. I could by then read and write and the little dark haired man with his briefcase and spectacles had nothing to teach me. None of the children were very interesting, except for one of the boys who took to looking after me. His name was Jacques. My mother used to take me to school and pick me up as well. My assurances that I could manage on my own, were to no avail. I begged and pleaded with her but she said I was too young and irresponsible and could not be trusted with the hazardous business of crossing two major roads.

Another problem with me now was that I was taking my pencil in my left hand. I always reached with my left hand. I didn't know I was doing it. I didn't know it was in any way different to everybody else. My mother said in that determined voice of hers:

'I will cure you of this! My daughter is not going to be crippled.'

When she brought me home from school, she ordered me to sit on the chair and put my left hand behind my back. I did. She then took a long belt and tied it around me in such a way that my left arm was completely stuck to my back. My note-book was in front of me on the table as I sat on a few cushions; my pencil was in front of me and my homework was to fill two pages with letters – one lower case, the other capitals. I knew how to read and write. I did not know how to use the only available hand. A lump in my throat and tears running down my cheeks, egged on by her, I picked up the pencil.

Ж

I was most surprised when one day she did not come for me! I looked and looked for her until I was certain that she hadn't come and once I was really convinced of the fact, I felt, the World belonged to me. It was challenging me. I was going to take things in my own hands. I was going home on my own. Then Jacques spotted me, came up to me and offered to walk me home.

'I know!' I said, 'You too! You also think I can't be trusted!'

'No, no,' he assured me, 'I simply want to walk with you'.

'Won't you be late home and worry your mother?'

'She won't even notice.'

I envied him this freedom of a quarter of an hour with which he could do as he pleased. I declined his offer, however, and started my journey, looking carefully as I crossed the roads. I met Aunt Rachel when I was half way home. She was running to meet me.

'Where is my mother?' I asked.

'She is not very well,' was the short answer. Aunt Rachel took my hand and we walked the rest of the way in silence. I found my father at home with Auntie Amelia and a doctor. My mother was lying on her bed. She was very pale and her eyes were shut. I made towards her but Aunt Amelia stopped me.

'Mummy! Mummy!' I called out, but got no response. I wanted to shake her, make her look at me, talk to me. But Auntie Amelia's hand firmly led me out the room and into the kitchen where I was told to stay. I sat on the divan and listened to the muffled sounds coming from the bedroom. Tears were running down my cheeks. I felt my World sinking. My mother had left me and nobody cared. Later that afternoon she got up. I looked at her carefully and threw myself on her. She held me to her for a while and then pushed me aside. She was very tired and had to rest. Aunt Rachel came for me and I had dinner at their place. Aunt Rachel took a tray in for my parents. My mother appeared to be getting better when suddenly it happened again. She fainted. The doctor came. Everybody came and I was ushered next door. I was too worried to play with Elise and her little sister, so I sat and did nothing.

The kitchen sink was full of unwashed dishes. The floors had got very dirty and no matter how much I insisted on doing the washing up, or cleaning the floors, my mother wouldn't let me. I was too clumsy she said. As for the floor I was bound to make more mess than there already was.

This went on for two or three days. My mother was fainting every few hours. Everybody was in the bedroom and I had to stay over at Elise's. On the night of the third day, I walked back to our flat through the cold landing and listened at the door, but couldn't make any sense of what was being said. It was a very cold December night and it was snowing. Then I heard my father say:

'Enough is enough! I will call someone else.' He tore out of the room, passed me by without noticing me and slammed the front door as he stormed out.

The women were whispering in the bedroom but I could not hear my mother's voice. I crept in, through the dark hallway into the kitchen. The bedroom door opposite had been left ajar.

'She might be right,' Aunt Amelia was saying, 'It might very well be … ' I didn't catch the word, ' … and and if this is the case, well … he better find a doctor or else … I would hate to think.'

'Shhhh … she is coming round again,' whispered Aunt Rachel.

I tiptoed to the door but couldn't see anything. There was a prolonged silence and I thought that I had been found out but then my mother's voice, very quiet and slow, said:

'Where is … ' I didn't hear whether she was asking for me or my father.

'Don't talk my dear,' Aunt Amelia said, 'The doctor will be here soon.'

The doctor? But he was here a few days ago! Why didn't he give her a medicine then? I crept back into the kitchen where the fire had died in the stove. I don't know how long I sat there shivering and crying, but I was sure my mother had died and nothing else mattered. If only she wouldn't die. I am sure I will be able to do the washing up; even light the fire in the kitchen stove! I was making promises: to like my teacher better, to really do my homework, to eat everything on my plate, if only she would live.

Suddenly there was a noise. My father had returned with another man. They went into the bedroom and all was quiet for a little while, then I heard the man's voice:

'How on earth have you let her get into this condition? She has an internal ... I will have to operate immediately and I am not certain of saving her. Quick, give me a hand. There is no time for an ambulance ... We'll take her in my car. You, here is the number, phone my clinic and tell them to prepare for ... ' The man's voice continued to give orders. I remembered some of the words as they were said in the silence of my collapsing world .... I didn't understand what they meant. I only felt what they implied. They took my mother away. I watched them from the darkness of the kitchen. My father was holding her legs, the doctor her shoulders. She was quite lifeless.

I understood much later that she had had an internal haemorrhage and that she had had an extra-uterine pregnancy. I also understood that Bulgarian doctors were not supposed to look after Jewish patients; that the first doctor had been Jewish, but had been unable to establish a diagnosis and that the doctor who had saved her life, had done so against the new rules. He was a Bulgarian.

I lived through some very shattering weeks, staying at Elise's, seeing my father only briefly in the evenings when he came to report on my mother's progress. But in the first few days, when her life was still in danger, I saw him cry and then I felt everything was lost. Slowly my father's face brightened. He started to smile again and my world began to regain some of its light. I went to our flat and washed the floors. They were part painted wood and part parquet which I polished. I washed up the crockery, that had piled up in the sink, without breaking anything at all and I made my mother's bed as she was coming home soon. She had stayed in hospital for over a month. I can still remember her pale hand on the sheets and her sunken cheeks.

Chapter Seven

The 'New Laws'

My mother made a slow recovery. The doctor came to see her often and when he did, we had to leave them alone together in the room. The door always shut behind us as he was lifting the bedclothes and I was terrified that he would hurt her. One day, on my return from school, I saw a yellow notice above the door of our flat. It said in thick black letters: 'Jewish residence.' When I got in, I found my mother sitting up in bed, stitching yellow stars, like buttons, on the lapel of her coat.

'Why?' I asked, 'What is it for?'

'So that it is known that we are Jews.' she said and added quickly, 'Don't ask me any more questions. I am tired. Go and wash your hands, they look filthy.'

Since my mother's operation it was arranged that Jacques would pick me up in the mornings and walk me home after school. His mother didn't mind as they lived quite near us. The yellow notice above the entrance door hurt me, but the yellow star scared me.

'Will I have to wear one too?' I asked

'No,' my mother said, 'You are too young.'

'Does this mean I am not Jewish yet?'

'No, stupid! You are Jewish, but you are too young to wear the star of David.'

Encouraged by this reply, I pushed my luck:

'But Mum, why did you not always wear this star? Why the notice on the door now? Weren't we Jewish before? Why is it NOW so important that we are Jewish?'

'Oh, you are trying! Stop your harassing questions and go and wash your hands.'

'I have.'

'Then go and do your homework.'

I had done it, but there was no room for discussion in her voice and I gave up.

I always listened carefully to my parents' conversation, though when things became important, they spoke French. Nonetheless, I could piece together some of it, and I realised that now, Jews were not allowed in the streets after nine o'clock in the evening.

Since Kira had left, my parents never went out without me. When we did go out, it was for visits to my aunts and of course, we had to come home before 7pm 'à cause de la petite', which of course, meant me. This meant that the 'New Laws' didn't affect my parents very much but with the approach of summer and the lengthening days, they appeared to need a social life 'after nine' and we became frequent visitors next door.

During my stay next door, when my mother was in hospital, I hadn't taken much notice of their way of life, but now that I was happier, I found some differences in their household, which I liked very much. They always seemed to have visitors. On every occasion, we found people sitting around the huge table, snacks were served by Aunt Rachel, there was laughing and talking. They seemed relaxed, happy. We had never had this sort of atmosphere at our place, and what there was, was for adults only.

I sat, bewildered, admiring Elise who dared speak. The adults would listen to her and give her an answer. It was beautiful. But then, she was so clever. Her father, Uncle Samuel, had a shop. He made glasses for short sighted people. He had a strong baritone voice and liked singing. So, as the level of the slivovitz in the bottle went down, his voice became louder. I can still remember the words of a song he sang. It was about a peasant girl pleading with her beloved to come back to her. And he really put a lot of feeling into it. Eventually people would join in, and I would hear my mother's lovely voice, and feel warm and happy. Later, they would gather around the radio covering their heads with a blanket and listen to something forbidden. Radio London, they called it. Eventually the visitors would leave. The Bulgarians could go home. Jews who lived in the block, like us, could also go home, but others who were not allowed in the street after nine, stayed the night.

A strange incident happened at that time. My father had been sent away by his firm, and he was not coming home for the night. My mother and I were having dinner in the kitchen when there was a knock at the door. My mother went to see who it was and left the kitchen door ajar. I heard Aunt Rachel's voice:

'They are after Herzl tonight … he is here … but I can't hide him; they know about us … you must hide him, please! For just one night.'

'Are you out of your mind?' my mother whispered, ' … my, my husband isn't here … '

'Exactly! He would never agree, I know! But you, you sympathise with his views, don't you? After all, your own brother …. '

'No … I daren't. If he ever found me out … why he would …, no, I can't.'

'They will find him, I am telling you! They will torture him.

He has only come down to recruit some more people. They will kill him. Please!'

'Where is he now?'

'Here. Right here.'

My mother shut the kitchen door and I couldn't overhear them any longer, but I understood that a man was hustled into my room that night – I slept with my mother since my father was away – and that my mother got up before dawn. I heard them talking in the kitchen, then he left and my mother returned to bed. It was still dark. I felt that this was a very serious matter and didn't ask any questions. Also, I realised that my father was not told, therefore I never mentioned anything to him. The only thing that struck me about this incident was that my mother had helped somebody who feared for his life.

Chapter Eight

The Jewish Ghetto

One day I went across the landing to Elise's and was sent straight back.

'Beatrice is ill. You can't stay.'

I went back to our flat and the memory of Misho, my little friend who, one day, didn't come to play with me, then died, came to my mind.

'What's wrong with Beatrice?' I asked.

'We don't know yet.' my mother said briefly.

Elise was sent to her grandmother's.

'The symptoms are no more serious than those of ordinary flu,' I heard my mother tell my father over dinner,' but with this epidemic of ... '

I didn't understand the word.

'What's the epidemic of?'

'A children's disease.'

'What is it called?' I insisted.

'It's called 'infantile paralysis'!'

Now, that was difficult!

Some days passed. The doctor was coming twice a day to see little Beatrice, and my mother would get the news from Aunt Rachel over the balcony – this was as near as the women dared approach each other.

'This is it,' she said after a few days, and she was crying, 'she can't move at all ... it's total ... '

I got involved with books and games, but my interest was renewed when Beatrice got better – she wasn't contagious any longer, and we could visit her. I remember her little body, limp and motionless on the bed. It was awful. The Bulgarian doctor still came to see her, risking being struck off for treating a Jewish child.

'Massage and exercise are the main things now,' Aunt Rachel said, 'I will take her for massages until I learn how to do them myself.'

I remember Aunt Rachel, bent over with the heavy little body on her back, for Beatrice had put on weight, going to the clinic. She had to take her on her back, because Jewish people were not allowed to take taxis. Special massages were given to Beatrice's legs, in a bath with an electric current. That sounded frightening. Aunt Rachel would take the child – she must have been about four at the time – out on the landing, and would spend hours trying to get her to lift her leg onto the step, until eventually, we were told, Beatrice had actually managed to climb one step by herself. This must have taken months because by then, it was time to go back to school, but the authorities closed the Jewish school down and forbade Jewish children to go to any school; so I stayed at home.

One day, an order was issued, which stipulated that all Jews, living in the centre of town, should move to the outskirts. I heard my parents say that more German troops were expected in Sofia and that they didn't want to see 'all those Jews' around.

A friend of my mother's came to visit us; so did some neighbours; they all tried to comfort us, saying that all this was going to stop soon. My mother was crying; I cried too. Her despair frightened me.

The adults around me were talking of war. My parents reverted to French as soon as they realised I was listening keenly. It was puzzling and frightening. When my cousin Yani and I played war, he was shooting and killing the enemy in one corner of the room, I was looking after 'the children' – in the other. In my parents' war, there was no shooting, no fighting, only this tremendous fear.

My father came in one afternoon and announced in a jubilant voice that his sister, my aunt, had agreed to have us move in with them.

'We can move in as soon as you are ready!'

'I bet your sister will make my life a misery, but we have no alternative.'

My aunt lived in 'a poorer quarter' of town and now I realised it was the Jewish district. The map of the 'City' had been marked in such a way, that no Jews would be found within the central areas. So, within a few weeks, this underpopulated district witnessed a great influx of people.

It was in those few weeks, prior to moving out, that the bombardments started. At first, there were air-raid warnings only. The sound of whining sirens in the night made my heart shrink with fear yet I didn't know what I was afraid of. Sheets of black paper were spread over the windows and no light was ever put on before we had made sure that the black shutters were down.

'The shutters!' my mother would shout if my father as much as made a movement to put the light on before she had finished pulling them down, '*They* will accuse us of helping Churchill!'

'Who is Churchill?' I asked and was told who he was.

'Why should we help him, if he wants to throw bombs on us?' I asked, but this proved too complex.

The basements were arranged as air-raid shelters with bunks

and first aid equipment and we had to run down three flights each time the alarm went. The sound of the exploding bombs was frightening.

'They are aiming at the Depot,' people were saying, or, 'They want to get the railway station.'

'What for?' somebody asked.

'To stop *them* transporting German troops to Yugoslavia, that's why.'

'They want to get the petrol storage cylinders,' somebody else said.

The doors opened suddenly and a strong gust of hot air came in. Women were screaming, children crying; one couldn't see for dust and soot.

'The RAF know their business,' somebody said, and I was certain the voice was jubilant. We were all choking. Then the 'all clear' came and the permission to go back upstairs; home.

'If this isn't a petrol explosion, I don't know what is!' the same voice said.

My aunt lay down restrictions as soon as we moved in and, as we had only one room and I had to sleep with my parents, I could hear more of what was said and therefore, I knew a lot more of what was going on. We could use the kitchen only when my aunt wasn't there. We could keep only a few items in the kitchen cupboards which meant that my mother had to go to and fro between the kitchen and our room when she cooked.

'I will help you.' I said.

'You keep out of this.' she said.

'I will talk it over with her.' my father said.

But nothing changed.

It was for me, the first time in my life that I was in such close proximity with other people. My cousin David was very handsome and always had lots of friends round; some boys, some girls. The flat was very large. It had a central hall and four bedrooms, a lounge and a large kitchen. We occupied one of the bedrooms, my cousin had the other, my aunt and uncle – the third, and the fourth was let to a widow and her son, who was a student, like my cousin. They were in the same predicament as us, having had to leave the town centre.

The central hall was filled with heavy walnut furniture, and was only used as a passage-way now. So, many times I hid under the large table and from between the carved lion-paw legs, spied on my cousin and his friends. Unfortunately, these pleasures never lasted long, because my mother would find me and make me go to our room. It was a very hot summer and Jacques had fallen ill to the same disease as Beatrice. I was told that he might never be able to use his legs again. This was very sad. I did see Jacques though, some months later; he was riding a large tricycle and had some strange attachments to his legs. He could wheel the tricycle, but he couldn't walk.

The street where we lived now, was wide and had no trees. There was a grocers' shop across the road and a pack of noisy children playing in the middle. My mother made it clear that I was not going to play in the street. What she didn't know was that the noisy children held no attraction for me, so I stayed home and played on my own, or read stories.

As there was no school to go to, September found me hanging aimlessly around. The widow was said to be 'neurotic' and her son was a 'mummy's boy'. My mother often imitated her, mockingly. There was a girl my cousin was not supposed to see. My aunt was very firm about it and I heard some loud voices from their lounge:

'You are to be a doctor! You've got to drop her!' my aunt's voice was high pitched; my cousin stood up to her, and I admired him for it:

'I will see whom I want!'

'Don't you answer me back! If it weren't for me you would be some office boy, or worse.'

I retreated quickly because it all sounded very dangerous.

Ж

One day my father came home looking worried and tired.

'What now?' said my mother quickly.

'We can't be employed any longer.'

'What do you mean?'

'As I said. We are not supposed to be employed, and that's that.'

'But how … how can we survive ….'

'We won't.'

I burst into tears.

'Oh, stop that,' my mother said to me, and to my father, 'So, you got the sack?'

'No, I haven't.'

'The hell with you! Why didn't you tell me straight out, you scared me.'

'This is not the point, is it? Glavtchev will let me work at his home, fair enough. BUT HE IS NOT SUPPOSED TO! Do you understand? It's against the 'new laws'. So sooner or later, he will get scared and drop me; and who can blame him.'

Soon all the men came back from their offices and they all had to stay home or just hang around like me, like all the children who had no school to go to and, as September was slowly drawing to its end, and the leaves were turning yellow and rust on the trees, one could see men, sitting outside the houses, smoking and talking, and still the children played in the middle of the street. We didn't see my other cousins and aunts now, because they had all moved very far away and as my mother put it, we 'didn't feel much like visiting right now.'

So, when the adults in the flat bored me, I could go and play with my new friend Rosie – in the next block – who had a lovely collection of dolls and dolls' houses and we spent hours giving the dolls a comfortable middle class life, in their 'salons' and drawing rooms.

ЖҀ

One morning an excited voice, somewhere in the flat, shouted:

'There is a blockade!'

We were still in bed. My father jumped up and opened the door, looking out while putting his jacket over his pyjamas.

'What are they looking for?' he asked as he walked out of the room. He left the door ajar however, and my mother and I could hear what was being said.

'I don't know,' my uncle's voice answered my father's question.

'I went down for some groceries. There is a soldier with a gun downstairs ... ordered me up and also said to lock the door and not to communicate between flats.'

'I wonder what they are after. Did you ask him how long this is going to last?'

'I did. All he said was, that only children were allowed to go to the shops for provisions and that, before noon. They seem to be searching.'

The street was strangely quiet. We could hear the heavy pacing of boots and then a voice, shouting:

'Shut the windows and stay in!'

Everybody came out of their rooms now, sleepy and frightened, and they sat in their pyjamas under their dressing gowns, pondering over the situation.

'I wonder whether there might be some members of the

resistance hiding in the area; or maybe there are guns hidden somewhere; in any case they have been tipped off.'

'If somebody is hiding some member of the resistance, why would they tell?'

I couldn't help thinking of that night when a man slept in our flat and that my father didn't know about it.

'Who are the resistance?' I asked.

'They are brave people who are against the Nazis; they have to hide in the mountains.' my cousin explained.

I thought that we were all against the Nazis. The pondering continued until somebody said:

'It's 11.30, she has to go and at least get us some bread.'

'Are you afraid?' my uncle asked me.

'No,' I said and I wasn't. It was so good to feel that I was going to be useful. I was given two shopping bags and a small list of what everybody wanted.

'She can't carry that much,' my mother said.

In the end they came to an agreement over what I could or could not do, and I went down.

There was a soldier downstairs at the entrance.

'You go across the road and back!' he said to me 'nowhere else. And don't talk to anybody!'

I nodded and started walking, venturing a glance to my left and to my right as I was crossing the road. There was something macabre in the total silence of the street. There was another soldier outside the shop and yet another inside it. I had to hand my list in, pay for the goods and go out without saying anything. The soldier took the list from me as I was handing it to the shopkeeper, looked through it and passed it on. As I was walking back, I saw four soldiers and another man walk into the entrance of the block next door. I didn't really know at that point, whether I was frightened or not. I felt numb; if only I could understand why. But I didn't, and this didn't help.

In the hours that followed, life at the flat became intolerable.

My uncle came across an object of mine in the hall and he kicked it against the wall muttering:

'That ...ing child is such a nuisance.' He muttered it loudly enough for my father to hear. Only once before that, had I seen my father in a rage like this and I had lived in the fear of another one ever since. This was to be another one. He went for my uncle, his eyes glaring, his fists tight and his jaw twitching. I was paralysed with fear at the sight of him and hid in my mother's lap and started to cry. My aunt shouted to my father to get hold of himself. My cousin got involved too and the widow shouted to her son to stay out of it. I don't quite know whether my father actually hit my uncle. My mother and I stayed in our room. Eventually my father came in and shut the door behind. He was pale but calmer, his hands were running though his hair as if to smooth it over,

' ... my child ... he is not going to touch my child ... ' he was saying.

'Calm down now,' said my mother 'he wasn't really going to touch her,' her voice was working itself into a high pitch. I looked at them, worried.

'Don't you tell me what to do!' he shouted at her.

We sat, all three of us, quiet and distant. I felt them wrapped up in something beyond my reach, something I did not understand. My mother was sobbing now, my father was pacing up and down the small space available, and I sat, my helpless hands in my lap, sensing that they were far apart from each other and neither of them took me in.

The blockade lasted three days. The soldiers came to the flat and searched. They looked in cupboards and under beds, they tapped the walls and the floors, felt the mattress and eventually, they left.

On the morning of the fourth day, I woke up and heard noise in the street; people's voices, children playing, cars. The blockade was over.

Chapter Nine

The Men are Rounded Up – We are Deported

Winter was now approaching and the main worry of the adults around me was money, and whether we would have coal to keep warm.

My father went every day to Mr. Glavtchev's house, where he worked for him and I knew he was being paid. I don't know what my father did at the house, but I knew that Mr Glavtchev was a tobacco exporter, that he traded with Germany and other countries and that my father was kept late at work and on these occasions Mr. Glavtchev and his son would walk him home, only he had to take his yellow star off and my mother worried because there were penalties for doing so.

'Don't worry' my father said to her 'the Mayor is Glavtchev's personal friend. He will fix things for me.'

'The Mayor is a Nazi,' my mother said and my father threw his arms in the air in desperation.

It was in the middle of the afternoon, one cold November day, when we heard the widow's voice in the entrance hall. She had just come in and was shouting:

'They are taking all the men! They are taking all our men! They are collecting them from the street … '

Quickly my mother and I went into the hall, so did my aunt with my uncle peering from behind her.

'What are they saying? Our men? Do you know anything more?'

The widow was holding her scarf against her forehead and her face was full of nervous ticks as she spoke. I averted my eyes, I just couldn't look at her.

' … men … men are gathered at the school … and there are lorries there … they have taken them from the street … they gave them half an hour to go home and collect some personal things … all men under 40 …. '

'Do you know where they are sending them?' my uncle asked.

'Poland, where else!' she said and burst out in sobs. I looked up at my mother. She looked pale and said:

'They will take him on his way in.'

My aunt started to cry for my cousin who was not at home either.

'I told him to stay home! That wretched girl!' My aunt's lament contained more anger than anxiety.

Suddenly the front door opened wide and the widow's son came in. She threw herself against his chest – he was a lot taller than her – and sobbed desperately. He put an arm around her and said:

'I understood what was going on as soon as I turned the corner, so I took the star off and walked slowly past them. They didn't stop me.'

He seemed pleased with himself.

What exactly is happening?' asked my uncle.

The widow's son took a deep breath and pushed his sobbing mother away.

It seems that all men between 18 and 40 years of age are being sent to labour camps.'

'No, no!' shouted his mother 'you don't know that! It's Poland they are being sent to!'

I remember the long glance he gave her before saying slowly:

'I don't know.'

'Nobody knows anything,' said my uncle.

'You don't have to worry.'

'No, not for myself,' he said thoughtfully. 'It's my son .... '

My mother took my hand and led me to our room where we sat, doing nothing waiting and hoping my father would come home. My mother's face was so sad, so tragic, that I didn't dare ask any questions. There were so many questions flashing through my mind but like so many others they remained unanswered. What was a labour camp? Why was Poland so frightening? How and why did they force people to go to places and do things they didn't want to do? If my father was sent away, how were we to survive? My mother, as usual, made me eat my dinner despite my telling her that I was feeling sick. Her anguish made her tight-lipped, and there was no room for my plea.

I was in bed, the covers up to my chin, watching the shadows on the ceiling, when my father finally arrived.

'Ohhh' my mother took a step toward him but her legs bent under her weight and I thought she was going to collapse. My father took hold of her, put her on the bed and sat down beside her, holding her hand.

'I know,' he said, 'Glavtchev told me. I know you worried but the only thing to do was to stay there until late. He walked me home.'

'How about tomorrow?' my mother asked.

'It doesn't matter. They are going to call up each and every one of us.'

'He … he can't … do something?'

'I could … 'fail' the medical.'

'There is that?'

'Yes.'

'How do you 'fail' it?'

'It has to be heart or ulcers. For heart you do vigorous exercise just before the examination in order to speed up the heart rate, for ulcers you swallow a coin or something!'

My father didn't fail his 'medical' and when the little white envelope came, he had to go. Eventually we received a card from him, telling us where he was. It was a village, about two hours' train journey from Sofia and we could visit him once a month. We could bring him food parcels. Of course, when he was 'mobilised' he had to hand in his food coupons, so we didn't have his rations.

They went one by one. My cousin, the student, and then all the younger men from the street. One could see only old men in the street now, and boys and lots of women and children.

My uncle remained the only man in the flat. He would see to it that the black shutters were pulled safely down and when the alarm went, he would see to it that all the fires were put out before everybody went to the shelters.

One afternoon I came back from Rosie's to find a lady visitor in our room.

'This is my daughter,' my mother said to her, and then to me: 'This is Mrs. Glavtcheva.'

I greeted the lady and sat down by the stove.

'So you see,' the lady was saying, 'if there is anything my husband can do, please tell us. I can't tell you how sorry we are about all this. But it's not going to last long. We all hope that. Churchill said he will be ready for war in '44'.

'Is that what he said?'

'Yes, I heard it on the BBC myself. Anyway these are the facts. How can we help?'

'Well,' said my mother, 'if we are to be sent away, I would like to go to Shoumen. I grew up there and my step-father, step-brothers and sisters still live there. I was brought up there.'

'Sure, I will tell my husband. The Mayor will do this for him. Now please take this,' and she handed my mother an envelope.

'What … ?'

'My husband owes it to your husband, his wages, I can assure you.'

The lady left quickly. My mother returned to the room closed the door quietly and sat down.

'There is going to be a massive deportation,' she muttered and as her hands went up to her face, she started to sob, 'Oh my God! How am I going to cope … ?'

I wanted to comfort her but couldn't think of what to say. I put my hand on her lap and looked at her.

'You don't even know what it's all about, do you?' she said to me.

'No I don't, please tell me, I so want to know.'

'You are too young for these things.'

My aunt knocked and walked straight in.

'What is it,' she said, 'I gather something is wrong.'

'We are going to be 'deported',' said my mother,'There are more German troops coming and they don't want any Jews in Sofia.'

'Oh, my God! Where? When? How did she know?'

'Her husband is a friend of the Mayor's and he warned him. He offered to help if he had any Jewish friends. Not that he can help much, but at least we can be sent to a town of our choice.'

'But what about us? Where are we going to go? And where are we going to live?'

'They will send us to towns where there are Jewish communities and impose us on the local Jewish families.'

My aunt thought for a moment, then said with a glint in her eyes:

'You know something? Just as well!'

'What are you talking about?'

'Well, the way I figure it, as soon as any more Germans come here, the RAF, are going to bomb relentlessly. So, just as well we won't be here.'

'You may be right.'

My aunt paused for a while then said quickly:

'There is going to be a wedding.'

'What?' my mother said surprised, 'Who?'

'He has ... compromised her.'

'No!'

I was dying to know what they meant.

'Yes, she is expecting ... ,' my aunt said meaningfully, 'and there is no knowing as far as I am concerned, that it is his.'

'Oh, my God!'

My aunt left without saying another word. She hadn't taken the news about the forced evacuation very badly and I noticed that my mother had calmed down.

'Will we be going to Shoumen then?' I asked.

'So it seems.'

I went to bed rather happy about the news now. In Shoumen there were a lot of people I had heard of, but most interesting of all was a baby girl born a few months earlier to my mother's niece.

'Will I be allowed to look after the baby?' I asked.

'Possibly.' said my mother in the darkness.

I felt that she had relaxed and chanced my question:

'Mum, who is expecting what?'

'Go to sleep and stop asking questions which do not concern you.'

Ж

When our yellow slip arrived, telling us to leave Sofia for Shoumen within three days, I had a temperature of 102 and my throat was so sore I couldn't talk or swallow. My mother said it was tonsillitis although my tonsils had been removed when I was four.

'She can't have tonsillitis if she has no tonsils,' said my aunt.

'Yes SHE can,' said my mother. How am I supposed to cope? With my husband away and a sick child!' my mother complained.

We were only allowed hand luggage. We were supposed to hand our key in at the Town Hall and leave everything as it was, as we had done with the key to the flat at Moskovitch Mansions and where, prior to that, we had handed in our radio.

'What are they going to do with all those keys?' I wondered.

Mrs. Glavtcheva came again and my mother gave her some valuables for safekeeping. We were the first ones to get a yellow slip in the flat but before we had packed, the others received theirs too. My mother went to see Aunt Amelia and came back quickly because I was alone. Aunty Amelia's family were sent to another town.

'When will we see them again, Mum?' I asked.

'How should I know. Do be quiet,' said my mother, 'I have to finish packing. How on earth am I going to take you!'

She decided to send a telegram to her step-brother in Shoumen, announcing our arrival in the hope that someone would be waiting for us at the station. There was no telephone in the flat so my mother went to talk to the doctor and get his advice as to how to cope with me during the journey. She came back some hours later, pale and distressed.

'What did he say?' I asked.

'Our doctor is Jewish and he is not allowed to practice,' she answered (as if we didn't know), 'and the Bulgarian doctors are not allowed to treat Jewish patients.'

It sounded like a death sentence.

The following day, I was wrapped up in a blanket from the neck down. My head was covered by a woollen hat, then by a woollen scarf. A Bulgarian neighbour helped transport me and some suitcases to the taxi which took us to the railway station. There, a porter put me over his shoulder like a rolled carpet, and deposited me in the carriage where he left me on the bench.

I was unable to move my arms or my legs, and with the hat and scarf having slipped somewhat, during my transportation, this left me with a very limited view of my surroundings. Eventually my mother got in, and put the hat back in position. The train was full of German soldiers, but our carriage was specially reserved for 'Jewish evacuees'.

I don't remember much of this journey. The train was very crowded and my mother had to hold me on her knees. Eventually some people got off, and she put me on the bench. My temperature must have shot up, for I remember the walls of the carriage slowly getting covered with flowers. They were all spring ones – snow drops and crocuses and violets. I wanted to pick some and smell their scent, but someone was holding my hand down and I couldn't reach.

Chapter Ten

Arrival at Shoumen – The Ratniks!

I had, in fact been to Shoumen in the days when my grandmother was still alive, and I remembered the house well. It had been built by my grandfather for his first wife. When she died, leaving him with four children, he married my grandmother who only had one child – my mother – and who was a widow herself. It had been a 'marriage de convenience' and my mother always maintained that her mother was not treated well in that household. My mother, (a girl of ten at the time), grew up alongside her two step-brothers and two step-sisters but never became very fond of any of them, except for the eldest brother Marco, who, my mother said, was the only one who treated her with warmth and understanding.

Uncle Marco and his young wife, Victoria, lived at the house. Aunt Clara was said to have been an 'introverted girl' – she married a Shoumenian and lived in the same street. Aunt Caroline married a rich man and lived in Sofia and Uncle Alf was also married and lived in Shoumen. I knew of my cousins Elsa, Albert and Sheri – who were the children of Uncle Marco and Aunt Victoria. It was, in fact, my cousin Elsa who had had a baby girl recently. My grandfather was once again remarried.

I remembered the house. It stood in its own grounds, quite majestic. Stone steps led up to the porch, where the carved wooden doors stood behind four stone pillars. Above the doors, carved in wood and forming part of its frame was a quotation from the Bible in Hebrew. It's meaning I learned later: 'If I forget thee Jerusalem ... '

I remembered the majestic hall with its ceiling-high Venetian mirrors. They were placed in such a way, facing each other, that when I stood in front of one of them, I could see my reflection ad infinitum in the mirror behind. I also remembered the paintings on the ceilings, decorated with plaster in various shapes among which baby-angels, pink and plump, wrapped in flimsy cloth were floating in what appeared to be the sky.

Another striking thing about the house, was ... 'the bath' in the garden .... It was a stone structure, and heat was actually coming through the walls and the floor and steam was coming in through thin pipes all around making everything hazy and unreal. There was a bath, which was too large to be called a tub and too small to be called a pool, nevertheless they still called it 'the pool'. I remembered sitting on a wooden stool, looking at the naked women around me, wondering at their large hanging breasts, as my mother threw cool water over me, probably to prevent me from fainting in the intense heat.

Adjoining the 'bath' was the washroom. I remembered Aisha, the Turkish maid, feeding the wood-fired furnace and stirring the washing in large metal tubs. Carried by the wafting steam was a pleasant smell of 'clean'. There was, also, the garden. The apple and pear trees, and the cherry tree. I could not have been older than three or four at the time and found this all so different from life in our flat and I remarked that 'they were very rich' and my mother had laughed and said:

'My step-father owns half the high street.'

I could never quite fathom how anyone could own 'a street'.

My father had added his opinion:

'The old chap has worked hard to get all this fortune and his sons are wasting it away. Specially the red one.'

Ж

The train journey to Shoumen took twelve hours. I was awake when we got there. My mother leant out of the window to look for her step-brother. Eventually she became agitated as she realised no one had shown up. She got off, found a porter who took the cases down, then as he was coming back for me, there were voices and greetings and I heard my mother ask:

'Where is Marco?' but I didn't hear the reply.

Then she was standing in front of me, smiling:

'Sheri has come for us!' and to him: 'She is ill.'

Next thing I knew, I was lifted up and carefully borne in my cousin's arms. I was still wrapped tightly in the blanket, as I sat up between the two of them in the one-horse drawn phaeton through the strangely deserted, blacked-out streets of the town.

My cousin, who was no older than 15 or 16 at the time, looked warmly at my mother above my head and answered all her questions.

'How is your father then?'

'We hope he is well, said Sheri tentatively, 'he ... is in Somovit.'

I learned later that Somovit was a special concentration camp for known communists.

'My God! Since when?'

'Albert is there too.' Sheri said instead of a reply.

'Albert too! ... but he is only a boy!'

'He is old enough.'

'So you are the only man in the house now.'

Sheri didn't answer. He asked the coachman to stop the horse, cleared his throat and said slowly:

'You ... won't ... be able to ... stay at ... the house .... '

'What? Don't they ... doesn't the old man want me to ... ' my mother's voice broke.

'No, no!' said Sheri vehemently, 'It's not like that! It's full of Sofiates. They are everywhere. They came before you did, and we were forced to take them in ... by the Town Hall .... You don't know what it's like!'

'How naive I am,' my mother said bitterly, 'to have used contacts to arrange to come here. I was always led to believe I should treat this as my own father's home. Ha! I would have been better off among strangers.'

Sheri asked the man to continue the journey.

'We are going home now though. Until you find a place.'

'Yes. Where will we sleep if it's full.'

'In my parents' bedroom. Mum is alone now, so we have put up two beds for you in her bedroom.'

I must have missed a lot of this conversation because my attention was divided between the streets we were driving through and my throbbing head and throat.

The first thing I remember of the end of this journey is a view of the large hall, called the 'salon', with mattresses laid out so as to leave a narrow passage in the middle, and there were people sleeping on them. Then I was put on a narrow bed by Sheri's gentle arms, and just before I went to sleep I caught a glimpse of the familiar angels on the ceiling.

It was more than a week before I recovered and was allowed to get up and wander around the house. I found nothing of the splendour I had remembered from my first visit. The 'salon' still had its mirrors, but their frames weren't shiny any more and the mirrors themselves looked tarnished. The carpets had disappeared and the bare parquet floors were dull and patchy. There were bundles of clothes everywhere and electric rings on which people were cooking in dirty looking aluminium pans.

Wandering in the garden I came across my grandfather. I knew he wasn't my real grandfather, but he was nice and he talked to me.

'Hullo little one,' he said, 'How are you? OK?'

He was sitting in the garden although it was quite cold. He was a heavy man with bushy grey hair and sparkling blue eyes. Sheri had the same eyes, only his hair was black. My grand father held in one hand a string of amber worry beads, which he was sliding one by one along the string. With his other hand, he was leaning heavily on his walking stick. He had a watch on a chain in the pocket of his waistcoat.

'I am fine now,' I said, 'Aren't you cold out here?'

'No. Are you?'

'No, I am not, but I am not allowed out.'

'I'll let you into a secret, little one: I am not allowed out either but I don't always do as I am told. Do you?' and he winked at me.

I nodded and sighed. It would be so marvellous to do a few things I wasn't allowed to do! But then, I didn't want to upset my mother by disobeying her. My grandfather searched furtively in his pocket and slipped a coin in my hand:

'Do something you are not allowed to do!' he said, 'Now you better run along, otherwise I'll get the blame for you.'

I ran into the house where I bumped into Aunt Victoria. Aunt Victoria was tall and very handsome. I pulled a face and said:

'Imagine I was like this!'

'God forbid!' she said throwing her arms in the air.

For some reason I found this little game very exciting. Probably because she didn't brush me aside or just tell me to stop the nonsense. So, from then on wherever I saw her, I pulled a face and she would throw her arms in the air and we would laugh. She must have found me very tiresome but never said so.

Now that I was well, we went to visit Elsa and her baby. Elsa's husband had also been sent to forced labour and she lived with her parents-in-law. Her father-in-law was a very rich man and his house had been searched more than once for gold and other riches. Elsa was a good looking young woman with sparkling blue eyes, same as Sheri's and granddad's. She was very pleased at my offer to look after the baby. She couldn't wait to be able to go out. The baby's name was Gigi.

We visited aunt Clara too. She had a son, my cousin Joseph who was about Sheri's age. He was a strange, quiet boy with ginger hair. His father was called Gabriel and I found that name very funny. Wherever we went, everybody asked my mother, whilst looking significantly at me:

'Does she eat her dinner now?' or 'In our house no one leaves the table before they have emptied their plate.'

And each time my heart sank with embarrassment, my hands went cold and damp and I wanted the floor to open up and make me disappear. How on earth did they all know?

Shoumen was, and probably still is, a particularly provincial town influenced greatly by the Turkish legacy of the Ottoman Empire which had occupied Bulgaria for 500 years. The town is not far from the Black Sea coast and was divided into four distinct communities, the Bulgarian, Armenian, Turkish and Jewish quarters.

Main Street runs through the Bulgarian quarter for about two miles, then just beyond the beautiful Tombul Mosque it changes into Jewish Street, cutting through the Jewish quarter and leading through The Park and out of town. The Park was at the Jewish quarter's end of town, and was a favourite for courting couples as well as for family picnics and walks. (Of course, one had to go through the Jewish quarter to get there.)

The Tombul Mosque, built more than a century ago in pink stone, its walls chipped and its gate broken, looked nonetheless imposing and solemn and I can still hear the muezzin's voice calling the faithful to prayer.

From Mosque Square two roads branch off and climb up, the one on the right – to the Armenian, the other to the Turkish quarter.

As soon as I was well enough, we moved into a room that my mother had found for us. Our landlady was a young woman, now alone with her little girl. The house faced the main street. The side gate led into a courtyard and the main entrance to the house was from the back. We occupied the spare room whose windows looked out over the street and was so low, that when I stood by it, I was at the same level as the passers-by. The landlady's room was adjoining ours and both opened onto a hall from where one could also go to the kitchen and bathroom. There was an outside staircase leading to the upper floor where our landlady's mother-in-law lived on her own.

The old woman was completely deaf. I had never in my life seen a deaf person. She talked incessantly in a low monotonous voice and most of the time I could not understand what she was saying. Talking to her was impossible; she tried to lip-read, but always failed, I didn't realise she understood everything wrongly and the conversation became hilarious. I laughed at the funny exchange but my mother pinched me severely pointing out that this was not at all funny but very sad. The old woman was deaf, but not blind or stupid, so she turned to me and said in a clear voice:

'Not at all my child, don't worry. There is so much rubbish spoken, I can assure you, I am better off not hearing it.'

Soon the Jewish quarter was full of Sofiates and every spare room housed a family from the capital. Under the deep snow, the overpopulated quarter found its organisers and in what formerly was the cultural centre, a school was now set up by a teacher who was too old for the labour camp.

There weren't enough children of the same age to form conventional classes but we formed two groups and instead of real learning we read books in class, (which, I later found out, were relevant to the schools' syllabus). I went to these classes with pleasure because there was no effort involved, no homework, no pressures. Sheri was a regular visitor of ours. He used to come round with a load of wood on his powerful shoulders, for our pot-belly stove. He always had a joke and a smile on his face and we used to like his visits.

I found a new friend. Her name was Minka and although she was my age, boys were interested in her and I found this both frightening and interesting. She had an older sister.

'Of course, she has her period already,' Minka said to me.

'What is that?' I asked, having never heard the word before.

'Hasn't your mother told you?'

'No.'

'Well … it's … a period, you know. Blood from … down there.'

'Blood!' I was shocked, 'How do you mean 'blood'? Where does it come from?'

'Well, I don't really know, all I know is – when you have it, you are a real woman.'

'Oh,' I Said 'I will never have it.'

'Of course you will, stupid! You are a girl, aren't you.'

'Yes.'

'So? Of course you will.'

I wasn't so sure.

From that time on, I watched my mother closely to try and detect any signs of this 'real womanhood' but I never did. I made a few miserable attempts to hint at it, so as to get her to tell me, but she never said anything.

The snow in Shoumen was deeper than in Sofia and it stayed

white longer. After school, we used to take our sledges up the hill of the Armenian quarter and shoot down, our noses and cheeks red with the biting cold. But, with nightfall, I had to go home whilst the others were allowed to stay out longer. By nine o'clock, the whole of the Jewish quarter was deserted. The only passers-by, were the Bulgarians going to the pub in the Park.

Often there were air-raid warnings and we were advised to gather in the centre of the house, and stay away from all windows. This was the best we could do as there were no shelters built in our quarter and we were not allowed to go to the public ones. So, these occasions found us, my mother, myself and our landlady hugging her little girl, seated on the floor in the middle of the kitchen. There was seldom any conversation on these occasions and I remember most of all the deep silence that followed the whining of the sirens. In Sofia too, there was a silence between the time the sirens stopped and the bombs started to fall, but here somehow, the silence was deeper, but then, Shoumen was never really bombed, but some bombs were dropped not too far out of town , on the German barracks.

Eventually the snow began to melt and the sunshine became warmer. There were rumours that the men would be returning home, but nobody knew anything for sure. One night I was woken up by a great noise coming from the street. There were voices, some singing, some shouting. I sat up on my bed, frightened to death. My mother, who hadn't gone to bed yet, came in from the kitchen, got me out of bed and just as we were leaving the room, something made a terrific noise and the window pane smashed into little pieces. We left the room quickly and went to the kitchen, where the landlady sat, her baby in her arms, crying.

'What is it, mum, what is happening?' I asked.

'It's probably members of the Hitler Youth, the Ratniks, drunk. Coming back from the pub in the Park.' she said.

I could hear the smashing of glass, gun shots and singing voices. ' … to kill our enemies, the Jews!' was the refrain of their song. I had heard it before.

'They have guns too,' said the landlady, 'God knows if they haven't killed someone'.

The voices grew more and more distant and eventually died out. Still, we waited for a long while before we dared to go into our room. We couldn't switch any lights on because the stone they had thrown, had not only broken the pane, but also torn the blackout paper. So, in the dark, my mother cleared the glass the best she could, shivering with the cold night air coming in through the broken window. She found a piece of brown paper which she put across it, then we went to bed.

Real fear must be a very tiring thing, because I had promised myself to keep my mother company in an effort to reassure her, but fell asleep immediately.

Sheri arrived early the next morning, even before we were up. His arms were loaded with some wooden planks which he dropped on the floor.

'Hi! Are you alright?'

My mother ushered him into our room.

'See for yourself,' she said. She allowed him to look at the scene for a few moments before she enquired, 'How about you? Did they break any windows at the house?'

'No. Not us. They seem to have done most of their stone-throwing up the street. By the time they arrived at our end they were either too tired or had run out of stones. Thank God you are not hurt.'

'No, we are alright. What are you going to do with that?' asked my mother pointing to the planks.

'I will make some shutters for your windows. I don't know yet how we are going to fix them, but I will work something out.'

Throughout that whole day, all the old men and boys

worked to provide everybody with shutters, to protect us from similar attacks. There was no school that day as everybody was engaged in the operation. So, before nightfall, as I went down the street having spent the afternoon helping Sheri, all the windows were covered by these improvised shutters and as the street was free of passers-by, it had a sinister ghostly appearance which made me run rather than walk.

That same night the Hitler Youth – Ratniks, made a similar attack on our street again and, having found the windows protected, they put even more venom into their verbal attack and more impact into the throwing of the stones which in hitting the wood, produced a series of hollow sounding bangs. We stayed in bed.

Chapter Eleven

We Get Thrown Out – My Father is Back

Our landlady's husband was the first one to turn up. He just walked in one evening as we were all sitting around the table in the kitchen. She stood up, her fork fell from her hand, and she screamed. He took her in his arms and she sobbed on his shoulder. My mother nudged me to get up and we went into our room.

The following day he told us that he had been building new roads to speed up the advance of the German army into Yugoslavia and that, as far as he knew this was what all the 'mobilised' Jewish men were doing. He also confirmed the news that they were all coming home, but not for long.

For some reason, unknown to me, the atmosphere at the house became strained. We could no longer just walk into the kitchen. My mother had to ask permission for us to take our meals. The same applied to the bathroom. Also, we no longer sat together in the evenings as we used to. Now, as soon as we had finished our dinner, my mother and I had to go straight into our room and stay there.

'Of course,' I heard Aunt Victoria say to my mother when she complained, 'she doesn't want another young woman around her husband. You wouldn't either.'

It all came to a head when our landlady picked a quarrel with my mother. I don't know how it all started, but my mother was very hurt. Many bitter words were exchanged:

'You go and find yourself a place!' the landlady was shouting, 'you are not wanted here, don't you understand! I don't want to see you on Monday. Do you hear me? By Monday you have to go! Go!'

'I didn't want to come here!' my mother sobbed, 'I didn't impose these laws. Where do you want me to go with a child? In the Street?'

'I don't care where you go, but go you will!'

My mother shut the door and cried desperately.

'Never mind mum,' I tried to comfort her, 'we will find another place. We don't want her husband, she can keep him!'

'There is nowhere to go! Everywhere there are only women, and the same would happen again ... to think that there is no room for me in my own father's house ... '

'Never mind, Sheri will help us find another place. He will know where.'

'How? How am I going to be out by Monday ... ' she sobbed, 'What am I going to do?'

It was, once again, an evening full of despair, gloom and tears and there seemed to be no way out.

In the morning I asked not to be sent to school, but to be allowed to help find a new place to live. But my mother insisted that I go, and so I did, my heart heavy with disappointment and worry. When I came back from school, my mother took me by the hand and we went to Aunt Victoria's for dinner. Sheri was his usual cheerful self. He assured my mother that he knew of a woman in the Armenian quarter, a very nice lady, who had a room to let and she didn't mind Jewish people. Suddenly, in the middle of this conversation, to our great surprise, my father walked in. I didn't recognise him at first. My mother jumped at him and started to cry. He was back! He was going to take things in hand now and the wicked landlady would see that we already had a father and didn't need hers.

The following afternoon I learned that we were going to move into that room Sheri had mentioned. Our landlady was a widow, a doctor's widow, and she lived with her daughter.

Chapter Twelve

Madame Arshalouise – David is Left for Dead

Madame Arshalouise had pale blue eyes and a halo of silver hair. To me she seemed tall and she looked very distinguished. My parents had moved our few possessions in and my father came to meet me from school and take me to our new home.

The house stood on top of the hill in the Armenian quarter and it was large and impressive. Not as large as my grandfather's but a lot more so than our place in the Jewish quarter. There were two entrances to the house both from the patio; the one leading into a small entrance hall and the other into a larger entrance hall both of which opened into the salon.

We were going to have the small entrance hall as a kitchen, and one of the bedrooms. Our kitchen looked out onto the garden, but the bedroom looked out on disused land behind the house. Here, the salon held a different attraction – a grand piano which, I was to find out, Madame Arshalouise enjoyed playing in the cool darkness. It was a beautiful shining thing, with beautifully made metal fixtures in the front as candle holders. The keyboard, when you lifted the lid, was covered in a soft green felt cover. Her favourite piece was a Tchaikovsky barcarole which to this day, when I hear it, takes me back to those sad, uncertain, days. On the wall of what was going to be our kitchen, hung a large portrait of a man whom I immediately took for God.

'Mummy, is this God?'

'No, silly. It's Tolstoy.'

'Who is Tolstoy?'

'A writer.'

He most certainly could have been God. With that long white beard, and those penetrating eyes!

One by one, all the men returned home. Many of them, like my father, having left their families in Sofia, had to come and look for them now in a strange town, cooped up in rooms in other people's houses. My cousin Albert, Sheri's brother returned very ill. He had contracted malaria and was ill for a long time. His father, my Uncle Marco also returned, so did my Aunt Caroline's eldest son, David and her husband. So, in the daytime, Jewish Street was more animated now. There were also more comings and goings after the forbidden hours since the young men were back.

Late one night, a tapping on our bedroom window woke us up. I half sat up in bed and saw my father get up and walk to the window. The windows opened inward, and only the black paper blinds separated us from whoever it was that stood outside.

'Who is it?' asked my father and his quiet voice couldn't quite disguise a tremor.

'Uncle, uncle, it's me, Sheri.'

'Sheri! For goodness' sake, come in round the front will you! What on earth is wrong?'

'I can't come in' Sheri whispered 'I have to go. Have you

seen David tonight?'

'David? Which David?'

'Aunt Caroline's David:'

'No, we haven't. Why, what's happened?'

'He is not in' said Sheri 'He hasn't come home and there are some police about, and some Ratniks. If they find him in the street, he's had it. I must go now, sorry to have scared you.' And we heard him walking away.

My father closed the shutters and secured them.

'Peculiar.' he said, 'very peculiar. If David is out, why is Sheri taking such risks himself? They might find them both! As it is, there is only David'

'I don't know,' said my mother, 'I don't understand where could he have got to. Young men! Looking for trouble! Let's hope he gets away with it.'

My cousin David was a handsome young man and a gifted pianist. He was from Sofia and did not know many people in Shoumen, but Sheri and Albert were born and bred in Shoumen and knew everybody! So, David was introduced to and met up with other musicians both from the Bulgarian and the Jewish quarters; they enjoyed playing together, set up concerts in the Jewish homes, so the Bulgarian players could go home 'after 9pm' – the others either slept over or risked being caught as they went home. We never went to any of those concerts, but we knew about them.

It was at those musical meetings that my cousin became friendly with the mayor's daughter who was also a pianist. They fell in love and saw each other quite often but although they tried to keep their relationship secret, it became known to members of the Hitler Youth who didn't like the idea. So, one night, in fact that particular night, they had followed the couple into the park and when it was just after the curfew at 9pm. the Ratniks, five of them, grabbed hold of the girl and ordered her to be quiet, they beat up the young man and she was made to watch. They punched him and kicked him and then, leaving him unconscious on the ground, they fled, taking the girl with them.

When he didn't come home at 9pm., his father contacted Sheri and Albert – the cousins, and asked for help. These two knew of David's attachment to the girl and the risks he would take and set out immediately to search for him, at no small risk to themselves.

It was in the early hours of the morning that they found him and carried him home. There was a doctor in the Jewish quarter who was called out to look after David. He did his best though he had no access to any drugs.

I was fascinated by the romance but the ending was much too frightening. Recalling it now, I cannot imagine how it was that my mother, who was always so careful that adult conversation shouldn't reach my ears, hadn't intervened in this instance.

Physically, David recovered, and for some years led a normal life, or what appeared to be a normal life. But some years later signs of substantial brain damage emerged and to this day he drifts aimlessly through life.

Since it was impossible to see anyone in the evenings, my parents visited members of the family in the late afternoon, when they came to the Jewish quarter to pick me up from school. After such visits, we would walk home and spend the evenings in Madame Arshalouise's kitchen, where it was warm, talking to her and her daughter. At 7.30 I would be sent to bed. As I lay in the dark, I listened to the sounds that came in from outside. They were different than the ones I was used to. In our flat in Sofia there was the sound of traffic and the city noise, at my aunt's there was less traffic but more voices, whereas here, as we were on top of a hill and near the edge of the Armenian quarter, as I lay in bed, in the dark, I listened to the sounds of songbirds and crickets. Crickets sound most peculiar to someone from the city. I listened to them for a very long time and wondered whether they were singing serenades to the lady crickets or lamenting for some reason or other. I listened very carefully but could never establish whether their singing was sad or happy. The only other sound was the occasional dog barking.

One day, soon after David's incident, a yellow slip arrived again and, once more, my father had to go to a labour camp. My mother cried and my father tried his best to comfort her, but there was very little he could comfort her with. He had to go in 48 hours. We had dinner and, as usual I was sent to bed and my imagination took flight to the sounds of the night.

I imagined that we lived in a big house in Sofia and that there was a party. There always was a party. There were many people, all wearing beautiful clothes and my mother was the queen of the party because she was the most beautiful. There were many sorts of foods, oh, fruit and chocolates and sweets and all the things I had forgotten the taste of, and everybody laughed and there was music. I don't know why I thought of food in those day-dreams, since I didn't like food at the time, I was told. Sometimes, when my mother had been particularly hard to me over my dinner, I would imagine that I was grown up, and beautiful and I was the queen of the party. That particular night, I had an addition to my dream – a prince who fell in love with me. I had drifted off to sleep and was woken up by a peculiar noise. It took me some moments to wake up fully and realise what was going on. My father was sitting up in bed, and he was crying. HE WAS CRYING! He had his face in his hands and my mother was holding him. I could just make out the shadows.

'What sort of a man am I … ?' he was sobbing, 'I can't even provide for you … and here I have to go and leave you …. '

I was frightened. I was so frightened that I hid my head under the covers not to hear any more, not to see my father so helpless so desperate, and I cried to myself.

Chapter Thirteen

We are Alone Again

The Jewish quarter was emptied of men again. This time even our teacher had gone and we drifted aimlessly in the street which, with the approach of summer had become covered with ash-like fine dust and the town seemed asleep under it, like in some fairy-tale. Morale was very low among the adults. This rubbed off on us children as we felt that our games and the sound of our voices annoyed them and we stopped laughing and running as soon as an adult showed up. My mother and I used to spend these early summer days at my grandfather's house.

My grandfather, having been a very rich and influential man, knew many people in and around the town, some of them from the Turkish population who were farmers. It was these friends of my grandfather's who supplied the household with meat, butter and bread. Bread was a special luxury. With ration coupons we could only get half a loaf per person every other day and meat once a week. So by spending time at my grandfather's house, we were fed which was probably how we survived. Everybody took part in feeding me, since neither the lack of food nor my mother's constant complaining, made me feel hungry. Meal time remained a nightmare and my stomach convulsed with nausea. Still my mother relentlessly tried, sat with me, nudged me, cried, pinched my thigh and got very upset.

'Look what you are doing to your mother,' Aunt Victoria would say.

'Come on, Bambo! for me!' Sheri would say and I would burst out crying. But, the agony of my meals was forgotten between meals, at least by me. I looked forward to going out in the garden to play with my friends. My friends came to me, because this was the largest house and afforded enough playing space without crowding and at the same time we were near enough for the adults to supervise us.

Chapter Fourteen

The Chest in the Attic – Death of King Boris III

We were a bunch of children, running up and down the garden, climbing up the trees, but the day we discovered the attic was the best day of our summer. It was, of course, Minka's idea that we should explore the attic and so one morning we crept up the wooden staircase in single file. The attic spread over the whole house without any partitions but there were numerous thick beams behind which we could hide. We spread out to look at the old pieces of furniture which, covered as they were with cobwebs, had the strangest of shapes. Then, one of us discovered the chest.

'Look!' she cried and we all rushed to where she was. She was holding up the lid of the black wooden chest with one hand, with the other she pulled out of its depths a velvet garment. Soon we were all there, looking with amazement at this treasure of taffetas, velvets and silks. They proved to be long gowns, similar to the ones I had seen women wearing on old family photographs. We rejoiced over our discovery for a while, then we decided to go back down to avoid being discovered. Once safely back in the garden, we decided to go up as often as we could, put the dresses on, and play 'ladies'.

My mother was in the habit of taking me to the house and then going on to visit people. I always felt free when my mother was not around, so when my friends said that we could cut up a dress to make clothes for our dolls, I felt very excited about it. Now this would be something really forbidden to do! So, the following day and the whole of that week we took needles and thread and provided our dolls with a really exciting new wardrobe. At the end of the week, we decided to have a party where the dolls would be the children and we – the mothers. Unfortunately, the party never took place.

Aunt Victoria met us on our way down, took us all to the kitchen and spoke to us in a quiet but firm voice. She knew where we had been, and what we had been up to, all the time. She had heard us in the attic and had gone to find out what we had been doing. She saw that we had gone a little too far but hadn't told my mother a word about it. If ever I had wanted the floor to open up and swallow me, it was then. I had never been treated so decently. Rather than being reprimanded and punished, I was spoken to with good-heartedness and understanding.

'It's her mother's clothes, your grandmother's.' she said kindly 'It would upset her very much that you, her own daughter, has cut some of them up, so I suggest we don't tell her OK?'

'But … how?' I had never kept a secret from my mother and I wasn't sure I could cope with it.

'Just like that, we don't mention it,' she said.

The others went to their respective homes and I sat, sad and defeated in the kitchen waiting for my mother to come for me. I couldn't wait to tell her. I wanted absolution.

Ж

In the Armenian quarter, the air-raids held a different attraction. Here, instead of running to the basement and sitting cooped up in the narrow corridors with babies crying and women screaming, as in Sofia, or sitting on the floor in the middle of the kitchen, as we did in the Jewish quarter, we were told to go out and run into the fields.

Since we were quite near them, within minutes we were sitting wrapped up in blankets on the damp grass, listening.

The town was never a target for the RAF, but some way out of town, there were barracks and a military hospital housing German soldiers. We could hear the distant roar of the bombs, but I was particularly taken by the beauty of the fields and the night sky. I remember one particular night when the moon was shining on the tall, ripe wheat and I could see the stems waving at the touch of the gentle breeze. The crickets seemed to be singing to the beauty of the night. Wrapped up in my blanket, although there was no need for this, as the night was warm, I felt a strange longing and a wish to walk across the field, to feel the breeze on my face and the caress of the wheat stems on my legs. Of course, I knew perfectly well I would not be allowed to do it and didn't even attempt it, so it turned into a fantasy which joined the other fantasies I had before I went to sleep.

More and more often now, the adults talked about Poland and about our King Boris who would not let Hitler send us to Poland. Some people were of the view that the Germans were going to lose the war, but that they would make sure that they killed us first. The King, it was said, had refused Hitler the use of the Bulgarian army, because our army could not be sent to fight the Russians who had, a century or so ago, freed us from the Turks.

'But Boris is a German!' went the argument.

'His father was, yes, Ferdinand was a pure German, but even he, when he was chosen to be our king, took our interests to heart and put them first. And Boris, even more so! He will never sell us to the Germans to fight against our liberators from the abominable slavery to the Turks!'

During that week it was said that the King had been called to an audience with Hitler and everybody was certain that as a result of that we would be sent to Poland. The King returned, and nothing happened, then suddenly his death was announced. People cried and said that he had died to save us, that Hitler had given him a 'delayed action poison'.

'Don't be silly,' somebody argued 'He was most probably dead on arrival, only they didn't tell us.'

Since his son, Simeon, was too young to become king, a Regent was appointed who would do Prince Simeon's work until he became of age. Everything was very confused. People now believed that the new Regent was going to go against everything that the King had done. They talked and talked; they were irritable and worried, so, we children, had to try and make our presence as unnoticed as possible.

Minka's sister had a new boyfriend now and we spent a lot of time spying on them. We were dying to 'see' what they were doing, but never actually saw anything. Minka was certain they were 'screwing' and when I asked her how she knew, she said:

'See for yourself, they were alone here today' and she was pointing at a stain on the cover of the sofa in the kitchen. I stared at the thing not knowing what to make of it. I remembered Kira and wished I had asked more about the whole thing, but I hadn't, and not wanting to appear ignorant, said:

'I see.'

Chapter Fifteen

The Red Army Arrives – We are Free!

Sheri appeared on our doorstep early one morning. He was short of breath and perspiration was running down the sides of his face, his blue eyes were sparkling with excitement. We had been sitting in the kitchen, it was very warm so the door leading out on to the patio was open, and we watched him taking the four steps in one jump. He hugged my mother and lifted her off the floor:

'My Thracian Princess.'

'What is it? Why are you running like this?' my mother asked.

'There is definite information that the Red Army have crossed the Danube from Romania last night.'

'My God. Is it possible. We are free!' exclaimed my mother, 'How do you know?'

'Word was brought by the resistance.'

'Is there going to be any fighting?'

'We hope not. There has been a coup d'état.'

'Really! That's unbelievable.'

I sat there, bemused, not daring to ask any questions and

feeling that all this was very, very important.

'Yes, yes, the Regent has been overthrown and we are now in charge. As soon as we get the word from Sofia, we are taking action there too. This is why I came – to tell you to stay home. Don't go anywhere, don't open the door to anyone. Tell Madame Arshalouise too. I wouldn't like her to get hurt.'

I simply couldn't visualise the Regent who was a grown man, being thrown on the floor.

Sheri lifted me in the air and gave me a kiss:

'Be a good girl Bambo' and putting me down, ran off.

'Mummy, mummy, please tell me why did they throw the Regent on the floor?'

'Don't be silly'. They didn't literally throw him, they took his power away from him.'

'How?' I asked

'He was simply told to leave the Palace, and nobody took orders from him any more.'

'Mummy, why is the whole army Red?'

'It isn't Red, silly, it's only called so. Now stop asking stupid questions and let me go to talk to Madame Arshalouise.'

She left me at the breakfast table, possibly for the first time of my life and I quickly crumbled all the bread under the table and poured the hot milk into the sink. Then I sat back on the chair and tried to assess the situation. An army which was red, or called so for whatever reason, was coming and that was a good thing. That too didn't mean much to me, but then, maybe there were not reasons or meanings for everything. But if my mother had said that we were saved, maybe my father would come home and my mother wouldn't be so sad any more, and maybe we were not going to be sent to Poland after all and be killed there. That was reason enough, I thought.

The streets remained very quiet that day as the news spread and people stayed in. We had closed the shutters of all the windows in the house, bolted the doors and all of us sat in the salon where it was dark and cool. Madame Arshalouise played the piano, her head tilted backwards, her daughter was knitting and the needles made an unpleasant noise competing with the sound of the piano. My mother sat on her chair biting her handkerchief. Eventually we all went to bed and the night passed undisturbed but we were awoken abruptly very early in the morning by the sound of gunfire. In a minute we were all up and met in the salon. No one said a word but I noticed the worried looks my mother and Madame Arshalouise exchanged, then we heard shouting in the street and Madame Arshalouise's daughter ran to the kitchen and opened the shutters a little way before anyone could stop her. We ran after her and peeped out into the street.

A man was running and waving his arms in all directions, shouting:

'They are fighting! They are fighting: Stay in! Don't shut the windows they might break! Close all the shutters and stay in!'

People from other houses shouted:

'Who is fighting whom?'

'Us! Us! The Resistance! We are fighting the Fascists! Down with the Nazis! Long live Stalin!'

Madame Arshalouise's daughter closed the shutters and secured them, then turned round and said, her voice filled with emotion:

'They are coming. Our saviours are coming and saving us for the second time! God save the Red Army! Long live Stalin!'

That meant Russia, I knew that much. Why hadn't anybody said to me that this was what we were waiting for? Then I would have known that we were waiting for something to happen, something good.

'But this is lovely!' I shouted 'Papa will be coming home now, if we are saved! And Uncle Marco and Albert and everybody, and we will go back home!'

My words fell flat and I asked, discouraged:

'Aren't we?'

'We don't know yet.' said my mother.

Throughout the day we heard long exchanges of fire which seemed to come from the centre of town and although it never seemed to come closer, it kept us indoors and frightened.

In the evening, Sheri appeared again. He was wearing a strange green uniform and had a rifle hanging over his shoulder.

'My God! What is this?' my mother said, taking a step back from him.

'What do you think? It's a Sten Gun!' he said pointing at the gun.

'Are you a policeman?' I asked also afraid of him, as he seemed taller than usual in the heavy boots, the unusual looking shirt with epaulettes and the green cap.

'Afraid, Bambo?' he said bursting into his warm familiar laughter, 'You mustn't be. I fought today; we took the Town Hall, the Police Station, the Barracks, the Post Office, everything. They fled like rats out of a sewer.'

'You fought?' my mother said, 'My God, you haven't killed anybody have you?'

'I don't think so!' Sheri laughed again, 'The mere sound of the gunfire made them run. Many of them had fled during the night. The Red Army will be here tomorrow and we are preparing a victors' welcome for them. I must be on my way now. I am on duty tonight.' He gulped the last drops of the coffee my mother had prepared for him and made a face, 'Ugh! I never got used to drinking this rubbish.'

He gave us both a kiss and was on his way.

The following morning started off quietly, but by noon we could hear voices in the street. They were cheerful voices singing, and shouting:

'Long live the Soviet Union! Long live the Red Army! Long live Stalin!'

As for us, we were still inside, the shutters well secured

barely letting any air in, (and it was a hot September day) just some light through the slats. Soon the singing and cheering came nearer, along with the roaring sound of heavy vehicles.

It seemed to me that everybody else in the town was celebrating and I pleaded with my mother to allow me to go and look out through the window in Madame Arshalouise's kitchen which was the only one that looked out onto the street, and where I could hear her daughter joining in with the cheering.

'Stay where you are.' my mother ordered and I had to obey.

The sound was now so loud that we could not have spoken to each other without shouting and I felt my mother relaxing in her chair. To my great surprise, she started humming, her features relaxed and she was smiling. Oh, how wonderful this was! At last there was a smile on her face! Maybe now she would let me join in too.

'Oh, mummy, please, please, let's go to, the kitchen!'

She stood up, not saying a word, walked across the hall to the kitchen and I followed. The sun was splashing in through the wide open window, which after the semi-darkness of our room made me squint. I ran to the window and the two women let me lean on the sill. Then I saw the amazing sight. Heavy lorries and tanks were driving slowly up the hill and the line stretched as far as the eye could see. On them, were hundreds of soldiers, some sitting on the seats, some standing and some hanging onto the sides. They all wore dusty grey-green uniforms and heavy even dustier boots. They were smiling though, and waving to us. There were people running with the convoy, throwing flowers and in the windows people seemed to be piled one on top of the other, all singing and cheering.

'Are they the Red Army?' I asked.

'Yes,' my mother answered, 'they are.'

I looked up at her, surprised at the emotion I had detected in her voice. I saw her eyes shining with tears, and once more, she joined in with the singing.

'Is it Russian, mummy? Can you speak Russian?'

'Yes. It is Russian. It's very much like Bulgarian. It's also a Slav language.' and she went on singing.

When the shouting and the singing in the street stopped, we all sat in the kitchen and had tea together. It was like a celebration, and they kept talking about having been saved, about an end to the laws against us Jews and I thought that life was going to be different. It wasn't going back to what it was, it wasn't going to be sad like it had been up to now, but it was going to be different. I didn't know how different, but it couldn't be too bad if we were not going to be killed.

Chapter Sixteen

The Russians – Volodya and the Colonels

Towards the end of the afternoon, we heard heavy footsteps outside followed by a loud banging on the front door. The women looked at each other and I saw panic on their faces.

'This is Volodya! Open the door, I won't do you any harm!' a deep voice shouted. I realised again that this was Russian and to my surprise, I could understand!

'Don't open the door!' hissed Madame Arshalouise to her daughter who had made a gesture as though she was going to, 'There are maybe many of them out there. They will ... attack us!' We were all standing now, I was clutching my mother's hand and shaking with fear.

'I am the Colonel's batman,' the voice came up again, 'I am looking for lodgings for both comrade Colonels, please open up.'

'I suppose we better talk to him,' said my mother, 'Otherwise he might break the door down. He might be genuine.'

'Yes, I suppose so.' Madame Arshalouise said and we all walked to the front door. My mother opened it slightly and we could see the shadow of a tall man. Because of the curfew, he had to come in before we could switch the light on.

'I am looking for a room for my Colonels … do you understand me … we need room ….'

The light went on, and we saw a slim tall very young man, with a broad smile, straw blond hair and red cheeks.

'I want to inspect … see … the house … you understand? For my comrade Colonels.'

The women relaxed and Madame Arshalouise showed the soldier around. They came back to the kitchen together and as he noticed me, came straight up to me, sat on the chair and put me on his knees. I wasn't used to this sort of treatment, besides, I wasn't a little girl any longer, but didn't know what to say.

'I … me … I have … you understand, I have – no had a little sister.' He stroked my hair, 'Same hair… same little sister.' He looked at me just as I was sneaking a glance at him, 'Don't be afraid' he said to me, 'Volodya won't harm you… my sister, she is dead – kaput – the Germans kaput, all village dead.'

He sat quietly for a moment, then put me on the floor and got up. His face was sad now, and although I didn't understand everything he said, I felt that I liked him.

'My comrade Colonels will have that room,' he said 'I will bring them now.'

Madame Arshalouise nodded as the choice had fallen on her own bedroom.

'I go and bring, now. I will come and clean the room, and the Colonels' clothes and boots. I will not need the kitchen. Horosho?'

'Yes,' my mother answered as it seemed that she was the only one to understand him fully.

'We come back after dinner,' Volodya said, touched his cap with two fingers as a salute, and left.

'Is he in the Red Army?' I asked.

'He couldn't be more than eighteen years old,' said my

mother, 'Isn't it awful!'

'Don't they usually requisition schools and such places?' asked our landlady.

'The soldiers maybe, but he was talking about two colonels.'

'Mummy, why did he call them 'comrades'?'

'I am scared stiff,' said my mother, 'good job there are locks on the doors. Don't forget to lock yourselves in.'

'No, we won't, but please wait until they come back, don't go to your room yet' pleaded Madame Arshalouise.

'Ah ... lovely Russian soldiers!' said her daughter dreamily.

A slight knock on the front door made us all jump again, but Sheri's voice followed and reassured us. My mother ran towards the front door and came back with him. He looked very tired and sat down heavily on the nearest chair.

'What have you been doing? How is the family? Have you got Russians in the house? my mother pressed him with questions.

'I haven't been home,' His voice was weary, 'They can look after themselves there, there are plenty of them, and some men too. I was worried about you. You OK?'

'Sort of.' my mother told him about Volodya's visit and the requisition of Madame Arshalouise's bedroom for two colonels.

'Well, colonels would be OK I suppose,' said Sheri slowly, 'It's the soldiers... they have been drinking and raping something terrible.' he sighed, 'It's understandable, maybe; they have been at war for years. I was worried about you... all women here... they have been drinking anything they could lay their hands on. Would you believe eau de Cologne?'

Nobody said a word.

'Are you hungry?' my mother asked.

Sheri shook his head. He was looking down at some spot on the floor and still shaking his head said:

'We don't know what it is like ... war ... these men ... like beasts. They are absolutely forbidden to drink, think about it –

an officer is allowed to shoot a soldier on sight, like that, in the street, if he is drunk. And they still drink,' he looked up before he said, 'and rape. I am not trying to scare you but to warn you. Lock yourselves in. I suppose the Colonels are genuine, so you have to let them in.' He got up,' I must run. Take care.'

'What is rape?' I asked

'Oh, shut up with your questions!' my mother said impatiently.

Sheri put a heavy hand on my head and said:

'Rape, Bambo, is when a man makes a woman do something she doesn't want to do.'

'Sheri!' my mother scolded him. He gave her a light kiss and a tap on the shoulder, and left the room.

'Why do you drive yourself so hard? You want to win the war single handed or something?' my mother followed him.

'Until all our boys come down from the mountain ... and back from the camps .... ' I heard him say, his voice fading.

Volodya's arrival followed soon after that. He walked in, smiling at us and ushering in a man and a woman, both in uniforms.

'Comrade Colonel,' he said to the man, 'this is our landlady.'

The colonel bent from the waist down towards Madame Arshalouise, but the woman shook hands with everybody enquiring about our names, then patted me on the head. Their uniforms seemed very formidable, with the trousers widening from the knees up, and the rigid epaulettes that made their shoulders look wide and square.

The officers went to their room, led by Volodya who came out in a couple of minutes, carrying their clothes. He asked for a brush and went outside where we heard him brushing vigorously; he then came back in and asked for shoe polish and brushes, deposited the clothes carefully on a chair and went out again to polish the Colonels' boots. All smile and chat had disappeared from his face while he was doing this and we watched him come and go, and listened to his brushing and polishing with amazement. Then, in he came again, a pair of boots in each hand, a smile back on his face again.

'There!' he said 'Now ... to bed!'

He picked up the uniforms and left the kitchen.

We all went to our respective bedrooms. My mother locked our door as quietly as she could, not to let our suspicions become obvious to the Russians.

'I wonder if the batman sleeps with his colonels,' said my mother.

'He might go and sleep with the other soldiers, wherever they are.' I said.

My mother didn't answer, and as the darkness enveloped us, I felt free to let my mind wander, to go back on all the things that had happened that day, so many of which I hadn't understood. Men. Women. According to Kira, they liked the forbidden thing they did, only they wouldn't admit it. As far as I could gather from Minka's sister's behaviour, both her and her boyfriend wanted to do it. Then why was it that an officer would shoot a soldier if he did it? And why would women have to be forced, if they liked it anyway? How awful it was to think that a soldier, like Volodya for instance, would get shot! But then, a lot of people had been shot and killed in the war. I knew it, but I hadn't thought about it. It had been something adults talked about, something they had heard of. It had been remote and speculative. But tonight, Volodya had said that his little sister, his whole family had been killed. The Germans had killed them. That was real, direct. That meant that the speculations about people killed in Poland were true. I was frightened. Will Sheri go to war now? Will he kill Germans? What if they killed him? My mind was full of questions, frightening, disquieting questions to which I couldn't find any explanations or answers, so I took refuge in a deep agitated sleep. When I woke up, in the morning, I saw my mother turning the key slowly and opening the door just enough to peep out into the hall. She closed the door immediately and, unaware of my gaze, rested her back on it, her features expressing great amazement.

'Mummy! Mummy!' I whispered 'what is it?'

'It's Volodya!' she said, 'he is asleep on the floor, outside the Colonels' room! Like a dog.'

Chapter Seventeen

Living with The Russians

In the days that followed, people relaxed and the sense of insecurity and fear eased up. Slowly people started to leave their homes, just to the corner at first, then daringly, from one quarter to the other. People's faces changed; I could see smiles and happy expressions as my mother and I took a walk to the Jewish quarter to visit the family for the first time in two weeks, since the Red Army had arrived. We got used to seeing Russian soldiers in the streets, heavy lorries transporting 'the Red Army' roaring up and down the streets and people always waving at them, some with a handkerchief, others waving a clenched fist. I found that odd, it seemed more like a threat than a greeting but my mother said this was no laughing matter, this was the Reds' greeting, and this is how it was going to be.

Also, people talked about the Russians being very fond of watches. The story went that they simply helped themselves to whatever they liked and just doled out receipts worded: 'Boris took the car.' or 'Ivan took the watch.'

'But why?' I asked.

'Because they have no watches.'

'But then how can they tell the time?'

'Don't be silly! Some of them do have watches, but only very few. They are poor people, peasants, and peasants can't afford watches.'

I didn't think it was right to go and just take whatever you wanted, but then no one had said that what the Russians were doing was right. Only we were not supposed to criticise them, I thought, and I left it at that.

Aunt Victoria said with conviction that now that the Red Army had 'taken' the country, the men would be back soon.

'I wish it were the Americans.' said my mother.

'Shhh!' Aunt Victoria scolded her , 'Shame on you! You are in Marco's house!'

'I don't think like him and you know it,' said my mother, 'I only hope they live up to his expectations. My guess is he will be bitterly disappointed.'

Since the Red Army had arrived, there were other changes for us. We could take the yellow stars off our lapels now, we could walk in the streets after 9pm., we could go to the centre of town without fear of the Hitler Youth or anybody . Being a Jew wasn't such a fearful thing any more. I remember my cousin Elsa saying with a deep sigh which made her generous bosom swell out impressively:

'The Red Army will soon calm down and anyway all these tales about watch snatching are just gossip anyway. They are heroes! They have arrived here after four years of bravely fighting the enemy! Soon they will settle down, there will be peace and our lives will be ten times better than before the war! There will be no exploitation, everybody will be equal ... '

'Shut up girl!' my mother interrupted impatiently, 'You are talking as though you are addressing a Party meeting.'

'What of it. These are facts. Our liberator Stalin will make our lives worthwhile. Enough oppression, down with capital-ism!'

'Ha, you should talk! I hope you don't carry on like this to strangers, everybody in town knows you married money!'

I wondered whether some day, when I grow up I will have breasts like Elsa's. Later I heard my mother tell Madame Arshalouise about that conversation:

'If she weren't my brother's daughter, and I didn't know her as well as I do, I would think she was a real Red. She is simply repeating the words she has heard my brother say. He is an idealist, in his mouth they are not big words but that vain girl, honestly! If you ask me,' and here my mother lowered her voice 'I don't think life will be very easy under the Reds.'

'No, I suppose not. But at least we are free from the Nazis.'

'Yes. I am enormously grateful, but far from optimistic.' Whatever was said about the Russians, at least they didn't hate us, they were not going to send us to Poland and kill us! I expressed these thoughts, and my mother said:

'Life under the Russians will be difficult, you can take my word for it.'

'But why do we have to be 'under' somebody?' I enquired, 'Before the Germans came, before the war, were we also 'under' someone?'

'No,' she said quietly, 'No, but things will never be the same again. This war has changed the world.'

Chapter Eighteen

My Father is Back Again

'When will papa come back?'

'If he comes back.'

'Why not? Why not?'

'This is war. The Germans might kill everybody on their way as they retreat. And who knows who will be on their way .... '

I understood that this was 'adult' talk. This was true and frightening. There was nothing more to be said. My father would come home if he is alive. No man had returned yet from the labour camps and I chose to be hopeful.

We got used to the comings and goings of our Colonels and Volodya shadowing them like a faithful dog.

'They are Jewish.' said my mother.

'How do you know?' I enquired, surprised.

'By their name, it's a Jewish name.'

'I couldn't tell.'

'It's because they are Ashkenazi and we are Sephardi.'

'What? But this is like our name!'

'It's different denominations, that's all.'

'What is that?'

'Oh, leave me alone! It's simply different Jews, now stop asking questions!'

Was there no end to the things I didn't know? I walked away, my head down hurt by this brick wall against which I bumped so often.

There was a new addition to my life since the Red Army had come into our country. Newspapers. I had never paid much attention to them when I was young. Afterwards, they were forbidden to us, now newspapers were freely available and my mother got one every day. It talked of distressing, terrible things. The bold letters in the headlines told of inquisitions carried out on the resistance, men and women, when they were caught by the Nazis, to get information about their comrades, or their future activities.

Violence was a novelty to me, and now haunted my nights. The human body and its vulnerability, the human mind and its ingenuity to find means to make people talk. The papers talked of heroes and heroines who died under torture but did not betray their comrades. That we were alive today because they had chosen to die.

I woke up one night and heard a male voice. I sat up on my bed, frightened to death. My mother grabbed me, and made me shut up pressing my face against her chest. I now realised that the voice came from outside the window. It was a deep, sad, panic stricken voice. It was pleading with somebody for forgiveness and his words were separated from each other by the sound of lashes.

'Please ... please ... tovarish ... I will ... never again ... I promise .... '

There was no response but the sound of the lash. An arm, with clockwork regularity hitting the poor man with what could have been a belt.

'Please ... I promise .... ' the voice was weakening and the beating continued.

'Shut up you dog!' I heard from the other man, and realised it had been spoken in Russian; more hissed than spoken.

My mother pressed her hands against my ears but I could still hear the voice and the lashes. I don't know how long this went on for. Eventually the voice became weaker and weaker and finally stopped, so did the lashes.

My mother and I cried and cried as quietly as we could.

'Mummy, please let's go and help the man! He will die out there!'

'There is nothing we can do for him. He is probably dead.'

'This is awful, mummy! Why? why? Why couldn't he forgive him? He promised not to do 'it' again? What more could he have done? Why are people so wicked?'

'Go to sleep now,' she said.

We never opened the shutters of our bedroom again.

Ж

My father turned up one evening. He just walked in, looking like a beggar, tired and bearded, a little bundle under his arm and his shoes tied to his feet with a string. My mother fell into his arms and I followed. Having got over the surprise of his arrival, we went into the kitchen where my mother prepared his supper; we had already eaten. Then we told him of the Red Army's arrival, of Sheri in uniform, of the colonels in the house. Then he told us how the Red Army had freed him too, how he had made some of the journey back by train without paying anything and how he had had to walk some of the way. because there were no trains running. He had been on his way for three days.

Then, they discussed among themselves about returning home, to Sofia. It seemed that a phase of our lives had come to an end; that, at least for us, life would soon resume its normal course: I would be returning to school, my father would be with us all the time, we would be free again and I could sense that calmer, happier days seemed to be coming. Finally we all went to bed.

Since the terrible incident outside our window, my bed had been moved from under it, to another wall, facing my parents' bed. We switched the light out and in the deep silence I listened to the October rain. The summer was over now and the night was chilly. Even the crickets were quiet. Since the 'incident' I always tucked my head under the bedclothes to avoid hearing anything, should 'it' happen again. After a while, I couldn't breathe and uncovered my face. It was then that I realised my parents were talking. I felt that what was being said was not meant for me, so I pretended I was asleep by breathing evenly – and listened attentively. My father was talking:

' … millions, millions, apparently. In concentration camps. We had heard human voices you see, from those freight carriages, so now we know – they were being transported to the death camps. Mass killings, what they say is unbelievable, but apparently true. In gas chambers … '

'But who were they? The ones in the trains you saw?'

'Jews, from Saloniki I think, but although most of the people in the camps were Jews, I mean the ones that were killed, there were others as well.'

'But why? Why?'

'Specially built chambers … with gas pipes … filled so much, that when they died, they were still standing … '

I felt cold. I couldn't take any more and tucked my head under again, shaking with cold and fright. Now I could hear my father's voice even under the bedclothes, he was crying and wasn't careful to whisper any longer:

'They made soap out of the fat … human fat … they made lamp shades from the skins …. '

'Stop it, please stop!' my mother was saying, 'I am sure these are just rumours, please calm down.'

'These are no rumours. I heard it from a Russian officer in the train. He had SEEN it. The camp. Auschwitz, in Germany; walking skeletons … the survivors … in the end they didn't quite manage to kill them all … they had run out of room …. He had seen the inquisition rooms, the operating theatres where they used people as … and he was now going to Berlin to kill, he said. Kill women and children only! If you had only seen him as he spoke …. '

I pressed my hands against my ears. I couldn't cry but my whole body shook. I don't think the enormity of what was said penetrated my brain but some of it did and as I fell asleep that night, and for many nights afterwards I dreamt that I was being chased by something awful. It was very very tall, and could have been a bear but I saw no details, just the shape, as tall as a house and I was running in what seemed to be a maze. I turned corner after corner, hoping to find an opening, a way out but instead, more and more complicated patterns of partitions appeared. My legs were soft under me, and each time I lifted a foot it took a great effort and I was losing the race. Although I ran all alone, beyond the stone walls of the maze, I could hear human voices, crying and screaming, begging for help. But I just kept running.

Chapter Nineteen

We Celebrate the New Year – Return to Sofia

Volodya became a regular visitor as he would come during the day to clean the Colonel's room, brush their uniforms and polish their boots. He often came to our kitchen and chatted to my mother. He told us how he had left his village when he was called up; how he had fought in France and Italy and also for Stalingrad; how he had arrived, with his unit, back at his village where he had hoped to see his family, but instead they found only ruins. The village had been burnt down, not a house was spared, not a soul had survived.

'And then,' Volodya said quite calmly, 'I swore to survive the war, to fight to its bitter end, and when we reach Germany I will, with my bare hands, kill! I will kill German babies – my sister had a baby – German old men and women, I shall set fire to villages.'

I understood most of what he was saying but my mother, probably assuming that I did not, let me stay. I listened fascinated and frightened. Hadn't a Russian officer told the very same thing to my father?

The Jewish New Year was approaching and my grandfather wanted us all to gather at the house for dinner, to spend that evening together to celebrate the New Year and also thank God for being alive and safe.

It really was a festive occasion. The salon had been cleared from all the beds and luggage and a long table set. All the men had returned and it was the first time that all the women had their husbands with them, and all the children – their fathers. I sat between my cousin Sheri who was wearing civilian clothes and my cousin Joseph – Aunt Clara's red haired son. Away from my mother's supervision, the meal went quite well for me. I listened to my uncle Marco's inspired talk. He was telling about the future and how wonderful for everybody it will be. Someone suggested Uncle Marco might become Mayor. My mother expressed her doubts; she didn't believe, she said, that a Jew would be elected and she was immediately attacked by Uncle Marco and his eldest son, Albert, who insisted vehemently that now, in the Socialist way of life, we were all really equal. I wondered. I thought people were equal by birth, by virtue of being human. But then, the Nazis had claimed that the Jews were inferior, which meant: not equal.

Late the following afternoon, there was a soft knock on our kitchen door, and my mother said:

'Come in.'

The door opened very slowly and the lady Colonel looked in shyly, then she walked in and shut the door behind her.

'Please forgive me Comrade,' she said to my mother, her hand hard and cool touching lightly my cheek, 'I wanted to talk to you .... '

'Do sit down, please,' my mother invited her, 'I can't offer much ... .'

'Don't worry, please don't worry ... I will only be a minute. Please don't tell my husband I came in to talk to you, please!'

'No, I won't. You can count on me.'

'And you too?' the lady colonel said to me.

'No. No. I won't either.'

'She is pretty reliable.' said my mother and I felt filled with pride at her confidence in me.

'Well, it's our New Year, isn't it?' the woman said.

'Yes. It is. Happy New Year. Here, I have some traditional cakes. They are ersatz of course, but we should be grateful for that too.'

'Oh, thank you! Thank you so much!' she helped herself, 'My husband doesn't want to know, he doesn't recognise religion. But we are Jewish, well only by tradition but I so miss the tradition of my father's home .... '

'I know what you mean.'

'They are both dead now. My parents I mean ... so I just wanted ... on a holiday ... to just remember them.'

'I am sorry. About your parents.'

'Stalingrad. Bombardments.' The woman's eyes looked moist.

'Was it very tough on you?' my mother said taking a deep breath.

'Well, not really, not in comparison with what others have been through.'

'Is it true, the concentration camps?'

'Oh, yes. Every bit of it. One great nightmare. But, how about you, it must have been tough for you too?'

'Yes, it was, but as you say, not in comparison to others. We have been lucky, we didn't know it at the time, but now that we know the truth, – we are alive and should be grateful.'

The woman got up.

'It seems so long,' she pulled at her rough uniform jacket, 'It won't be long now. Another year or so.'

'A whole year?'

' ... or thereabouts. I must go now.' she extended a firm hand to my mother.

'Thank you so much for the cakes. Happy New Year.'

And she quickly went out, as though she had waited all the time to be able to say the last words.

'Blood is thicker than water.' my mother said.

'Why doesn't she want her husband to know she came to see us?'

I asked.

'Because the Russians, the Soviet Russians don't believe in religion. They deny religion.'

But later, to my father she said:

'she was afraid of her own husband! That's how free they are!'

Soon afterwards my father left for Sofia. He was going to look for a job and a flat and then send for us. Most of the deportees were now returning to Sofia and the Jewish quarter was empty once more.

The Bulgarian Army had joined the allies and was fighting the Germans in Hungary and Czechoslovakia.

Sheri wasn't around to visit us and bring us wood but Volodya helped a lot. His smiling face and shining blue eyes brought laughter and light, but he would never accept anything to eat. Not even a cup of tea. Or what we called tea for lack of real tea. My mother was convinced that he had been warned by his superiors not to accept any food from the citizens, probably for fear of being poisoned. Though, why we would want to poison them, I never quite fathomed.

It was reported that documents had been found in the files of the Town Hall, which confirmed the rumours that all Jews would have been deported before the end of that year – 1944. I knew that deportation meant concentration camps and Poland. The Red Army had saved us by a very narrow margin.

Some three weeks after he had left, my father wrote and said that he had found a job at the American Military Mission. As there was no other work available he had decided to apply at such places where he could make use of the languages he spoke, and the Americans had been the first ones to offer him a job. He had also found a flat, well, a room in a flat, really. The new regulations stipulated that a family of three where the child was under 12 years of age, was allowed only one room. So, he had found us a room in a flat occupied by another family of three but their daughter was older and they had permission to occupy two rooms. I was very happy that we were going back. I was looking forward to school again, and to a more normal life. There had been fun and games in Shoumen, but there had also been a lot of fear and tears. I felt older somehow, and was looking forward to studying and reading books and getting to penetrate the enigmas of the adult world and understand so many things that were happening around me.

We went to see the family and say 'good bye', packed our few possessions and Volodya gave us a lift to the railway station in his jeep. The railway station was in total chaos. There were no timetables. The trains just came and went, we had to wait and see. There were many people, mainly Russian soldiers – men and women, and some civilians. We sat around all day. Finally, late in the afternoon a train pulled in. The loudspeaker announced that it was going to Sofia and we rushed to get on. Unfortunately we were outnumbered by people who moved faster. My mother ran, the crowd became denser; people were shouting and pushing. Suddenly I felt my hand slip from my mother's. I started to shout but nobody paid attention, the crowd dragged me along. People were climbing into the train through the windows, I was too short to be able to see around me, and as panic set in, I heard my name uttered by someone ahead of me.

'Yeeeeesss! That's me!' I shouted but my voice was lost in the noise, 'That's meeee!' I shouted again and again.

The train began to move. Somebody lifted me up and a strong pair of arms took me up and in through a window. I banged my head on the window frame, and as the train was gathering speed I found myself on my mother's knees.

The compartment was full of Russian officers. They all knew my name now and were all talking about their own children. There was a general conversation all about children but I was too tired to listen and as I was falling asleep an officer got up and offered his seat so that I could lie down with my head on my mother's knees. Then he wrapped his long overcoat, made of rough heavy material, around me. The security of my mother's nearness, the rhythm of the motion and the warmth of the coat wrapped around me, lulled me and I slept throughout the journey back to Sofia.

Chapter Twenty

A Room in Gladstone Street – Back to School

The train rolled slowly in and came to a halt. All passengers rushed towards the doors and so, eventually, did we. My father was waiting for us, but how we found him in the crowd, I shall never know. People were busily rushing around us in all directions. Most of them were men in military uniforms – all Russian. We managed somehow to get to the tram with all our luggage.

'Sofia is a ghost city.' my father informed us.

My parents sat on a double seat, both their laps and the floor by their feet laden with suitcases and holdalls, not all ours. I stood by the window and looked out as the autumn morning lit up the sky. It had rained during the night and the pavements were still wet. The hesitant November sun brought out the colours of the rainbow as it shone on the puddles left here and there by the night rain.

As the tram progressed, the horror story unfolded. There was hardly a building left intact. There were large holes in the ground where houses had stood. Odd walls added gloom to the scene, with their brickwork covered in soot; their gaping windows through which I could see the sky beyond. There were holes in the middle of the road too, and in one place where the tram rails had been blown up, they had been precariously replaced over the hole and as the tram sped over it, it made a frightening, hollow noise.

'It would seem that they did do us a favour by evacuating us.' my mother said looking out, over my shoulder, 'God knows how many people have been killed.'

'Yes and there is a terrible housing shortage. Everybody wants to come back but as you can see, half the flats are gone. By the way, Moskovitch Mansions has been hit.'

'No!'

'Yes. Not a direct hit though, just the third floor, our floor, as if it had been cut off with a giant knife.'

'My goodness! Can you imagine if we had been … '

'That's what I mean.'

'But how about the others … all our Bulgarian neighbours … ?'

'Many of them had decided to leave Sofia anyway, but many …. '

They fell silent for awhile.

'This is why we have to share now, is it?' my mother asked.

'Because of the housing shortage? I don't know. Strange things are going on. This new Government is replacing every key position held by an ordinary person, with a man of their own – a Red. And they are all peasants!'

'Sh … sh … sh … shut up!' my mother whispered.

'We are free now my dear, you seem to forget that.' said my father loudly.

'Tickets Comrade.' I turned round and saw the conductor standing by my father, who handed him the fare and took the tickets from his hand.

'Comrade indeed!' said my father angrily as the man walked away.

'Will you shut up!'

'He is not my comrade, and I am, by no means, his!'

'You better get used to it, because this is how it's going to be from now on.'

Our new home was a room in a third floor flat of a small block in Gladstone Street. It was a wide, tree-lined street with a garden square at one end. It was by far the most elegant flat we had ever lived in, and it would have been even lovelier to have had it all to ourselves. As it was, we only had the master bedroom, with the bathroom 'en suite', and a large balcony overlooking the back garden.

Our co-sharers had an 18 year old daughter and occupied two rooms and the kitchen.

'But why can't we use the kitchen too?' my mother protested.

'Whoever is first in the flat sets the rules,' my father explained patiently. 'This is how it is now. We have enough cooking facilities in the bathroom. It is a very nice bathroom, and it's all ours. They use the shower in what was the servants' quarters at the back of the flat.'

Moving in was no problem since we had little in the way of possessions. My father had arranged for three folding beds to be delivered before our arrival, so at least we had beds to sleep in.

On the following day, I was sent to the local municipal school. Secretly I was till longing for the French school, but as I realised the financial impossibility of being sent to a private school, I didn't even mention it. I was ushered into a large classroom of about 40 children, all my own age, all staring at me. The teacher, a tall lean woman, with grey hair and no make up, was standing by the blackboard. She extended a protective arm towards me, smiled sweetly and said to the class:

'This is the new comrade I told you about this morning. She has just returned from evacuation and, like our comrade Rachel, has missed two years at school. But we shall help our Israelite comrades to catch up with us, won't we?'

'Yes, Comrade.' answered the class.

Throughout the teacher's speech, I stood facing the class, not knowing where to look. I was vaguely aware of a girl in the front row. She seemed to be looking at me, smiling.

'Here, sit with Rachel.' The teacher's firm hand on my shoulder guided me towards the girl in the front row. The class was very quiet. The girl leant towards me and whispered:

'Call me Shelly.'

I smiled back at her, relieved to be seated, and no longer the focus of the class's attention. It had been a long time since I had sat in a classroom. Would I be able to catch up with all the material that I had missed? Will they accept me as one of them?

Chapter Twenty One

My New Friend Shelly

The teacher left the classroom and all hell broke loose.

'As I said, my name is Shelly,' the girl turned to me again, 'we only returned from deportation two weeks ago. I am catching up though. It's not difficult. I'll tell you all the books you need to buy, all right?'

'Yes, thank you.'

I realised that she was being friendly but wondered whether that was just because we had been placed on the same bench, placed together because we were Jewish? Because we had suffered the same fate, different from the rest of the class?

'Until you came, I was the only Jewish girl in the class,' Shelly seemed to have read my thoughts, 'I felt so lonely.'

'Did you? Why? Did they hate you?'

'No, not at all. They are all very nice; they don't seem to mind. It may be me, really, who feels different. I mean, how can I expect them to understand?'

'Yes.'

'We stick together OK?'

'OK. Tell me, why is everyone calling each other 'Comrade'?'

'This is how it is in the Soviet Union.' Shelly said gravely.

I was impressed with her use of "The Soviet Union' rather than 'Russia'.

'It has to do with equality,' she went on, 'In the Soviet Union, everybody is considered to be equal to everyone else.'

'How do you mean 'equal'?'

'Well, as far as I can understand, nobody is a 'Mister' or 'Madam' or 'Sir' or 'Lady' do you follow? It's always Comrade. Even Stalin, the greatest of them all, is called Comrade. Besides, everybody works for the Government.'

'How do you know all this?' I was full of admiration.

'We are studying these things, here, at school. The History of the Communist Party for instance.'

'Are we really?' It sounded wonderful. 'I so want to know all these things.'

'I must confess to being mildly interested in them.' Shelly said, 'Do you think Stalin is as marvellous as they say? That he is like a father to his people.'

'Oh, yes! He has done so much for his people. It's just incredible, Lenin and him, they are the greatest!'

'Yes, but I must confess, I don't feel very comfortable calling everybody, especially the teacher, Comrade.'

'I know what you mean.'

'But, am I right in saying that one is almost forced to do it?

I don't know how, but I feel compelled.' I said hesitantly.

'Yes, as though if you didn't, something will happen to you. Something bad.'

'So, you have the same feeling?'

The bell rang and the class returned as noisily as they had left.

'Sh ... sh ... sh ... careful,' whispered Shelly, leaning towards me and speaking into my ear, 'We are also studying Stalin's biography and ... '

'When?'

'Three times a week, after class,' she whispered as the teacher was coming in and silence was restored in the classroom.

Chapter Twenty Two

The Red Army Officer's Coat

When I came home from school, my mother met me at the front door and on her face I read disaster! 'What have I done now' I thought.

Without saying a word she took me by the collar of my jumper and, keeping me at arm's length, led me into the bathroom where something was bubbling on a noisy primus stove.

'Strip,' she said, 'Don't ask questions. Just do as you are told. We are full of lice.'

I began to take my clothes off and as I was doing so, my mother took them from me and dropped them into the bubbling tin basin. She was pushing them in and turning them round with a wooden spoon. The bathroom was full of steam and the smell of soap.

My whole body started to itch.

'How did we get them?' I asked when totally undressed. 'Where from?'

'The Russian soldiers. In the train from Shoumen, remember? You were wrapped all night in one of their coats. No wonder it kept you warm. It was alive!'

'How about my hair? Don't they go into the hair as well?'

'I'll check you, but I think we have only got the clothes' variety. The ones that go on the hair are a different species.'

She took a torch and parting my hair with the end of the wooden spoon, examined my scalp carefully, as I stood naked and shivering on the stone tiled floor.

'No,' she said finally, 'It's clear. Get in the bath now.'

For three days she boiled and ironed clothes, bedclothes, towels and socks. Finally she pronounced us 'clean' again, and I went back to school.

Shelly appeared to have awaited my return eagerly. She had prepared a list of books I would need, and she offered to come and help me buy them. Except for the odd newspaper and some bread, I had never actually bought anything before. The prospect of walking into a shop with money in my pocket and a list of books to purchase was extremely attractive.

'I have to ask my mother .' I said

'She will be only too glad to have the burden off her hands, I am sure.'

Somehow I doubted it.

After school Shelly accompanied me home.

'This is Shelly,' I introduced her to my mother, 'we are in the same class.'

My lunch was ready. My mother told me to wash my hands and sit down to eat.

Shelly sat quietly, looking on, not saying a word. I could detect disapproval on my mother's face, but didn't know what it was she disapproved of. Eventually, she began asking questions, and Shelly answered carefully, with respect, even reverence. I so wanted my mother to approve of my friend!

'Where do you live? What does your father do? Do you have brothers and sisters? Where did you live before the war?'

Shelly's father was an electrician. He had had his own shop for electrical repairs. But now people simply didn't have shops any more so he did repairs at people's homes. Did we need anything repaired? He was a very good electrician.

Shelly was reminded of the time and also, that her mother was sure to be waiting for her. Shelly left. There was no question of me, going out with Shelly for my books. I didn't even ask, and Shelly never mentioned it. I was certain that my mother's treatment of her, would make her mad at me, and that she would never speak to me again. I couldn't blame her if she didn't.

The following day, however, Shelly acted as though nothing had happened.

Shelly was in the habit of waiting for me downstairs in the street, so we could walk together to school. She also walked home with me in the afternoon. It meant a detour for her, and I never understood what prompted her to do it.

I was very pleased that we had to stay in after classes. The History of the CP, Stalin's Biography and Lenin's Biography. There was a great deal of additional material to study, dates to memorise, names to learn. The idea of being out after school, on my own, and that my parents couldn't prevent or interfere, made it all worth while. It even made up, at least at the beginning, for the unpleasant feeling the new slogans, new phrases, new 'values' engendered. That we were made to refer to Stalin as our Father; that our aim was to 'uproot our enemies – the imperialists' – wherever they were, under whatever guise. And worst of all, calling everybody Comrade.

But maybe that wasn't the worst, not in the long run. The worst was, when I realised that it was dangerous to do otherwise. The danger itself was neither spelled out, nor it's nature stated, but we knew it was there; and that, that was the worst.

One day, as we were walking home, Shelly asked:

'What do you do on Sundays?'

'Nothing much. Homework, mainly. Sometimes, if I have finished my homework, we visit my cousins; but mostly we just stay in.'

'You mean, you stay in with your parents?'

'Yes, of course. What else?'

'Don't you go out with friends? I thought that you had friends of your own.'

'Me? What gave you that idea? No, I only go out with my parents. The occasion hasn't arisen, but I don't think they would approve of my going out without them.'

Shelly fell silent for a while, then said thoughtfully:

'Don't you belong to one of our Organisations?'

'What organisation? I don't know what you are talking about.'

'Beitar, or Poale Zion or Maccabi.'

'No, I don't.'

We walked in silence for a while.

'I do,' Shelly said, 'we are organised in groups, and each group has a leader.'

'Really? And what do you do?'

'We have a Club. We meet, we hear lectures; mainly about Palestine; we study Hebrew. We are getting organised and we will fight for a free country of our own; where we will not be discriminated against, where we will be free!'

I looked at my friend. She had spoken with emotion, quietly at first, but now her cheeks were flushed, her breath short. I was surprised to discover all this, I was amazed at this little girl, lost somewhere in a small insignificant country like Bulgaria, expressing such views, and with such conviction.

'In Palestine?' was all I could say.

'Yes! You see! You do know!' She seemed pleased that I wasn't altogether ignorant of the subject so dear to her heart. 'That is where we belong, all of us! That is where we should build our future.'

'In a desert.' I said, realising that I had heard my mother say the same words, in the same tone of voice, about Palestine.

'Now it is, but not for long!'

'What can you do about it? What do you know about it all!' I challenged her.

'You must come to our club. Please promise you will! Please! I want you to meet them, I want you to talk to Paul – he is our leader. You will like them all, such real people, intelligent people! And Zvi, the guy from the kibbutz. He explained it all, how it can be done, how it is being done! But that more people are needed and there is a future for all of us there! Please say you'll come: if not to the Club, at least on Sunday, to Paul's!'

For a moment, just a brief moment, I felt her enthusiasm flow over me, but instinctively I knew that I must stop it there and then, I mustn't allow it to take hold, because I knew that my parents would disapprove, would not allow it. Also, because I couldn't really respond to Shelly's ideals; they didn't really fire me. It was her enthusiasm, her involvement, her emotion that impressed me.

'I would love to go to Paul's on Sunday, but I am pretty certain my parents won't let me. I'll ask though.'

'That would be wonderful. I promise you won't be disappointed!'

That same afternoon, I said to my mother:

'Shelly belongs to a Jewish organisation.'

'Does she?'

'Yes. She invited me to meet her group on Sunday. They get together at their leader's home on Sundays. She says they are very nice people. May I go?'

'I don't know. You better ask your father.'

I didn't mention Shelly's and the Group's ambitions for a new free country as I wished to avoid an outright refusal.

'No way,' said my father, 'you are only a little schoolgirl. You must keep your mind on your studies! You are not going to any group meetings.'

'Please daddy, all the others are the same age as me, why are they allowed?'

'Because their parents are loose people, that's why! Who are they anyway?'

'How am I to know, I haven't met them.'

My father laughed. I was quick to take the advantage:

'Oh, please daddy! Only this once!'

'How will you get home?'

'Shelly will accompany me.'

'All right. But only this once. And remember, you must be home by six – before dark, understood?'

'Oh, daddy, thank you!' I kissed him and did a pirouette carried away by my success in convincing him.

'Stop this nonsense,' he scolded me and I stood still, in case he changed his mind.

I couldn't wait to tell Shelly.

Chapter Twenty Three

My First Dance

Sunday finally came. I was allowed to wear my new dress made out of an old blanket. It felt warm and the dressmaker had tried her best to make it fit and look nice. It had not been an easy task, but still, it was the first new dress I had had in years and I felt elated, even though it was quite scratchy. For the first time in my life, I expressed the wish to 'do' my hair. I had often wanted to, but hadn't dared ask my mother's permission and assistance.

'Don't be silly,' she said , 'Your hair is much too thin. You can't do a thing with it.'

'Besides,' added my father, 'I don't want you all dolled up. You are still a child.'

I polished my old shoes and sat down to wait for Shelly, trying to keep still. Finally she arrived.

'Home by six!' my father reminded me as we were leaving.

'Is this our new 'havera'?'

We were ushered in by a tall young man whose hand lingered on my shoulder. He had used the Hebrew word for 'friend' or 'comrade'.

'Yes,' said Shelly.

'I am delighted to meet you, Havera, .' said the young man.

I looked up at him and met his gaze. The way he looked at me, made me feel ill at ease. The expression in his eyes didn't confirm his words, they were saying something else, something which I couldn't understand and found disconcerting. Nobody had looked like this at me before.

'What is your name?' he asked.

I mumbled my name. His hand was still on my shoulder.

'Isn't this lovely! A French name, absolutely enchanting!

'There were many people scattered around the room. Some older, and others – my age – whom I was used to thinking of as children. They didn't behave like children though. They talked to each other, in smaller or larger groups, in a very adult way. Some had glasses in their hands and the liquid in them looked alcoholic, rather than soft and I could just imagine my father's disapproval, should he ever find out. For the first time in my life, I was among people my own age, and older, outside the classroom and without my parents' immediate supervision. I felt frightened and elated at the same time. I didn't know which was stronger.

'My name is Paul.' He was still behind me, as I stood in the doorway observing the room. Shelly was by now deep in conversation with a boy at the far end of the room.

'Will you dance with me?' Paul asked.

He took hold of me before I could answer. I had never danced before. I felt sweaty and clumsy and did my best to follow his step.

'Your hair is beautiful.' he was holding me gently.

'It's too soft.'

'That's the beauty of it. It's so light. It flies when I as much as breathe on it, then it falls back, right into place. Beautiful.'

I knew for a fact that my hair was no good. My mother had told me so, and I found Paul's flattery unnecessary. Whatever he wanted to get from me, I thought, he won't get it. I wasn't that sort of girl.

'Will you join our group?' he now asked.

'I don't think so.'

'Oh, but why not?' his disappointment sounded genuine. I looked up at him to see whether he meant it, and once more I met his eyes which made me look away. What was it they contained?

'I don't know.' I said a little breathless.

'But you must.'

'Why 'must'?'

'Because we need every Jewish person to help in the fight for a free country of our own. Don't you think we have been maligned, killed, discriminated against, hated, enough? Don't you think we owe it to those who died to secure a safe and wholesome life for their children? Don't you think that it is up to us, our generation to see to it that it never happens again, never!'

I felt dizzy. I didn't know what made me dizzy; perhaps the mere fact that I was spoken to as one speaks to a sensible person, to an adult.

'Yes, all this is true.' I said.

'There you are! Then why not take part in the building of this new country where no one will be ashamed that he is a Jew?'

'Because I am too young. Because I know nothing about all these things; how can I fight or build or take part in something that's so large, so ... big ... so remote, that I can't say I really comprehend it!'

'Firstly, you are not too young. You are a lovely, strong, intelligent person; there are trained people in Palestine, they will, in turn train you. There is a lot of work to be done. Our country is a beautiful one. A country of sunshine and palm trees.

'A desert.'

'Yes, no doubt, but we can make it into a garden! It is

possible, it has already begun. Isn't it challenging to you – to be part of it?'

'I must complete my education first.'

The dance was finished. Paul went to see to the record player and I walked, self-consciously, towards the corner of the room where Shelly was sitting on the floor, engrossed in a conversation with the same boy.

'Sit down,' she said as she saw me coming, 'this is Harry.'

I sat down and shook hands with Harry.

'What do you think of Paul? Isn't he just – everything?'

'Yes, he is very nice.'

Shelly glanced at me with her dark brown, penetrating eyes.

'You don't mean a word you are saying,' her eyes said, 'you are afraid to say what you think.'

I looked away. What did I think? I couldn't honestly say, not even to myself. Not much, probably. I hadn't often been asked my opinion. I wasn't used to having one. That might have been the honest answer to her reproach. Was I aware of it? I doubt it. I just felt mixed up.

Suddenly everybody moved away from the centre of the room. Paul stood in the middle of the floor, a violin in his hands. He bowed slightly as he pivoted and looked around. He came to a halt facing us; put the violin under his chin, placed the bow on the strings and stood motionless awaiting people's attention. While the last murmurs died out, his eyes rested on me with that deep disconcerting light in them. I looked down.

He started to play softly, but as I relaxed and began to take the music in, my eyes fell on Shelly's wrist watch. It's hands were stretched out at exactly 180° – it was six o'clock! My first impulse was to run, but I realised that I was trapped. I looked at the door, across the room, behind Paul who, his eyes now shut, seemed to have forgotten the whole world, borne as he was, by Sarasate's Gypsy's serenade. My back was moist with perspiration; my throat dry. I wasn't listening to the music any longer. All I wanted was, to get out. It seemed that hours had passed when Paul, at last, stopped playing. Everybody applauded. I jumped up wanting to reach the door as fast as I could. But I found myself in Paul's arms.

'Did you enjoy the music?'

'Yes; yes very much, but I must go now, immediately, please.'

'She must go home early Paul. Her parents don't allow her out on her own.'

Shelly was standing behind me.

'Yes, of course!' Paul preceded us towards the door. 'I'll get your coat, come on, I'll take you home.'

'No, no, there is no need, please .... '

If my father saw me with a boy (and Paul was by no means a 'boy') he would kill me and most probably him too.

'Her parents don't approve of her mixing with boys, Paul. I'll take her home.'

'As you wish.'

God! The humiliation of it all!

'I hope to see you again soon, Havera, very soon.' Paul held my hand.

I tried to smile, but most probably the result was a twisted grimace. We rushed off.

'Don't worry,' Shelly said, 'we are not terribly late.'

'He said six o'clock.'

'OK, so it's half past. It's not the end of the world. You can't be expected to watch the time all the time! How can you ever enjoy anything?'

I didn't think my enjoyment came into it.

'You don't know my father.'

'Surely you should be allowed to have friends of your own. After all, you are nearly 12 now.'

My mind was totally absorbed by putting one leg in front of the other, and getting home as quickly as I could.

'Shall I come up with you ... perhaps I can explain?'

I didn't want her to see my father's anger; I didn't want her to realise his total mistrust of me. We parted at the corner and I ran.

I walked in, breathless. My mother was lying on her back, her eyes half closed and red-rimmed, her hand dabbing her cheeks. She was sobbing noiselessly. My father's eyes flared at me with that wild look that I feared so much.

'Do you know what the time is?' he roared.

I didn't know exactly, and even if I did, I would not have been able to speak.

'When I say six o'clock, I mean six! not seven!' I stood frozen on the spot. Guilty.

'What loose people have you been with? What have you been up to?' His finger was pointing at me, accusing me. I looked up and happened to notice the time on his wrist watch; it was a quarter to seven.

'It isn't seven o'clock yet!' I said in one breath 'It's only a quarter to … and I have … '

'Don't answer back! Look at your mother! She nearly fainted with worry over you! What were you up to all this time?'

'Nothing, I can assure you … I simply didn't know the time …. '

'Couldn't you ask? What were you busy doing, tell me!'

'Nothing dad … 'I was sobbing now, '… there were other … children there … they are all members of the same group … Beitar … they just talked … someone played the violin …. '

'The violin! That's fine! If you can't do as you are told, you can listen to the violin at home from now on. No more, do you hear? That's it!'

'But I have no watch …. '

That was the last attempt I made to plead my cause, to save my dignity, then I just gave up and stood there, looking down, and tears of frustration and bitterness ran down from my eyes onto my shiny old shoes.

Chapter Twenty Four

The Red Scarf

Shelly was waiting for me outside, as usual, when I left home for school in the morning. It was a little late and we walked quickly, side by side. And as we walked we talked without looking at each other. I still felt the humiliation of having had to rush home, obedient to my father's will.

'I haven't done anything for geography today.' she said.

Relieved that she hadn't mentioned yesterday's events, and having prepared my geography lesson, I gave her some of the details which she tried to memorise.

On Mondays, we had a biography of Y.V. Stalin class after school and my mother had given me so many sandwiches, that my satchel was ridiculously bulky and awkward to hold. I kept passing it from one hand to the other. Shelly offered to carry it for me.

'No! Why should you.' I protested.

I had began to wonder about her silence in connection with yesterday's fiasco. Her silence worried me. Was she cross with me? Did she disapprove of me too? Of my obedience to my parents? My concern to meet their demands, to gain their approval, their love? If that were the case, there was nothing I could do – I loved my parents and wanted them to love me, and

I most certainly wasn't going to go against their wishes to please her!

At the school gates we were stopped by an older girl:

'I see you don't have your Red Scarves, Comrades.'

We looked at each other.

'We haven't got them yet,' Shelly said firmly.

'How do you mean, you haven't got them yet?'

'We only came back from deportation a week or so ago. We haven't had the time to get our scarves,' I left the talking to Shelly, 'but we will – now.'

A Red Scarf signified that one was a member of the Stalin Youth Organisation.

'Your names please,' asked the older girl.

'Can you enrol us?' Shelly asked innocently.

'Yes. I can also check up on you and report you. If you are telling the truth – you should be all right. If not – you'll be punished. A member of the Stalin Youth Organisation doesn't tell lies.'

'Look,' said Shelly quickly, 'we are late as it is. Let us in, we will have our scarves tomorrow, promise!'

'What's the matter with you then?' The girl turned to me 'You dumb or something?'

'I am not! Let us in now. We'll have our scarves tomorrow.'

She moved away from the gate and we ran across the large school grounds to the building.

'I suppose we'll have to join immediately.' I said

'I suppose so. I have to ask my mother for the money.'

'Membership fees? How much is it?'

'I don't know. Not too much, I don't think.'

We contacted the class activist who was responsible for the enrolment of new members. In fact everybody had to be a member. All it involved, we were told, was regular payment of the membership fees, wearing the Red Scarf at all times, attending all the meetings as requested and behaving honourably in the street.

'I have decided against the Stalin Youth.' Shelly said to me the following morning.

'What? But why? You were so full of admiration, not so long ago? Besides, you know you can't get anywhere without being a member.'

'I am not interested any longer. It won't do me any good. I am emigrating next year and I don't have to paint myself red to secure my future here. I have no future here; none of us has.'

'I am going to university.'

'You may be. Then you better keep up with them.'

She was rather short with me, but there was nothing I could do about it. I paid my membership fee and got my scarf and membership card.

The following Monday, the same older girl was at the school gates.

'Ah, it's you two again,' she looked at each one of us in turn, 'good, good.' she approved of my scarf, then turned abruptly to Shelly, 'What about you then?'

'I am not joining.'

'Just like that?'

'Yes.'

'And why, may I ask?'

'You may not,' Shelly retorted and turned to me, 'come on, we are late.'

'Why were you so nasty to her?' I asked Shelly when we were at a safe distance.

'Oh, the silly cow. Who does she think she is anyway. Taking it all on herself, like she comes directly after Stalin himself! What are they trying to prove anyway.

Can't you see, it's all a pretence, a make believe business. I don't have to pretend. What is more, I don't want to pretend. I am getting out of here!'

The girl was at the gates on the following Monday once

again. As we walked in, she pulled me by the arm.

'Wait a minute,' and to Shelly, 'you may go in.'

Shelly took a few paces inside, and waited for me, half turning her back to us.

'It isn't advisable to be seen with that girl all the time, you know.' she said to me in a confiding tone.

'Why not?'

'We don't want reactionary elements to poison our minds with their propaganda, do we?' As she spoke, the activist girl moved her head in the direction of my friend, her eyes never leaving mine.

'She is my friend.'

'If you know what's good for you, you must soon put an end to this, so called *friendship* and you may consider yourself lucky. I told you privately. It could have come to you from a much greater height. Besides, you do care about your future education, don't you?'

Filled with contempt I walked away before I had said something which I might later regret. I was extremely irritated and on the verge of losing my temper. I broke away from the girl, walked over to Shelly and said as loudly as I possibly could:

'Come on, Shelly, let's go. I can't wait for this afternoon! What was the title of the American film we are going to see?'

I looked back and saw that the girl was watching us. I hoped she could hear me as well.

'I love American films! They are such fun!'

Shelly grabbed me by the hand and we ran towards the building.

'What possessed you?' Shelly asked when we were far enough, not to be heard.

'There must be a limit and that was it! '

We stopped running and I tried to catch my breath. Shelly swung me around, as she was still holding my hand, and hugged me warmly.

'I am so pleased you did it! So very pleased!' she said in one breath, 'I had begun to think that you couldn't stand up to anyone! That you didn't have as much of a character as I thought you had!' she took a deep breath, as we were still panting from the long run and went on, 'Forgive me for being so frank, but I am so pleased I was not mistaken about you, I had to tell you!'

Without awaiting my reaction, she started running again along the corridor, towards our classroom, pulling me once more, by the hand.

Chapter Twenty Five

Greeting Enver Hodja

Three times a week, Shelly hurried to her club, whilst I walked slowly to my after school classes. There were exams to be taken at the end of each course. I was mildly taken by Karl Marx's dialectics, but this is as far as my interest went; the rest was just something I had to do. One of the classes was devoted to the Stalin Youth Organisation. We listened to lectures about our new State, which was now a proud Republic, having done away with the 'decadent King'; about our new progressive State headed by the hero of Leipzig – Georgi Dimitrov, a State where everything was 'from the people – for the People'; about how honoured we were by the Soviet Union's friendship and assistance in our development as a People's Democratic Republic. The list was a lot longer and it got more and more preposterous as it went along.

One evening we found the meeting hall decorated by huge posters of a rather handsome man's face. We didn't know the face and, intrigued, waited to hear what it was all about.

'This, Comrades,' the secretary pointed at one of the posters, 'is the Comrade Enver Hodja, the Head of State of our brothers and neighbours, the Democratic Republic of Albania.'

Albania? All we were ever told about Albania, in geography, was that it had also been under the Ottoman empire like us, but never recovered properly and was an underdeveloped country whose religion was Muslim. Now we were brothers!

We listened for two hours to a lecture about Enver Hodja – his biography. his `underground' work against the Nazis during the war, his general contribution to the development of the Communist Party in Albania, his 'progressive' views, his merit in the fight against the 'imperialist aggressor the King Zog'. In the end, we were informed that Enver Hodja was arriving the following day for a State Visit and that we have to be at the school at 7am, from where we were going to meet the great man.

This, of course, meant that we had no classes in the morning, and Shelly, not having attended the meeting, didn't know about it. Luxuries such as telephones weren't very popular in those days and I couldn't take the risk of going to her home to warn her after the meeting, since my mother timed by absence from home to the minute.

It was still dark when I left home the following morning at a quarter to seven. It was very cold and foggy. My mother made me wrap up as warmly as she could. I had a scarf wrapped twice round my neck and over my mouth and was told under no circumstances to inhale the cold air directly; only through the scarf!

There were few people in the street and the pavement was slippery with frost. The school courtyard was bubbling with people. We were arranged in rows of four abreast, like on a May Day parade, and marched out of the school gates. The activists were busily running alongside our bulk, trying to get us to sing 'The International', but what with the cold and fog, all they got were some pathetic screeching noises, squeezed out of our vocal chords. Having to give up the singing, the activists decided to make us shout slogans.

'Long live Stalin! Long live Lenin! (forgetting that he was dead) Long live Enver Hodja! Long live the Communist Party!' – they prompted us:

'Now in that order – one, two, three: Long live .... ' A few voices came up and died out before the end of the phrase. The activist accompanying our group walked between the rows and repeated the slogans, looking at each and every one of us; eventually she got us going.

I looked around, whilst shouting, and realised how ridiculous we all looked. Shouting our heads off, impassive if not bored expressions on our faces, red, runny noses, pink cheeks and lips turning blue with cold. I looked down and decided to drop out. The activist moved in, between the rows before I spotted her.

'What's the matter with you Comrade? Have you lost your voice or something?' she shouted over the noise.

'Sorry ... I was adjusting my step .... '

'What?'

'I was out of step!' I shouted right in her ear.

'Proletariat of the World – Unite!' she shouted in my face, meaning I should repeat after her, and also, perhaps, that I hadn't quite duped her. I stuck out my tongue to her back as she walked out of the row, then, suspecting that she would watch me, formed the words with my lips without uttering a sound.

Daylight peeped shyly from behind the thick grey clouds. The wind cut into our skin like razor blades as we walked towards the Railway Station. Eventually we were made to line the pavement, other schools, already lined the opposite side, and further down, all the way from the Station to the National Assembly, where Enver Hodja was going to have lunch with the Prime Minister.

Albanian and Bulgarian flags were distributed all around and we had to wave them as we shouted. Now that we were stationary, the cold was biting viciously at our bodies even through our clothes, not to speak of our faces and hands, exposed to its merciless attack. I had to remove the scarf from around my neck because my breath had moistened it, and the cold had frozen it. I hated the Albanians, Enver Hodja and us, our idiotic attitude to all this; above all, I hated myself for being part of this 'spontaneous' welcoming party.

Eventually the long black Soviet limousines Z.I.S. showed up at the far end of the Boulevard, we were prompted to shout welcoming slogans and wave the flags. Realising that our ordeal would be finished soon, we all shouted 'Long live Enver Hodja', waved the flags and jumped up and down, more to warm up, than with love for the man.

Wrapped up in fur coats, with Russian type astrakhan hats on, the Heads of State smiled benevolently and waved white plump hands at us as the limousines sailed slowly by. As soon as the cars disappeared in the distance, we were told by the activists that we should be back at school at three o'clock in the afternoon and were dismissed.

I made my way home the best I could; I had no experience in walking about town on my own, and in the intense cold, lost my way a few times. Finally I got home. I never admitted that I had lost my way.

'You're not going anywhere! ' said my mother when I told her that I had to go back in the afternoon. 'Look at you! You are all blue and red, you'll catch pneumonia.'

'Please mum, I must go. We were virtually ordered to go.'

'They are not going to tell me how to bring up my child! Besides, why is it Shelly didn't even know about it when she came to pick you up this morning?'

'Shelly wasn't at the meeting last night, she didn't know, this is why .... '

'You said,' my mother interrupted me, 'everybody had to go!'

'Yes, but Shelly didn't … she never does … she is emigrating … . '

'Anyway, she had more sense than you did, not to go.'

Oh, the injustice of it all! Shelly had sense now! She had been described as 'loose', so had her parents! I had been told not to see her any more than I had to, and now SHE had sense! I felt so indignant, I was suffocating.

'Shelly doesn't care about her record with 'them'!' I shouted, 'but I, I do! Shelly is emigrating next year, on her own, with a group call 'Aliyat Hanoar' – so she doesn't care. Will I be allowed to emigrate, on my own? No! I will have to go to university, therefore I have to watch my record.' I was surprised my mother allowed me to finish this outburst.

'Just watch how you talk to me,' was all she said, and as I was still impassioned with her injustice, she added, 'don't look at me like that!'

I looked away.

I hadn't enjoyed the morning, far from it, and I wasn't anticipating the afternoon with relish, either. I was still cold, my fingers were red and stiff and, in any case, I didn't know why we had been called back.

'You are not going anywhere.' my mother said in a voice that allowed no reply.

I learned in the morning that they had gone to the square outside the National Assembly, to listen – and cheer – Enver Hodja's address, delivered from the balcony of the Assembly. All secondary schools, and all adults – members of the National Front Organisation had been a 'spontaneous' audience to the Albanian during his two hours long speech.

A week had passed before we had the next meeting and the cold and frustration of that day had, by then, faded away. On the way to the hall, we joked about who was going to be paying us a visit that week, and what would the temperatures be, but a surprise awaited us as we entered the hall.

The Secretary was standing on the rostrum (usually we had

to wait for her), stiff, leaning on her stretched arms which seemed to support the weight of her body, the palms of her hands flat on the desk. She was looking straight ahead , at no one in particular, her face seemed tense and expressed impatience. We fell silent as we walked in, and tip-toed to our seats.

The Secretary let a long moment pass before she spoke, and when she did, her voice was low, the words spoken one by one seemed to, be thrown at us, hit us.

'Today, Comrades,' she said sweeping the hall with her eyes, 'we are going to look into our consciences, into our worthiness. We are going to find out who, among us, is worthy of being a member of our Organisation, and who – isn't. Some of us, it would seem, have not asked themselves what it is that they have engaged themselves in when joining our Stalin Youth Organisation. Some of us, are not worthy of being among us. Those, shall be singled out and expelled, in good time.' She cleared her throat , her eyes sweeping the hall constantly. She shifted the weight of her body from her arms onto her legs, stood up, her back straight and continued, 'Today, Comrades, we shall make those of us, who hadn't asked themselves that question until now, ask it – and answer it! Here and now. Today, we shall give everybody an opportunity. The opportunity to come forward and through self-criticism tell us why they think they are not worthy of our ORGANISATION, of being among us.'

She paused again, her eagle eyes scanning each face; the hall was dead quiet. 'Today,' she went on, 'you will have the judgement of your own comrades to contend with, which, I anticipate, will be lenient. But, as of next week, we will have the privilege of the presence of our District Secretary. And he is NOT lenient.'

She sat down now, on the chair that had stood behind her all the while, crossed her arms over her generous bosom, leant back, and added, 'I am waiting, Comrades,' Pause. 'I am waiting for those of you who know they have something on their conscience to come forward with their self-criticism.'

No one moved; it seemed that people had even stopped breathing; the fear was almost tangible. I wondered what it was she meant. Was my non-attendance last week a reason for 'self-criticism'? I looked obstinately at an ink stain on the desk when, in the dead silence I heard my name called. I must have stirred, because I heard the Secretary's voice, loud and clear again:

'Yes, YOU.'

I looked up; our eyes met. I stood up.

'I would like to hear your self-criticism, Comrade.' she said slowly, a tinge of mockery in her voice.

I found my throat dry and incapable of uttering a sound. I cleared it as best I could, perspiring under the heavy glance of the woman on the rostrum.

'I missed the afternoon meeting last Wednesday.'

'And why was that, Comrade?'

'My mother … wouldn't let me go out again … it was … very cold.'

'Oh, mummy's girl!'

I looked down.

'It WAS very cold!' she roared.

'Yes, Comrade Secretary, it was and … '

'It is winter now you know? Winters are usually, rather cold. Does your mother knit a cocoon around you, and tie you to herself every winter?' The soft mocking whisper changed suddenly into a high pitched attack. 'In winters like this, in most appalling conditions, in the mountains, in the bush, our Comrades fought for freedom. Many gave their lives in the process; some, luckily survived – they are our pride today. People like Enver Hodja, whom you chose to ignore, IS one of them! And your mother, thought it was too cold for you?'

Her mocking tone brought up some laughter, but nobody

dared laugh too loudly; I felt them careful, trying to please her, yet fearing of being next in line.

'What have you to say?'

'I told the truth, Comrade Secretary.'

'I will check with your mother.'

'Yes, Comrade Secretary, please do.' I sat down.

'Wait!' her hawk eyes pierced me once more. 'We haven't finished with you! Comrade Christine has something to report, and perhaps it was your mother who told you what to do on that occasion too.' I stood up again, my knees shaky.

Christine was our activist.

Her voice came loud and clear from the back of the hall:

'Last Wednesday, when attending the arrival of Comrade Enver Hodja, I noticed the Comrade in question not participating properly in the proceedings. When I brought the fact to her attention, she made a childish excuse. It was reported to me, that when I went away from her, to attend to my duties, she stuck out her tongue behind my back. Also, I realised that she was pretending to be singing or greeting but actually – wasn't. I found this to be an insult to Comrade Enver Hodja.'

By the tone of her voice, without looking back, I realised that she had finished. In the dead silence, I realised that everybody in the hall was happy not to be in my shoes.

'What have you to say, Comrade?' The Secretary's voice was impatient.

I said nothing. I couldn't. I was desperately fighting the tears which were already burning my eye-lids.

'You will not be expelled Comrade.' the Secretary said slowly, emphasising every word, 'your membership card will not be endorsed, not this time. But there must not be a second time. Three endorsements mean withdrawal of your membership. And you know the meaning of that, don't you?'

I nodded.

'Is that perfectly clear?'

I nodded again.

'Yes Comrade Secretary.' my voice was more of a shriek than anything else.

'Good.' she said slowly, this time the weight of her glance shifted from me to a sweep around the hall.

'I will see for myself what your mother has to say about your non-attendance.'

Her eyes, having done a full circle, rested back on me.

'Yes, Comrade.' I whispered.

There was a long silence. I sat down slowly half expecting to be called again.

'Now you see Comrades what we mean by self-criticism,' there was a benevolent half smile on her face, 'what we want is, each and every one of us to be able to search his or her conscience and find their own faults, be aware of their conduct. This is the only way, we think, to become worthy citizens of a Proletarian Democratic Republic. Not only should we search ourselves, but our comrades too. Our friends. Our brothers and sisters. Our fathers and mothers.'

When I got home I felt feverish and sick. My mother took one look at me and said,

'You look like you have failed an examination or if not – you certainly have a flu!'

I told her briefly what had happened.

'They won't tell me how to look after my own child!' she was indignant. 'This is rubbish!'

I stayed in bed, feverish, for two days.

Shelly came every day to bring me her notes. She sat for a while by my bed, then left. We were never left alone to talk. When on the third day I was well enough to go back to school, she spoke to me as soon as I was out of the front door.

'Please tell me what happened? I know I put my foot right in it for you, last Wednesday when I went upstairs. I waited for a while, then when you didn't turn up I thought that you were not well, and went ... upstairs. Your mother thought ... '

'It's alright, forget it.'

'No, please tell me! Your mother was so funny. She seemed so suspicious of you having left home so early, and me – not even knowing about it. She was so mistrustful, I am sorry.'

'Forget it, it's all in the past now.'

I told her about it though, and about the 'self-criticism' I had been subjected to. I could talk about it now; it was in the past and I had learned my lesson.

'It's quite awful, if you ask me'

'Yes, it is.' Shelly said,

'And you know something? I simply can't accept it! ... that you subject yourself to all this, just like that, almost willingly.'

'I have to.'

'Rubbish; no one has to! You can come away with us. It is an open door out of this gloom! It is the only way of life for all Jewish people .... '

'You talk like a pamphlet,' I lost my temper, 'you saw my mother – she won't trust me from here to the corner, how do you expect me to leave the country on my own? As for my father, he is petrified that some boy might touch me and I have to reassure him all the time. You saw the fuss he made over my being home half an hour later than the time set by him!' I calmed down a little, my friend was looking at me with awe. 'So, you see, I have the wrong parents for that sort of thing; but nonetheless, I love them. They are the only parents I've got. So, please let's leave it at that.'

Shelly never raised the matter again.

On Monday morning, Christine, our class activist, informed us that there was going to be a special meeting after classes. Shelly's club wasn't meeting that day, so she came along with me to the assembly hall.

We were surprised to be addressed by the Headmaster this time. He hung a poster on the wall behind him, then turned to us:

'This, comrades, is Marshal Tito – the leader of the Democratic Republic of Yugoslavia – our beloved friends and neighbours.'

It was a repetition of the meeting we had had before the visit of Enver Hodja, only the names were different. Marshal Tito's visit was scheduled for the following day; the programme was the same. It was difficult to keep a happy smile and not to show how fed up we were with it all. Little did we know, that this was but the beginning. That the noose was going to get a lot tighter.

'Why can't he postpone his visit until June' I said to Shelly on the way home, trying to joke about it.

'I wonder how many more of these visits there are going to be and how often. You realise of course that we are missing a perfectly good school day in his honour! In the end they will ask us to pass the exams. Still, I am happy,' she added, 'I'll have a lovely day off, and get up at 10!'

'Comrade!' I looked up as we bumped into the secretary.

'Everything is in order with your mother,' she said, looking down at me, 'you will have no more difficulties in attending our functions. She understood very well, when I explained.'

'Thank you Comrade.' I mumbled. She walked off.

'What did she mean?' asked Shelly.

'The cow, she has been to see my mother. It's about last week. She wanted to make sure that I will be there tomorrow afternoon. Oh, how I hate it all!'

I was nearly in tears; the secretary didn't believe me and had to make sure with my mother, and my mother didn't believe me; she had checked up on me with Shelly!

Shelly, tactfully didn't say a word. We parted at the corner and I expected to find my mother in one of her 'states' because I was late, due to the unscheduled meeting. To my surprise, she didn't say anything and when I informed her of the following day's outing, she only said:

'You better wrap up warmly.'

She never mentioned the visit she had had from our secretary.

Ж

That term ended my primary education. To gain admission to the Secondary School, or Gymnasium, one had to pass exams in all subjects and obtain a diploma. Pupils with marks above the average were exempt from those exams and were issued automatically with a diploma. I was one of the latter. A fact my parents took great pride in. My friend though, had to take all the exams, since her marks were below average; she eventually failed both maths and geometry but was given a second chance to re-sit them in September. That gave her the summer months to prepare herself. If she failed then, she would not be admitted to the Gymnasium and would have either to leave school or go back and repeat the last year. Shelly wasn't too perturbed because of her intention to emigrate.

My mother though, insisted that her failure was due to her interests outside school, proving once more – she said – that Club meetings and Sunday gatherings were detrimental to one's education.

My diploma in hand, my father said to me:

'Now, I can tell you that if you still want it, you can go to the French school next term.'

I had given up hope of ever getting into my dream school and his statement was a complete surprise. I flew at him, ecstatic and kissed him:

'Oh, papa, thank you! I am so happy! Thank you so much!'

He freed himself slowly from my embrace:

'All right, all right, no need to get excited. You'll have to be a good girl and work hard.'

'I will, I promise!'

We became aware of a strange noise coming from the street. It must have been very loud, because our room was at the back, and the noise reached us even there. There were voices, cheers, shouting. Being conditioned to fear all unexpected situations, we fell silent and looked at each other. My mother was the first to react. Her features relaxed and she strode towards the door decisively. She ran down the stairs – my father and I followed, still uncomprehending.

People were running in the street, waving the latest editions of the newspapers, singing , shouting and kissing each other. Somebody had put their radio on a window sill of a flat opposite, for everybody to hear. Eventually we were able to make some sense of what was being said:

' ... unconditional surrender ... armistice ... the Germans have surrendered unconditionally, the Allied troops were marching into Berlin ... '

'It's all over! The war is over!' A woman stopped and kissed my mother.

A man running down the street, waving a newspaper, also stopped and shook hands with all of us:

'Congratulations,' he was saying, 'we won!'

My mother turned back to go upstairs.

'It's finally finished.'

We followed her.

'Now,' she added, 'it remains to see what peace is going to be like.'

Chapter Twenty Six

Lycée Français St. Joseph – Shelly Emigrates

As soon as the school term was over, my mother took me to the French School for an interview. We were received by the Mother Superior, who had a warm, kind face. She talked to my mother and occasionally looked at me and smiled. I was very nervous, knowing that they were talking about me, not quite understanding what was being said.

'Are you prepared to lose a year?' my mother turned to me with a smile, 'You will have to spend a whole term in a special preparatory class where you will only study French. It will enable you to cope with all the subjects in the following term – they are all taught in French.'

'Yes, I would.'

'That's wonderful!' said the Mother Superior in broken Bulgarian. They went on talking and I observed with interest the nun's clothes. I couldn't see her skirts, hidden behind the desk, but her head-dress was fascinating. Her shoulders and chest were engulfed in a white, stiff, armour-like material, which seemed as if moulded over her black bodice. The head-dress itself had complicated white pleated sides, covered by a long black cloth, which fell loosely over her shoulders. Most of all, I was impressed by her hands. They emerged from the black sleeves, long and delicate, resting motionless on the desk, holding one another. The fingernails were cut short, yet this fact didn't alter in any way the elegant appearance of the hands. I was shaken out of my dreamy observations by my mother's hand squeezing my shoulder.

'Say, 'au revoir ma mère' – this is how you should address the Mother Superior.'

'Au revoir ma mere.' I said.

'Mais elle a un très bon accent! Pas mal du tout ma petite,' the nun said with a broad smile and emerging from behind her desk, she came near me and her hand touched my cheek gently. I blushed.

'You will be starting on the lst of September, when the new term begins' my mother said sweetly to me.

'Au revoir Madame.' the nun said to my mother and showed us out of her office. Another nun escorted us through a long dark corridor towards the heavy wooden carved door.

When it was shut behind us, my mother said:

'You will have to work very hard. It's an expensive school, and if you don't – it's no point spending the money.'

'I will, I promise I will.'

'We'll have to wait and see.'

"Thank you so much mum!"

'I hope you won't disappoint us.'

'No, I won't! I promise!'

Ж

I suppose, summer is always a little boring when you are twelve and a half years old and when you have no homework to do and you are not allowed to see your school friends. I spent my mornings trying to help my mother with the housework, but somehow I was never allowed to actually do anything. I would start sweeping the floor, and seemed to get so carried away with it, that when my mother spoke to me, she had to call out loud more than once before I would respond. She called this 'having your head in the clouds' and 'not concentrating on what you were doing', she also thought that I did it on purpose. And I, knowing that I was so eager to be of help, despaired at my own unreliability and inadequacy.

It was at that time that I took an interest in the newspapers again and, whenever I could, I read them. I read about the trials in Sofia and Nuremberg – against the War Criminals, in Nuremberg, and their agents in Bulgaria. There were lengthy transcripts of the cross examinations that went on in the Courts. The detailed descriptions often accompanied by pictures were horrifying. Especially the pictures. Pictures of Bulgarian policemen, who, having trapped members of the Resistance, like foxes in their holes, would have their picture taken. They would stand there, one foot on the corpse, in one hand – a bloody head, held by the hair; in the other – rifle with a bayonet, and wide, victorious smiles on their faces. On closer inspection I could see that the body on the ground was decapitated.

That picture haunted me for many nights. Then there were other pictures. Pictures of human shadows in strange striped clothes, looking at the camera with watery, bewildered eyes, not quite understanding what was happening; not, perhaps, quite caring any longer. Other pictures, of piles of children's shoes, human hair, soap made of human fat; I cried at those pictures, I didn't want to believe that those things were real, that somewhere, all those thing had been done to people. I asked my mother.

'You mustn't read the newspapers,' she said, 'you are too

young to understand these things.'

There was something else in the papers which drew my attention. The reports of the goings on in Palestine. It seemed that the Jewish population there, as well as Jews throughout the whole world were demanding that the Balfour Declaration be honoured. There were reports of underground movements to free Palestine from the British, reports of illegal immigration, of clandestine movements all over Europe. I thought about Shelly; it seemed that her dream was coming true and I wondered whether she had already left.

I heard my parents talking about sons and daughters of people they knew, who were 'leaving'. I heard them talk of the dangers. It was illegal to leave Bulgaria, and it was illegal to immigrate into Palestine. I pretended I was asleep at night, when they talked about these things, but they never mentioned the possibility of our 'leaving'. I heard my father talking about his brother, whom I didn't know and who lived in Palestine. Now, for the first time, I heard them mention him, his sick wife and his two children. I had two cousins in Palestine! My own father's brother lived there. How could he and his family live, by their own choice, in the desert?

Shelly came to visit me one sunny afternoon, and my mother agreed reluctantly to let us go and sit in the garden square. I told Shelly about the French school.

'I will go for a while to State Gymnasium,' she said, 'then, I am leaving, well before the end of next year.'

'But it's illegal.'

'So?'

'How can you do it, if it's illegal?'

'I am not the only one. All I have to do is – wait for my turn. We leave Sofia by night, on foot. We reach the Yugoslav border and from there – to Italy. Once in Italy, we are looked after by the Jewish Agency. They organise everything.'

I looked at her, incredulous. It was as if she were telling me fairy tales, only she believed in them! I told her so.

'But it is true! We will get there one way or another, we'll fight the British, we will have a free Jewish State!'

To me, parental consent was the main hurdle.

'How about your parents? Are they not ... concerned?'

'Of course they are! But they will follow me and we will be together – there, in our country, in Israel!'

'Israel' I said dreamily, not having heard the name before.

'How about your education?'

'Education, education, that's all you have in your mind! There are more important things to do than read books and divide fractions! Besides, it's never too late. I can always go back, and study.'

I had no answer to that.

'I must be going now,' Shelly stood up, 'I'll try and come again before the term starts, or before I leave.'

'Yes, that would be nice.'

We shook hands clumsily.

'I'll stay here for a while,' I said and she walked away.

I sat on the bench and looked over, across the lawn, at the large oak trees and their rich foliage. Soon it would turn yellow and rust, and it will be time to go to school. Some noisy children were playing in the middle of the lawn. I could still see Shelly walking away. I was certain she didn't understand me. I walked home slowly, fearing that she might turn round and see me; I waited until she had turned the corner and then went home. I never saw Shelly again in Bulgaria. It was many years later that I bumped into her in Tel Aviv; she was married and had just had a baby boy.

Chapter Twenty Seven

Rakovsky Street – Comrade Aslanova

I found my father already at home, speaking with an unusual degree of excitement:

' ... and a kitchen, all to ourselves!'

'Are we sure to get in?' asked my mother, and I understood that they were talking about moving flats. 'I must see it, we can't just say 'yes' before I have seen it.'

'I am telling you – two rooms and a kitchen. The other family have also two rooms, they use the bathroom as a kitchen, but we will be allowed to take our baths when we want to.'

'Charming.'

'No one lives better now.'

'Great consolation that is to me.'

My father threw his arms up in the air.

'I can only do the possible. Do you want to go and see it now?'

'Only if it's sure we'll get in. There may be others ... '

'I am telling you, it belongs to the Methodist Church, it's American sponsored and it was offered to me, as an employee of theirs. You can always say 'no' if you don't like it.'

'Sharing with a family with two kids!'

'They are Jewish.'

My mother shrugged:

'I don't care.'

'Oh, please yourself!'

'All right, let's go and see it.'

Rakovsky Street climbs up from the Dondukov Boulevard towards the Alexander Nevsky Square, in the middle of which the Cathedral of the same name stands, magnificent, with its stained glass windows and gilt domes.

The block called Doctor Long, is situated in the middle of that stretch. If one climbed all the way up, past the Alexander Nevsky Cathedral, one would end up at the National Assembly.

The National Assembly used to be the King's Palace. In the days of King Boris's reign. The Palace had stood in the middle of a vast garden and the building itself had not been visible from the street. The garden had been cleared up now and turned into a square, probably a smaller copy of the Red Square outside the Kremlin. On one side of this square, stands Georgi Dimitrov's Mausoleum, erected after his death and where his embalmed remains are placed for everyone to see.

He died upon his return from an audience with Stalin, in Moscow in very similar, mysterious circumstances to those surrounding King Boris, who died upon his return from an audience with Hitler, in Berlin.

Rumours had it, that Dimitrov had wanted to take a more democratic line, following in the footsteps of Tito, but he must have been less cautious in his approach, for he was exposed and, of course, eliminated. He was never officially 'discredited', though, unlike so many others.

Ж

We moved in towards the end of the summer. The flat was on the fifth floor; both our rooms opened into a central hall, as did our co-sharers' – the kitchen and bathroom were at the other end of the flat, across a little corridor off the main entrance hall.

Our co-sharers, the Solomons, had a daughter a year or two younger than me and a boy of eight. I became friendly with Erica and we spent a lot of time together, queueing up for our mothers' shopping. We spent hours downstairs at the green grocer's, waiting for the vegetables to arrive from the market. Only when the van finally turned up, did we find out what we could purchase. If my mother had asked for a kilo of tomatoes – and provided there were some available – we had to purchase a kilo of green peppers as well, or a kilo of carrots. Many times, he would sell us only half the quantity of the vegetables we wanted and double, the imposed one. The green grocer's took us two to three hours.

We would then proceed to the grocer's, where there was already a long queue. If we had been asked to purchase some sugar, by the time our turn came, there would be no more sugar left and we would be told that a delivery was expected in the morning.

The following morning, we would get up early, to be at the grocer's before opening time. By 6am a fairly long queue had already formed. It was the only way of obtaining some of the precious sugar which, of course, had to be accompanied by a kilo or two of something quite unwanted, like dry beans or lentils.

On the first of September we went to our respective schools, and the problems of shopping were left to our mothers.

As soon as I walked through the gates of the French School, I realised that I hadn't made a mistake, that this was what I had always wanted. September is a warm month in Bulgaria. The early morning sun shone on the school grounds where girls between the ages of fourteen and eighteen, all wearing the school uniform – a black satin over-dress with a white collar – walked together in twos and threes, or stood in one place and talked.

There was no disorder or unnecessary noise, no shouting or wild running about.

I was an outsider. I didn't know anybody, but I felt less afraid of this fact than I had done when I first returned from deportation, and went to the State school. I stood near the wall, at one end of the grounds, wondering whether I would be accepted as one of them?

Eventually, a nun, standing at the entrance to one of the buildings, gave us instructions as to where to find our class-rooms. The 'old' girls, all knew where to go, but the new ones, including myself, waited for their names to be read out by a young smiling nun with sparkling blue eyes and pink cheeks; we formed two classes, and were led into the building, the young nun accompanying our class, told us in perfect Bulgarian that, as we were there to study French, Bulgarian would be banned within the boundaries of the school and only used on very special occasions. I was sharing a desk with a girl who had long plaited jet-black hair framing her face. She had fiery black eyes and a lovely fair complexion. We smiled at each other.

'My name is Margaret.' she said.

I told her my name; we felt at ease with each other. It was obvious to me that she was wearing a bra. No doubt she also had her period for in my mind, those two things went together. I sighed thinking that I might have it too one day, and wear a bra.

When the bell rang, the nun urged us to go out into the fresh air; Margaret and I walked out together and paced around and talked until the bell called us in again, and, already, in those short ten minutes, I felt a part of all this, which only 45 minutes earlier I had observed as an outsider.

Ж

A few weeks after we had moved in, late one afternoon, the door bell rang twice; both families' names were pinned on the door with instructions to ring once for the Solomons', and twice for us. I went to see who it was. A short fat lady stepped in, saying:

'I want to see your mother, comrade.' and proceeded towards the kitchen without waiting to be asked or shown in. I followed her.

'Good afternoon, comrade.' she said to my mother who, sitting on the kitchen divan, looked up, surprised.

'Good afternoon. Please come in.'

'Yes, yes,' she looked at a note-book, which she had produced from her pocket, 'My name is Comrade Aslanova. I am the National Front Secretary for the block.'

'Pleased to meet you.' said my mother, but the Secretary cut her short, implying that she had no time for unnecessary politeness.

'You have been in the block … let me see … well, quite a few weeks, haven't you? You must have been busy settling down and all that, and you haven't joined our National Front Meetings yet. Are you, in fact, members?'

'Well, no. .not really, you see, we haven't quite recovered from deportation yet. In our previous … place … we didn't stay long enough … and my health hasn't been what it used to be … '

'Yes, Comrade, sure, we understand. No harm done. You can join now.' She was already writing a receipt, my mother sent me for her purse.

'The Block meets at the library, do you know it? At the top of the road? On the first Wednesday of every month. You will have to attend the district's meetings too; also once a month, but we will advise you as to the exact day in due course.' She took the money and handed my mother the receipt.

'Your membership cards will be given to you at our next

meeting. If your Comrade (meaning 'husband') attends meetings at his work's group, he won't have to come to ours, but we will issue him with the membership card. Do you understand?'

'Yes, Comrade, thank you very much.' my mother got up, expecting the woman to leave, but she now turned to me:

'What about you, Comrade? Are you a member of the Stalin Youth, or are you old enough for the National Front?'

'No, no, I have my Stalin Youth Scarf.'

'I didn't think they had much activity at the foreign schools. Do they?'

'I can't really tell, we have only just started, but I am a member from my previous school.'

'Hm, we will have to look into this matter very soon; these foreign schools I mean, they are dangerous growths in our society and we mustn't let them turn malignant.' She opened the door and walked out. Obviously she was well acquainted with the geography of the flat.

'Ugh!' said my mother 'how awful.'

'Yes. Once out of the grip of the Stalin Youth, they grab you by the neck and straight into the National Front.'

'Is there a 'Stalin Youth Organisation' at the French School?'

'No, of course not.'

'Aren't you worried about your record then?'

'University, you mean? I don't know any longer. If the school is approved by the Ministry of Education, and its Baccalaureate recognised, then there would be no reason to deny us university, would there?'

'Logically, not; but things aren't all that logical any longer.'

'In any case, I was fed up with all their stupid meetings, and activities and spyings.'

'We still don't know who are the spies here.' said my mother. It had, by now, become a habit to whisper.

Chapter Twenty Eight

Special 'Treat' For Comrade Rashkov

My father's position at the American Military Mission had become permanent. He was in charge of all local personnel. He told us how the Americans had everything shipped over from the States, even their toilet paper. They lived in luxury, were fed with – what to us were – delicacies and that there was an abundance of everything.

American personnel were often changed and although they brought everything with them, they seldom took anything away with them when they left. So in only a few months my father had been able to purchase a complete bedroom suite, and, for my room an exquisite three-seater settee, which became a large double bed at night, a table and four chairs, a sort of large 'secretaire' with a flap that I used as a desk, and shelves for my books, and a compartment with two doors, where I stored my clothes. Eventually a low table was placed by the settee and a Philips radio was put on it – a whole world, which at night was my own.

There had always been books around. My mother was an

avid reader of novels and my father of political and historical non-fiction. There was a drawer, however, where I knew some books were kept – but I was not allowed them! So finding myself alone for a few minutes I opened that forbidden drawer and withdrew a large volume. The title was – I now know, but didn't understand it then – The Decameron. I tried to read it but didn't understand a word, so I put it back and forgot all about it. I thought my parents were just being fussy …. However, I read everything else that fell – 'legally', so to speak, – into my hands: Erich Maria Remarque, Stephen Zweig, Zelma Lagelof, Pearl Buck, Zola, and many others. Reading was one thing I was not prevented from doing and I went for it. I loved and lived with these stories. But, I was not allowed to read at night. When the Philips radio appeared in 'my room' – with its sparkling green light, my problems disappeared. I could read by 'the eye of the radio' and the book that fell into my hands just then was Gone With The Wind. Scarlett O'Hara became my heroine and I knew I had to become like her; independent, conscious of my needs, wilful and trusting that 'tomorrow was another day'.

However, for the time being, I was none of those things.

The Americans, my father told us, worked only five days a week and never spent a weekend in town. They had requisitioned villas in some in spa resorts, some in winter sports resorts, some – just out in the countryside. Once a month my father had to go around all these villas – all manned by Bulgarian personnel – to bring them their wages. For this purpose he was given a car and a driver. I was very proud of him and at the same time, incredulous that people lived in this way as a matter of course.

From those journeys my father always brought back gifts that the personnel had prepared for him – a cake from the cook, flowers from the gardener – and, believe it or not, toilet paper from the housekeeper!

On one occasion he brought back an enormous chocolate cake that looked quite unreal on our table! To me, its taste was incredible and alien as I could remember nothing of the taste of chocolate or almonds from the pre-war days. At such times, we had to eat whatever it was that he brought back, quickly and without leaving any trace in the dustbins. These feasts usually took place in my parents' bedroom, where we were least likely to be found out.

Comrade Aslanova, the woman who had recruited my parents to the National Front, lived in one of the bachelor flats on the ground floor. From her accent it was clear that she was a peasant from the Rodope Mountains, and we learned that she had come 'up' to Sofia only after the 9th of September. On that day in 1944, the Red Army had walked into Bulgaria, freeing us from the Nazi and Imperialist Aggressor. The 9th of September from then on became a national holiday – Independence Day and the question: 'What did you do before the 9th of September?' became – to some – a scary question.

Soon, it became general knowledge that Comrade Aslanova, apart from being Secretary of the National Front Organisation for our block, was also an informer who spied and reported on the goings on in the block. Rumour had it, that the network was even greater than that, and that there were informers on each floor too. For a while, my mother suspected our co-sharers, then she thought it might be the neighbours in the second large flat on the landing, but when the elderly man, occupying the bachelor flat on our floor, paid us a 'neighbourly' visit more than once in one week, it became clear that he was the one. He would always come by around supper time.

'Oh, I am so sorry, you are having supper; quite frankly I didn't look at the time, I ... '

'Not at all, not at all,' my mother would say, 'please take a seat. We are nearly finished, and you will have coffee with us in a minute, won't you?'

'If you insist,' he would sit heavily, his eyes scanning our plates, 'it is awful that we should have to eat vegetables that we don't really want, isn't it?'

My father would be about to agree when my mother would interrupt, giving him a short 'shut up' glance and when possible, a kick under the table.

'No, not really,' she would say, 'after all, the village co-operatives produce these vegetables and they have to be sold; besides, we love green peppers.'

'Maybe you are right. Have you met Comrade Aslanova? Isn't her accent atrocious?'

'She comes from the Rodopes and as far as I know, they speak the real, old Bulgarian language in those parts; here, our language is spoiled by all the foreign words that we have, one way or another, assimilated over the years.'

'I still think her accent is awful and she thinks she knows everything.'

'I don't know Comrade Aslanova very well, but I think the Party knew what they were doing in giving her the position. She may even have been a member of the Resistance.'

My mother did all the talking.

'I must go and pay a short visit to the Solomons'; it isn't very neighbourly of me to come and only visit you, but between you and I, I like you better.'

'All right,' my mother would say, ignoring the last remark, 'come to our lounge afterwards and we shall have coffee.'

'That's nice; if you can call this horrible muddy beverage – coffee.'

'We are lucky to be alive, and we have everything to be grateful for. During the war, we didn't have any coffee at all.'

At the beginning, my father would protest:

'What is the matter with you?' he would say to my mother. 'What sort of talk is this? We are free people now, it doesn't matter any more to anyone that we are Jewish. Surely we can speak our minds, at least where green peppers are concerned!'

'You don't understand, you miss the whole … '

'I am not an idiot! What do you mean I don't understand?'

'Oh, you are so naive! You exasperate me ! Can't you see he is trying to provoke us into talking against … against everything! Can't you put it through your head that when they say 'Who is not with us is against us' – they mean exactly that, and being against them can be as petty as criticising the bloody green peppers!'

'But surely they know we can't be against them? They know what we have been through, being Jewish and all that – the camps, the deportation, all the humiliations, doesn't this count any longer?'

'Not now, it doesn't.'

Eventually, they would all sit in our lounge – my room, and Erica and I would be sent to our kitchen to make coffee. We had a lovely time then. Like the witches in Macbeth, we put whatever came to hand in Comrade Rashkov's coffee: two pinches of salt and a pinch of black pepper, half the amount of sugar he wanted and a sprinkle of dill!

We never told our parents about it, and Comrade Rashkov never complained about the unusual taste of his coffee. He didn't dare! I wonder whether it was possible that our additives made the brown beverage taste better!

Chapter Twenty Nine

Dream Holiday in Borovetz

When I was very young, three or four perhaps, my mother used to put me in my sledge, wrap me up and strap me in, and pull me along on the hard snow for a stroll around the Christmas Market. There was a strong smell of pine, of incense and freshly roasted chestnuts. I stared with fascination at the shiny blue, red, gold and silver balls, the tassels and bells and angels on the stalls. We never had a Christmas tree, and I only learned why later, but still my mother liked the market, and we visited it every year back then.

Since the 9th of September 1944 there was no Christmas Market, Christmas was no longer called Christmas just the Winter holidays. Father Christmas still remained in the minds of all children, but was re-named The Frost Man. Eventually, he was dropped altogether.

At our school though, there were feverish preparations for the celebration of the holiday. There was a large Christmas tree in the Gym where we were going to have a party. We learned French carols, we baked cakes and made sandwiches and hung decorations and presents on the tree.

The party was a success and Mother Superior was very pleased. The best part of it all, for us, was that we broke up a lot earlier than all other schools: we celebrated the Catholic Christmas on the 25th of December, and then the Bulgarian, Russian orthodox Christmas – on the 6th of January. On account of the long holiday, we were given a great amount of homework, but there were no complaints. The nuns had inspired us to work hard.

Two days before Christmas, my father received an invitation to spend the holiday, together with his family, at the General's villa at Borovetz.

Borovetz is a winter sports resort, situated high up on Mount Rila. It's name means Pine Woods, and that's exactly what it is – tall pine trees, very few clearings and villas built so as not to spoil the natural beauty of the peak. The villas had been private properties; and the few hotels were all now in the hands of the Government. The Americans had requisitioned no less than ten of the villas. One for the General, one for each of the Colonels, the Lieutenants, the Marines and so on. They were all fully serviced by chefs, housekeepers and other staff, who were housed in two separate villas.

'How is she going to cope? What with the standards there and the service?'

'She will. We will have to watch her. No, I will. You will just relax and enjoy yourself.'

My parents could no longer talk about me in my presence in French, so they just whispered and I pretended I wasn't there.

The car came to pick us up early on the morning of the 24th December. I was allowed to sit by the window. I sat back, enjoying the luxury of the large black Buick and the beautiful winter scenery.

As soon as we left town, the road began to climb, gently at first and then quite steeply. All the way the road was covered with snow. The traffic had cut tracks, which the cold had frozen and I suppose the journey would have been impossible without the chains on the wheels.

Soon Rila's majestic slopes surrounded us, it's tall pines reaching for the sky, their branches heavy with white powdery snow. As the road, hugging the mountain-side, meandered up the slopes, higher and higher, new and more spectacular vistas opened up at each turning.

Eventually we seemed to penetrate the wood itself, the road became narrower, and the snow – softer. The chauffeur said that it must have snowed in the morning. Villas of different shapes and sizes appeared, from behind the trees, on either side of the road.

'This is it' the chauffeur said 'We have to leave the car here, the sleigh is waiting for us at the square.'

Indeed, a horse drawn sleigh, beautifully painted in bright colours, stood in the middle of what seemed to be the town square. As soon as he saw the car pull up, the man who was sitting on it, jumped down and came to greet us. We left the car and stretched our legs, numb from the long drive, then we got onto the sleigh. Our knees were covered with a soft, thick blanket. The chauffeur had joined the sleigh driver up front. The man pulled at the reins and invited the horse to pull us, with a deep-throated tz, tz, tz! The horse took a step and the bells round his neck broke the deep silence with their cheerful ring.

I shut my eyes. It was so wonderful, so fantastic! All this beauty, all this whiteness. In my mind's eye I imagined the horse replaced by reindeer and it wasn't too difficult to believe that I was sitting on Father Christmas's sleigh!

The man pulled back on the reins, this time with a loud oho! oop! and the sleigh came to a halt. We were outside a large white villa on two floors and shaped like a ship. Two balconies went all round each floor, like two parallel belts. As we jumped down, the front door opened and a man in a thick white pullover came out. The sun was shining in his face and he squinted at us:

'Welcome, welcome, come on in!'

'Sasha … you have met my wife. This is my daughter. Sasha – our Manager.'

My father introduced me. Sasha shook my mother's hand, then mine.

'I hope you had a comfortable journey.' he said to my mother.

'Yes, very, thank you.'

'Vassili! Come here, at the double! Take the ladies' coats!' the orders were given with a broad smile, which indicated that they weren't as tough as they may have sounded. Sasha turned to my father with the same smile;

'Eh, we give the orders now – tomorrow we will take them.'

'Cut it out Sasha.' said my father with a quick glance towards my mother who pretended she hadn't heard.

'The Bosses haven't arrived yet,' Sasha said as we followed him, 'So, let's have some fun.'

We found ourselves in a large drawing room, where a huge log fire was throwing bunches of light onto the flushed faces of a few people sitting around it.

'It's all right folks,' Sasha said to them, 'you can stay. It's our man from Sofia.'

We were introduced to the man sitting on the rug, whose name was that of a famous comedian. There were two young women there too.

'OK. sweetheart, you can stay on my lap until Uncle Sam arrives,' said the comedian, Tony Kostov. He grabbed one of the girls and put her on his knee. He then looked up at me, smiled and said:

'Sorry love. You will have to wait a few more years, but don't you worry, your turn will come!'

'Excuse him,' Sasha said to my father, 'he is not quite himself these days.'

'How can I be myself? My days are numbered. My hours are numbered. In fact I have started the count down. The Red noose is tightening around my neck, all our necks!' He emptied his glass and kissed the girl, 'Do you know who my father was?' he went on, 'Do you? Well then, can you blame me? Not for being his son – that is entirely his fault, at least he thought he was my father, anyway, no one can blame me for being his son, can they? Oh, yes, they can! Because who knows, I might share his views. Poor old man! Me, sharing his views! Ah, what the hell, let's drink.'

'His father was a cabinet minister in the previous Government.' one of the young women said to my mother.

'I know.' My mother's tone implied that she didn't need the girl's explanations, but she went on: 'He thinks they are going to send him to a concentration camp, you know, like in Siberia. His father committed suicide.'

'Oh, my love, do you have to?' Tony interrupted her flow.

'Sorry. I thought you weren't listening.'

'I was. Shut up.' he took a sip of the fresh drink Sasha had poured for him and turned to me, 'I will tell you the most wonderful ghost story. Do you like ghost stories?'

'Yes, I do!'

'Since when?' intervened my mother.

'Come on, let her have a ghost story. After all, these are ghostly times! I better hurry because our friend here,' he pointed at Sasha, 'will throw me out as soon as Uncle Sam shows up. We, this lovely and I, have been smuggled here and ... '

'They are here sir!' Vassili peeped in and disappeared immediately.

'Come on, the vanishing cream, quickly! Please stay here little one' Tony said to me as he walked away 'I'll be back with a ghost story for you! It will be such a good story, you won't have a wink of sleep all night, I promise!'

'I will, I will, please come back!' I said quickly.

Sasha shook his head as though he was feeling sorry for his friend. Tony, his girl friend and the other girl got up and went towards the adjoining dining room and from there through some French windows in a small conservatory and left the villa.

'I'll go and meet the bosses.' Sasha said.

There were four of them, all wearing officers' uniforms, and accompanied by four young ladies. Drinks were immediately poured and handed around. Everybody spoke English, but I realised that although they spoke the language, the girls accompanying the American officers, were Bulgarian.

I sat near the fireplace and looked at the burning logs. I looked at the flames as they became shorter, slowly dying, playing a last wild dance, turning the logs first red, then black, then red again and, as the heat receded, their edges turned to ash.

I was stirred out of my dreamy observations by Sasha who invited us to go and see our rooms, freshen up and change for dinner. I had read about people changing for dinner in books. Our rooms were on the first floor; so were all the Americans'. Only Sasha and Vassili had rooms on the second floor.

'You are in the Blue Room,' Sasha said, as he opened the door.

It was a large room with two tall French windows opening onto the balcony. The bedspread, curtains and a gathered drape which fell from the ceiling onto the head of the bed, were all in the same blue material. There was a thick blue carpet over the parquet floor. The bed was framed by built-in wardrobes.

'I hope you will find this comfortable.' Sasha said to my mother.

'Yes, thank you.'

'As for you young lady.' Sasha said to me as he walked over to the wardrobe. I followed him, but stopped as he opened the wardrobe door, and I thought for a moment that I was going to be put in there! We were all looking at him now. He paused, enjoying the suspense, his hand on the knob. He looked at each one of us, smiling; turned the knob, his arm reached inside the wardrobe, pushed the panel and disappeared inside! I walked over, quickly. Sasha had walked into the next room through the back of the wardrobe, which from the adjoining room, was just the door to another wardrobe. We followed him. We found ourselves in a room of a similar size to the first one. The sunshine was pouring in through the French windows. The decor was rustic, colourful. I was amazed:

'My God! This is fantastic! I have never seen anything quite like it.

'Go and freshen up.' my mother said.

'Should you need anything, there is a bell by each bed. Just ring, someone will come. I will leave you now. Dinner is at seven. Sasha left the room.

'Isn't this out of this world!' I continued excitedly.

'Now listen. You mustn't keep saying those things. Keep your thoughts to yourself. If you keep on like this, people will think that we come from some Rodope village!'

'Yes mother.'

'At table, you will find that food is served in such a way that you will have to help yourself. Watch the others carefully, and by the time your turn comes, you might be able to manage. Try not to spill food all over the tablecloth and most of all, eat your food, don't just turn your fork in it, as is your habit.'

'Yes mother.'

Ж

We couldn't change for dinner, for the simple reason that we didn't have a change of clothes. I had been wearing the blue dress all day, and all I did was to take it off, wash and put it on again. That didn't take long and so, I sat quietly on the divan and looked around me. The divan was upholstered in a cheerful Bulgarian folk motif, in a thick linen fabric; the floor was covered by a Bulgarian kelim. The sun, coming in through the tall windows lit up the colours and I thought that if I had a room like this, all to myself, I would never feel depressed or miserable no matter what happened. One couldn't, not in a room like this!

My father walked in through the wardrobe and put an end to my day-dreaming.

'Come on,' he said sharply.

The main feature of the dining room was a very long table; with two rows of high-backed chairs, and over it hung an unusual chandelier made of intertwined reindeer's antlers. It was beautiful.

Sasha came up to me and offered me his arm. I linked mine with his, and he led me to the table. I was pleased to find that my mother had been placed next to the General at the top of the table and my father next to her, whereas I was sitting next to Sasha at the opposite end. There was splendid tableware, scintillating glasses and so many knives and forks!

'Don't worry,' Sasha whispered to me, 'I will help you out.'

Vassili appeared at the door, wearing a white smoking jacket and white gloves holding an enormous silver dish. He went over to my mother and leant very slightly over her, on her left. She helped herself to some soup with poised solemnity.

Vassili moved on to the General.

'Do you want me to help you,' Sasha asked me as Vassili approached us?

'May I try it myself first, please?'

'Certainly. Do.'

I did. I might have been biting my lips and twisting my face as I did, but nothing was spilled. I sighed with relief.

It was a long and tasty meal. I kept helping myself to each dish as it came, and ate everything on my plate. Sasha poured some wine into my glass.

My father reacted immediately:

'Sasha, please! What are you doing?' his voice rose above the others all the way across the table. I blushed, but Sasha made a face to him without bothering to answer, and said to me:

'Drink up, cheers!'

I did.

When the meal was finished, Sasha took me to my father.

'She is a natural, your daughter. You ought to be proud of her,' and to me, 'Thank you for your most delightful company.'

'You must go to bed now.' said my father.

'Oh, let her stay a while! It is a holiday for her too after all.' Sasha said to him, but my father was adamant:

'No, it's bed time for her.'

I said 'good night' all round and, reluctantly, I went up to my room.

I didn't switch the light on. I walked over to the window and looked out. There was a full moon. The snow on the ground and on the branches of the pine trees shone brilliant white in the moonlight. The air seemed completely still. A squirrel must have ventured out of its hole and as it ran swiftly from one branch to another, it scattered powdery flakes, which glided slowly to the ground and all was still again. I moved away from the window and prepared to go to bed. How nice Sasha was. How beautiful all this was. I wondered whether life could be as nice as this all the time. Was it like this for some people? Probably, yes, since this place existed. It could not have been conceived by miserable people. How wonderful it would be if I were a few years older and Sasha fell in love with me, and took me away from my parents and their tiresome supervision and restrictions, and actually talked to me. He said that I had been good company. I didn't even remember what we had talked about, absorbed as I must have been with doing well during the meal ... but then, what if he had said that without really meaning it, just to please my father? What a disturbing thought this was! I was sad now; and I had been imagining such pleasurable things! I didn't succeed to cast off the unpleasant thought and couldn't go on with my imaginary new life; so, despondent and sad, I went to bed.

When I woke up the sun was pouring in through the windows. There was no trace of last night's melancholy. I had had a restful night's sleep. The room was warm; I jumped out of bed, got dressed and slipped quietly out. From the angle of the sun and the stillness in the villa, I could tell that it was very early. I tip-toed down the stairs and went into the drawing room where I found Vassili.

'Good morning young lady, did you sleep well?' he enquired politely.

'Yes, very well, thank you.'

'Come, I'll show you how to light the fire.'

I joined him in front of the fireplace where he was crouched. In the fireplace, there were a number of large logs resting on iron supports. Underneath them, there was a web of skilfully constructed thin, white pieces of wood.

'You have to light the thin ones first. They are called kindling. The logs catch on from them. Here, you do it.' Vassili handed me the matches and watched on.

'It's pine wood,' he explained as I was holding the flame under the wood, 'and it smells beautifully when it burns.'

Soon the pieces of wood started to burn quite wildly, the flames becoming longer and longer and licking at the logs. As they burned, they made little explosions and the smell of resin filled the room. It was beautiful.

'I finish my duties after I have served lunch,' Vassili said, 'Then I am free until dinner. Usually I go skiing, would you like to come with me?'

'Oh, I would love to, but I have no skis and I doubt that my mother would let me anyway.'

'Of course she will! Everybody skis here, otherwise, why bother to come to Borovetz?'

He obviously didn't know my mother.

'As for skis – we will find a pair that fits you in the ski-room.' Vassili went on.

'Ski-room?' I didn't understand.

'Yes, there is a small room, full of skis and skiing shoes etc. You can help yourself.'

The time between breakfast and lunch was spent sitting around and talking. The Americans drank whisky non-stop and my father kept remarking in Bulgarian how awful it was; my mother kept telling him to stop commenting in case somebody would hear him and understand what he was saying. I wandered around the villa, went to visit the kitchen with Vassili as my guide and, then, walked in the grounds. Lunch was served early to enable us to get to the ski slopes. Since everybody was going in the sleigh, my mother was soon outvoted and I was allowed to get a pair of skis and skiing shoes. At the foot of the slopes, there was a bar-café-restaurant and my parents, the only ones not participating in any of the ventures, sat on the bench outside and watched.

The Americans and their girl friends went up to the advanced slopes and did some real skiing, except for one of the girls who, like Sasha couldn't ski. Sasha found a small sledge somewhere and the two of them walked up and whooshed down the beginners' slope, with laughter and screams as skiers passed them by clumsily, almost colliding with them. They seemed to be the major attraction on the slopes since everybody around watched and laughed at their misadventures.

Vassili kept his promise and looked after me . He taught me first how to walk up with my skis on, and then, how to ski down.

'Keep the knees flexible. Light and flexible, like that, yes, all right, now let's give it a try; push yourself lightly, very lightly forward with the sticks and bend down a little ... '

Vassili had intended me to move across rather than down the slope. But by then, I had executed his advice, pushed myself forward, and was gathering speed down the slope. I wasn't aware at the time, that to make things easier for me, Vassili had waxed my skis. My speed was now increasing alarmingly. Vassili was skiing behind me, giving me instructions as to how to regain control, but I had by then reached the foot of the slope and was heading straight for a tree. I realised that I was going to smash into it if something wasn't done quickly and, without thinking, I sat down on the skis. My weight slowed me down and when I reached the tree, I just put my arms round it and came to a halt. Vassili arrived at the same time.

'Well done!' he said.

Behind him, I saw my parents. They were running towards us, their faces worried, gesticulating. I wanted to shout out something to reassure them that I was alright, but laughter prevented me from doing so. When they realised that I was not injured my parents calmed down and Vassili and I went back to the slopes.

As the sun began to set, the shadows grew longer and the temperature dropped, it was decided to call it a day. We all piled into the sleigh again, our noses running, our cheeks – pink with the exercise and the biting cold.

'Why don't you leave your wife and daughter here for a few days?' asked Sasha after dinner, and before he got a reaction from my father or my mother, he turned to one of the officers and spoke to him in English. He then turned back to my parents who were exchanging glances. I looked at my parents anxious to hear their reply, praying that they should say 'yes'. Sasha winked at me; my mother whispered to my father:

'Will you be able to manage on your own?'

And my father, perhaps a little embarrassed at the suggestion that he might not be capable of managing on his own, answered with a smile:

'Of course I will manage! Thank you Sasha, this will be a lovely break for my wife.'

'Great!' Sasha lowered his voice 'Tony and the girls will be back and we will have a really smashing time here.'

My father turned to me:

'Off you go to bed!'

'Ah, yes, you will be able to hear Tony's ghost story, won't you?'

'Yes, I am looking forward to it and thank you for asking us.' I said.

'You really must go to bed now.' said my mother.

I went up to my room where I fell asleep as soon as I was in bed.

My father, the American officers and their girl friends left in the morning. My mother and I stayed on for two more weeks. Tony, having returned from the staff villa, where he and the girls had been hiding, took the first opportunity to tell me his ghost story. He even came upstairs after I had gone to bed, wrapped in a white sheet 'to scare the life out of you sweetheart' – he did, but in such a nice, humorous way, that I laughed and didn't lose any sleep over it.

Every morning I lit the fire in the fireplace. I chose the day's menu with the cook and went skiing with Vassili and the others. My mother always came to the slopes, but remained an onlooker. She warned me to be careful, but never actually stopped me from doing any of the things I enjoyed doing. By the end of the holiday I was skiing down the advanced slope. It was straight and steep and I took it, my eyes shut, my face open to the biting wind, inebriated with speed.

I had a glass of wine with every meal; Sasha remained my table companion. He spoke French to me; I sang some of the French folk songs that we had learned at school. Eventually I was allowed to join the others around the fireplace after dinner and although the atmosphere remained that of a light hearted and jolly holiday, every now and then, Tony would say to my mother, his glass in his hand, his face flushed from both the drink and the fire:

'Drink now my love, and promise me that when your old man and I meet up in some concentration camp, you won't cry only for him.'

'Tony, please don't spoil it all!' my mother would plead with him.

'Reality, my love, must never leave us. This is what enables us to appreciate better this … refuge, this temporary, shall we say … delay, or reprieve.'

Then someone would change the subject.

For two weeks I lived in my day-dreams. For two weeks, I was the mistress of a room so beautiful, that I didn't mind it's solitude at night. For two weeks, I saw my mother relaxed, smiling, almost happy and in her happiness, she didn't deny me mine. I took part in the conversation at dinner and at other times, I exchanged witticisms with Tony, I flirted very shyly with Sasha at table and I skied to exhaustion with Vassili.

At the end of the two weeks, Sasha and Vassili sent us off with all the pomp and circumstance they could muster. My mother and I sat at the back of the black Buick and didn't exchange a word during the whole journey. I looked at the snow laden trees as they sped past us, the frozen river, the heavy gray sky and wondered what was in store for us. I knew where we were going – home; but where were we really going to end up? Where was I going to end up? I couldn't help the question bothering me. I had no answer. I wanted the car to turn back but I knew it couldn't and it wouldn't. It had to go on.

BOOK TWO

Chapter One

They Arrest my Father

A bell was ringing. I sat up in bed and realised that I wasn't dreaming. Someone had left their finger on the door bell. Sharp kicks on the door accompanied the shrill bell. My heart was beating so fast that I thought I was going to faint. A ray of light came from under the door and brought visual reality to the nightmarish noise. I heard my parents' door open and shut, quick steps towards the front door. Suddenly the noise stopped, and after a moment's silence, all the space outside my room seemed to be filled with men. They were talking loudly. I couldn't make out what was being said, but it sounded more like orders than anything else. My door opened and I recognised my father silhouetted in its frame. He switched the light on in my room. Some men appeared behind him, then pushed him aside and walked in.

'Go and bring your wife here,' a voice ordered.

Head down, holding his pyjamas against his body, my father obeyed.

It took me a few moments to get accustomed to the light;

when I did, I realised that there were three civilians and two Militia men in the room. The Militia men stood by the door, while the men in civilian clothes began to search the room. My parents returned, their faces chalk white. My mother handed me a jumper, which I put on over my pyjamas, and my socks. The water in the glass on the table was frozen solid. The men opened every book and note book, leafed through them, shook them; poked the mattress, the duvet, knocked on the walls, looked inside the lamp shades, inside the radio. When they finished with my room, they asked to be shown into my parents' bedroom. We were ordered to follow them and stay with them. When I asked to go to the toilet, one of the Militia men accompanied me and looked inside before allowing me in.

They searched the kitchen and the common parts of the flat. Throughout the search, for four hours, not a word was said. Only when they had finished with a room did one of them, always the same one, turn to my father and ask to be shown to the next room. Obediently, my father would volunteer:

'Yes, most certainly Comrade.' and he was stopped with a short 'That's enough'.

I tried to catch the eye of one of my parents. I wanted to find some reassurance; I wanted to read in their eyes that all this wasn't as scary as it seemed to be, that it would be over and forgotten soon, that it was some terrible mistake, that it had nothing to do with Tony's predictions, made in a half drunken state, during that wonderful winter holiday … but I failed.

Not once did either of my parents look at me; they didn't even look at each other. I understood later that they didn't want to be suspected of exchanging signals. Throughout this search, when time seemed to have stopped, I read worry in my mother's face, but my father couldn't conceal his fear; even I could see it. I felt that our lives had come to an end. When the search was completed, there was, for a moment, a glimmer of hope in my mind, that it was all over; but I was wrong.

'You!' one of the men in civilian clothes turned to my father, 'come with us.'

'But why?' asked my mother.

'Don't worry my dear,' my father's voice had a slight tremolo in it, 'the gentlemen have most probably some papers to check, the mistake will soon be found and all will be in order.'

'Go and get dressed.' the man ordered.

Only now did I realise that my father was wearing his trousers over his pyjamas. One of the Militia men escorted him to the bedroom, while we all stood in the middle of the hall in the freezing cold; no one looked at anyone else; no one said a word.

'See you later my dear.' My father kissed us.

'Where are you taking him? Where? I want to know,' my mother insisted, pleading with the civilian who had spoken before.

'Just an enquiry.' he said.

One of the Militia men gave my father a push in the back and they left. All was quiet now; we stood, my mother and I, numbed by fear and shock, looking incredulously at the front door which had just shut behind my father. Mr. Solomon, opening their door a fraction, shook us out of our torpor.

'What happened? Did they take him away?'

My mother replied flatly: 'They did.'

He now came out of their room, wrapped in a blanket.

'Did they search? Do you know what they were after?'

'They searched. They looked everywhere. God, everywhere! I don't know what they were looking for.'

'Was there no emphasis, like the bedrooms more than the kitchen, say?'

'No, they searched in the same way everywhere.'

Mrs. Solomon had also come out now and stood there, not knowing what to say.

A door slammed somewhere on one of the lower

floors and I thought that people were already going to work and school. I was wrong, it was only seven o'clock; it was too early. Mrs. Solomon must have had thoughts along the same line, because she ran to the front room and came back quickly:

'They have 'taken' Pastor Ivanov too! I just saw them getting into a black car? Three civilians and two Militia men with him.'

'Pastor Ivanov? From the 4th floor?'

'Yes, yes, I just saw him.'

'But why? I don't understand it.'

'Don't worry dear,' said Mrs. Solomon softly, 'go and get dressed properly, you'll catch your death here. Come on you too,' she said to me. 'I am sure they will come home latter this afternoon, both of them.'

My mother lit the fire in the kitchen stove and finally we warmed up a little. She was quiet and distant; I wanted to say something reassuring to her, but Tony's words, his predictions and warnings, coming back to me now, seemed to have just come true, and whatever words of reassurance I thought of, they didn't seem convincing at all; so I didn't say anything.

When the door bell rang, my mother dropped whatever she was holding, we looked at each other not knowing what to expect; my mother looked at the door, her features distorted with fear.

'I'll get it,' Mrs. Solomon shouted, 'don't worry.' There was a slight knock on the kitchen door, and Mrs. Ivanova, the Pastor's wife, walked in.

'What happened here? We realised something was going on. We could hear the commotion upstairs.'

'They searched everywhere ... '

... and they took him away?' Mrs. Ivanova finished the sentence for my mother who acquiesced, tears running down her cheeks. 'Same with us.' Mrs. Ivanova said sadly, 'Don't cry, please.'

'Do you know why? Do you have a clue, why?'

'No. I don't. But you mustn't worry.' She put a protective arm round my mother's shoulders. 'Such is God's will. He is testing us, and we must have faith in Him. I will pray for both of them today.'

I didn't go to school. We sat all day and waited for my father to return home. At ten o'clock my mother said:

'Let's go to bed. You might as well sleep in your father's place.'

When my father didn't come home the following day, my mother decided to pay a visit to my cousin Albert. As a member of the Communist Party, he was, she thought, the best person to advise her.

My cousin Albert, from Shoumen, had spent most of his late teens and early twenties in labour camps and prisons for communist activities. After the 9th September 1944, a free man in what he thought was a free country and a member of the CP, he had come to Sofia and was a student at the university. The previous summer he had married a girl student, and they lived in a flat which belonged to her father, not far from us.

My mother went to visit Albert and Mary on her own; I stayed home, in case my father returned.

'Albert thinks that they are checking on your father because he worked for the Americans,' my mother said when she returned. 'He thinks that they will probably keep him for a few days, during the enquiry. We will have to wait and see.'

'Yes, but why didn't they say anything to us, if it's as straightforward as that?'

'Albert told me that he wouldn't have expected them to. He said: 'it's the usual procedure'. 'I told him how they treated us and he was very embarrassed.'

A week passed, then another and another and still we had no news. I went back to school two days after my father's detention. I found that I couldn't concentrate and although I did my homework and read through the material over and over again,

I failed to retain any of it. I felt that some danger, some dark shadow was hanging over our heads and that my father's disappearance was but the first blow; I didn't know what else was in store for us; I was sure we would be hit again, but didn't know what kind of a blow or where it would come from.

With every passing day, my mother became more and more irritable. She complained of stomach ache and nausea. I worried about her health and did my best to help, but my mother was always dissatisfied and made it clear to me that I couldn't do anything right. In those first weeks, she saw her cousins during the day, seeking advice or maybe comfort, but no one could help and no comfort offered by Aunt Amelia or Aunt Mathilde served any purpose. She would not be comforted. My mother hadn't told me anything about those visits but one afternoon, when I came home from school, I found her in tears.

'What happened mummy? What is it? Have you heard anything?'

'Leave me alone,' she sobbed.

'Mummy, please tell me why are you crying?' I implored.

'Your Uncle Dori has forbidden Aunt Amelia to see me. Can you imagine, the only friend I have ever had … and her husband won't allow her to see me!'

'But why?'

'Oh, don't you understand?' she said losing her temper, 'We are marked people now! We might as well have leprosy!

When the third week of my father's detention drew to an end, and still we had had no news, my mother decided to 'do something'.

'I will go to the Militia Detention Centre. If he is detained, it stands to reason that he should be there,' I heard her tell Mrs. Solomon.

'How about the State Security?' Mrs. Solomon said.

'God forbid! I don't even want to think that he might be there! It's political, there … people don't always come out …

from there.'

'He might even be in prison,' Mrs. Solomon said more carefully now.

'My husband is not a thief! Nor a murderer!'

'One doesn't have to be a thief or a murderer nowadays, to be in prison.'

'He can't be in prison,' my mother reflected, 'for the simple reason that he has not been convicted.'

Mrs. Solomon didn't say anything and my mother went to the Militia Detention Centre. She came back, head down.

'Any luck?' I asked. She shook her head.

'They said he isn't there. I saw other women there. I spoke to one, whose husband has been there for three months! Can you imagine, three whole months! and without any explanation, or reason. She told me that I must go on looking for your father, they will never advise us where he is. That's how she found her husband, now she is allowed to bring him food parcels. I am going to obtain an appointment with the Director.'

'How?'

'I don't know yet.'

My mother did get an appointment with the Director of the Detention Centre, but when she went there, she was told that the Comrade Director had been called away on urgent business.

Aunt Amelia came to see us one afternoon. She was furtive, afraid that her husband might find her out.

'Listen,' she said to my mother, 'why don't you try and see some influential Jewish official? There are plenty who hold key positions. Reds, you know, or 'nouveaux Reds' – anyway, they might be able to help.'

'Who, for instance?'

'The head of one of the departments of the Central Committee of the CP is Jewish for one. How about the Jewish Agency? They might be able to enquire on your behalf. Also, what about your own brother? What about Marco, he is something or other in the party, isn't he? Although he is in Shoumen, surely he could pull a string here?'

My mother looked at her, a bitter half smile on her lips, her eyes dark:

'I am surprised at you Amelia. Don't you know what happens to a member of the Party if he as much as mentions a connection with a detained man? I don't want to cause Marco any troubles. He has suffered enough for them. The kind of man he is, he will soon suffer from them too, but it doesn't have to come through me.'

'I am only trying to help.'

'Thank you. With every passing day, I am becoming more and more certain that there is nothing anyone can do to help. I only wonder what is to become of me.'

Aunt Amelia stayed a while, but she was nervous.

'You must go now Amelia. Dori will find you out and he will be angry. At least *you* have your husband with you, go home to him.'

Towards the end of term I realised that I had let my studies slip and decided to pull myself together, I was going to end up at the bottom of the class. No one at school knew what had happened to us and my teachers were very surprised at my bad exam results.

I was told politely that if I were unwell, I should see a doctor. Margaret didn't know what to make of it all, but enjoying as she did having the top place uncontested, she didn't make any remarks.

I did pull myself together and studied very hard for the final exams. It wasn't easy, with my mother around – her red rimmed eyes, her bad temper and black moods, but I did quite well and climbed up a few places.

My mother kept going to the Militia Detention Centre every week on the day food parcels were brought in by wives. Every week she made up a small parcel and told the man at the desk, innocently, as though she had done it before, that she had brought her husband's food parcel. And every week he would look through his list, shake his head and say:

'He isn't here.'

Mrs. Ivanova did very much the same; she hadn't heard from her husband either, but her faith carried her through. She came to see my mother and although the two women were in the same position, it seemed to me that Mrs. Ivanova had more courage, more hope. She smiled, talked calmly, hopefully, whereas I hadn't seen a smile on my mother's face ever since my father's detention.

'God is testing us,' Mrs. Ivanova kept saying, 'He is testing our faith. Don't despair, I am praying for you. He is watching over us.'

My mother, a non-believer, just shook her head and shrugged. Three months after his arrest we found my father. It was on a 'parcels day' at the Centre; when my mother did as she had been doing for weeks, the man ticked his list and said, pulling the string to open the parcel:

'What have we here?'

My mother told me afterwards how she had tried not to show her joy, her surprise, her emotions, when she answered him:

'Just some home made cake.'

The man poked the cake in a few places then said:

'All right. Next!'

My mother was crying as she was telling me, and finally she said:

' ... you ... you see ... without my perseverance, I would not have found him! He would still be alone ... feeling abandoned ... oh, God what is to become of me ... '

The world outside mattered very little as we were totally preoccupied with our own misfortune. The relative calm that followed the discovery of my father's whereabouts, was soon followed by a worsening of my mother's restlessness. 'I know where he is, but this doesn't change my position at all. I still don't know how long he is there for and why he is there! How much more can I take?'

She had, by then, given up trying to get to see the Director of the Centre. Somebody had suggested to her that she should try and get an appointment with the Public Prosecutor. As for me, I was kept out, out of my mother's ordeal. I was just a silent witness to her anguish and an eavesdropper on her conversations with neighbours or friends.

Chapter Two

No News – My Mother Visits The Public Prosecutor

The struggles of the Jews in Palestine and all over the world to get the British to honour the Balfour Declaration; the illegal immigration of many Jews from Bulgaria and other European countries; and the final triumph – the declaration of an independent Jewish State – Israel, had all happened in the background of our own reality. All our family and friends were emigrating legally now that the Bulgarian government had opened 'the gates' for whoever wanted to leave.

People rushed and were leaving by the thousands every week, in case the Government changed their minds and stopped the emigration. Within a few months, Aunt Amelia and her family, Aunt Mathilde, my married cousins, and my father's sister, everybody in Shoumen, except Uncle Marco and Aunt Victoria; everybody had left.

We hadn't been able to visit any of them prior to their leaving because a meeting with us would have spelled danger for those left behind. The Solomons left just as the school term ended. The flat became lugubriously quiet.

'Who knows what kind of people *they* are going to put in the flat now,' my mother said, but her mind was preoccupied with her visit on the following day, to the Public Prosecutor's office. She returned from her appointment, excited:

'I saw him,' she said, because she didn't really believe he would see her. 'He took down all the details and I am going back to see him in a fortnight. He will investigate and tell me what it is all about.'

'Let's hope he will.'

'Oh, yes, he will, he was a very nice man.'

Two weeks later, she went back to the Public Prosecutor's office, and returned crying.

'What happened?' I asked her. She shook her head.

'He can't do anything ... or he won't do anything. Perhaps he knew it even then, but led me to believe that he will find out the reason for all this – and tell me! What is happening to us ... why? Why?' There was nothing I could say to comfort her.

We didn't have to wait long before new co-sharers were 'put' in the flat. Two days after the Solomons had vacated, a young man came to our door. He was tall with dark bushy hair and blue eyes; his weather-beaten complexion and his accent told us that he was a peasant from the South.

'My name is Stephan.' he introduced himself to my mother. 'I am a driver at the Central Committee. I will bring my bride tomorrow and we will have the front room. The back room will be occupied by one of our secretaries. She will be arriving tomorrow too.'

The 'Central Committee' meant 'the Central Committee of the Communist Party'!

My mother handed him a plate with some bread and salt on it, the traditional greeting to a new home. I saw her hand shaking; I only hoped that he hadn't seen it.

'Welcome to your new home,' she said, 'All the best to your

bride and yourself.'

Stephan took the plate and smiled:

'Thank you Comrade.'

When he left, my mother walked up and down the room, her hands on her cheeks:

'A driver at the Central Committee ... and a secretary from the same place – our crime must be terrible for them to watch us so closely. We will have to be careful ... very careful .... What a life this is going to be ... surrounded by spies .... '

It had become a normal behaviour of my mother's – she cried. She cried and sobbed in her little handkerchief. Eventually a new and frightening thing was added to this behaviour. She would start a long whine, then she would stay on her seat, her eyes vague, her hands tearing at each other while muttering all the time, sometimes incomprehensibly, sometimes repeatedly:

' ... how long ... how long ... my God, how long.'

Her posture, her voice, her swaying, were frightening. I wanted to bring her some comfort, I wanted to stop her swaying, I wanted somehow to force her to talk in her normal voice, I wanted to see my mother as I knew her. I would put my hand on her knee but she would brush it aside with an unpredictably violent sweep as though the very contact with me enraged her. On one occasion, when she pushed my hand aside, she shouted in a voice, suddenly high, aggressive, hatred laden:

'Go away!'

After an evening meal taken in total silence, we would go to bed. I slept in my father's half of the huge double bed, where there was no contact possible with my mother and, once the light was out, I would shut my eyes, my fists clenched, my body stiff with loneliness and misery, and wish vehemently for death. Death, of course didn't come, and I would fall asleep in the grip of the most awful nightmares.

Chapter Three

My mother's Illness – Stephan's Stephanka

One night, my mother's hand shook me out of my nightmare. She was squeezing my arm painfully and I raised myself up on my elbow.

'Wake up … wake up!' she whispered. I switched the light on:

'What's the matter mum?'

'Go and get someone … I am having … a heart attack … '

She was lying on her back, her eyes shut, her breath short, pale. I jumped out of bed and ran to the kitchen, got a glass of water, ran back and tried to make her drink, but the water spilled down her chin. I withdrew the glass and realised that my mother was dying and I didn't know how to help her and whom to call.

'Go and get Mrs. Stoylova …, ' my mother whispered. I put my coat over my pyjamas and ran down the stairs. The Stoylovs lived on the first floor and my mother was friendly with them. I didn't know them very well, and it struck me now, that I had to ring their bell – it was three o'clock in the morning. I was going to scare them to death.

There was no time for hesitation, my mother's life was at stake. I rang the bell and knocked gently at the same time. Soon, I heard a movement behind the door and I said:

'Don't worry … it's only me … ' the door opened, and Mrs. Stoylova, wrapped up in a large shawl looked at me; I went on:

'it's my mother … I believe she is having a heart attack …. '

'I am coming.' Mrs. Stoylova disappeared inside and came back soon, a little bottle in her hand. I had called the lift. We didn't speak. We found my mother as I had left her, pale on her pillows. I stood in the corner of the room. Mrs. Stoylova had asked me for a bowl of water and a lump of sugar. She poured some drops from the little bottle she had brought with her on to the sugar and I saw the brown liquid disappear into the porous surface. She slipped the sugar in mother's mouth. She then soaked a flannel in the bowl, squeezed it, and gently wiped my mother's temples and wrists; she then spread the same cloth on my mother's chest.

'Get me some vinegar,' she said to me, and I went into the kitchen again. Mrs. Stoylova dipped her finger in the vinegar and passed it over my mother's upper lip. The reaction was immediate, My mother moved her head, sighed and opened her eyes.

'Don't worry my dear … ' Mrs. Stoylova spoke in a low, soothing voice. 'You will be all right … ' My mother smiled faintly at her and her lips formed the words: 'Thank you'.

I don't know how long all this took. Eventually Mrs. Stoylova came up to me, handing me a glass of water.

'Here, drink up. You have had quite a fright. Go to bed now. She is all right.' She saw herself out and I went back to bed.

Ж

At the end of school term, we had received our reports from the hands of the Mother Superior in a short, solemn ceremony. The nuns had been given three weeks to vacate the building and leave the country. The building was requisitioned by the Government. We were all very sad, having to part with our teachers and our school. It was agreed that the day before the nuns were due to leave the country, we would go back to say our final 'adieu' to them.

On the day, Margaret came to pick me up.

'Which school are you going to go to next term?' I asked her.

'It will have to be the Fifth Gymnasium for girls. It's my regional ... whatever they call it. How about you? I am sure your regional school will be the Sixth.'

'Yes, it is. I have heard though, that as of next term that particular school will change – it will be one school from the age of 5 to 18, like in the Soviet Union and it will be called – wait for it – First Model Experimental school in the name of Josef Stalin.'

'Charming. And back to meetings, pestering activists, slogans and the like.'

'Margaret! What's the matter with you! We are in the Street!'

'Oh, I don't know I am fed up.'

I didn't answer for a while, then I couldn't help saying:

'I am fed up too. Everything seems to be coming to an end.'

'You sound rather gloomy. Are you going anywhere in the summer?'

'No. Are you?'

'Yes, to my grandparents' in the country. It's near a Spa resort where my mother takes baths. I have lots of cousins and aunts and uncles; we all meet there every summer, it's great fun.'

It sounded wonderful. A place in the country, crickets, sunshine and country stillness, the smell of freshly cut grass and wild flowers. What was my summer going to be like?

'Haven't you any relations in the country?' Margaret asked.

'No. My family were all Sofiates. I say were, because they have all gone to Israel.'

'Lucky people. Do you hear from them? What is it like to be out there?'

'One of my aunts writes sometimes. She doesn't say much except that everything is in Hebrew and that Hebrew is a very difficult language. They live in a place called Jaffa.'

'Aren't you going to take the opportunity and leave here?' I had a ready answer to this question:

'I want to complete my education first.'

'Oh, I don't know about that,' said Margaret, 'what if 'they' decide suddenly to stop all emigration and you are stuck here? Surely you could complete your education there?'

'I can't speak any Hebrew.'

'If I had the option open to me, I am sure I would learn Hebrew. You could too, after all it's just another language. You didn't do too badly in French.'

'Possibly.'

We walked for a while without talking. I felt Margaret's glance and looked down.

'I don't know quite how to say this … but you are not yourself lately. I have meant to ask you for some time, but didn't want to pry. If you think I am being indiscreet, please tell me, but only if you want to, please tell me what is the matter?'

I had never spoken about it and although many times I had felt the urge to talk, I knew that had I told Margaret – she was the only person I could tell – I would have possibly lost her friendship; she couldn't know and continue to see me, not if she cared about her own and her family's welfare. Now that we were about to lose sight of each other anyway, through going to different schools and the opportunity was offered to me to talk about it, it poured out in one breath together with sobs and tears of frustration.

'My father … has been … detained … my mother and I are

alone … and she is not well and I can't help her. She doesn't want me to. And we don't know what it is all about and how long it's going to last … my father worked for the Americans for a while, and this is the only explanation that we can find, but how long are we going to be punished for it? I don't know … if I haven't told you before, it's because I didn't want to … lose you as a friend … I so needed to have a friend … I know it was selfish … but at least when I was with you … I could allow myself to smile even laugh sometimes … at home, it's only gloom. My mother doesn't allow us to well, live, really, she is sad all the time, but that is not the point … the point is that … oh, forgive me Margaret, but the point is – not a word is said about what my father may be going through….'

I stopped as suddenly as I had started and tried to calm down. Margaret put her hand on my shoulder:

'I am so sorry! If only I had known … I … look, we are nearly there, wipe your face, we will talk about it afterwards, OK?'

On the way back, Margaret insisted that we went to the Alexander Nevski square. We sat on one of the benches. It was a warm early summer's day; the air was transparent. The large linden trees around the square were in blossom. Large, heavy, fragrant blooms danced at the end of their branches and the breeze carried their delicate scent.

'I would like to treat you to a trip to the cinema this afternoon. There is an American film showing at the Gloria Palace. I am sure we won't be given the opportunity to see American films for long. Shall we go?'

'I don't know … my mother doesn't like to be left alone … it's not fair to leave her alone ….'

'Let's go to your place, I'll talk to your mother, perhaps she would come with us. It will do her good.'

My mother declined the offer to go to the cinema with us, but couldn't refuse to let me go with Margaret who had 'invited' me. We saw a film called Rhapsody in Blue. I enjoyed it tremendously.

I went home straight after the film and, as we parted, we promised to try and see each other during next term.

I found my mother sitting, staring at the floor, her face closed. I felt ashamed for being in a good mood.

'You should have come, mum, it would have helped change your mood and ... ' She gave me a short reproachful glance:

'I had an attack while you were out enjoying yourself,' she said.

After the initial visit of our co-sharer, nobody showed up for well over a week and the tension mounted. Each time we came into the flat, we had to be careful about anything we said that could be overheard from the rooms – 'they' could have moved in while we were out. My mother took special care in trying to talk in her normal voice to me when we were crossing the hall and saying such mundane things as: 'I am so hungry' or: 'my bag is very heavy, I feel that my arms are growing longer'. Whispering was all right, provided we could explain it by saying that we were careful not to disturb anyone. Late one evening, we heard the front door open and close, heavy steps, then a knock on our door. My mother was teaching me to knit. I was handling the needles clumsily, seeing in my mind's eye a wonderful jumper that I would be able to knit as soon as I had mastered the craft.

'Don't say a word,' whispered my mother to me and, aloud, 'Come in.'

Stephan walked shyly in, closed the door behind him and touched his forehead with two fingers in the form of a salute.

'Good evening Comrade,' he said quietly. And, my mother, in a jovial, friendly tone:

'Good evening to you Comrade, come and sit down. Stephan sat on the edge of a chair. He started slowly, then, encouraged by my mother's smile:

'I am from Dragovo. A small village in the Rodopes. You

wouldn't know it. Anyway, my wife is arriving tomorrow and I wondered, she has never left our village before. She has never seen the city ... '

'Is there anything I can do to help?'

'Oh, bless you lady! ah ... Comrade I mean ... I ... this is what I had in mind. We, in our village, are simple people ... if you can help her a little ... I would appreciate it very much.'

'Why, certainly comrade, with pleasure.' my mother's enthusiasm made me look up at her. Stephan seemed relieved.

'May I smoke?' he asked.

'By all means.'

He sat back in his chair, lit a cigarette and took a deep, long draw from it. The fold in the middle of his forehead disappeared.

'I have travelled you see, Comrade,' he said, a cloud of blue smoke streaming from his nostrils, 'I have seen the world, I have seen what life in Europe is like, but my young bride – she hasn't.'

'Where have you travelled?'

'With the Army, see, I fought in Hungary, in Czechoslovakia and Poland – we fought the Nazis. I saw all those cities, their monuments and cathedrals and how people live. It does something for a man – travelling, you know.'

'Yes, I agree.'

'I enjoyed myself. I tasted a little of everything, you know what I mean. But when it came to choosing a wife, she had to be from our village. Women in the cities, Comrade, they are too smart, they know too much ... hm, no offence, I mean .... '

'Very wise, Comrade. There is nothing like a wife who comes from the very same background as yourself.'

'Please call me Stephan, My wife's name is Stephanka. I call her Stephka, for short – Stephan and Stephka, see?'

'This is charming. I am sure we will get on together fine, Stephan; and please don't worry about your wife. I'll help her without her realising it.'

Stephan stood up:

'Thank you so very much, Comrade,' he paused a moment. I felt that there was something he was going to add, and looked up from my knitting.

'About your … man, lady,' Stephan said quietly, 'I know, but you don't have to worry about me. I am a friend.' And he walked quickly out, without waiting for a reply. I waited a while, to allow time for Stephan to get into his room and said:

'Do you believe him?'

'I don't know,.' said my mother, 'I don't know what to believe any longer.'

The back room vacated by the Solomons was occupied by the Secretary on the following day. She moved in noisily, went to work noisily in the morning and came back home noisily in the afternoon. I don't know how she did it, but there was no way one could ignore the fact Maria was in. In the evenings, she had visitors and we soon realised that they were all men. We could hear their voices in her room, there would be the sound of records being played, the light would go off, then on again. The door would open, then close; and soon, there would be another visitor. This went on late into the night. The noise didn't disturb me, nor the thought of what was going on for I did not understand. My mother though, complained constantly about it.

Stephka, like her husband, was a typical Bulgarian peasant … Tall, slim but solidly built. A small upturned nose, blue eyes and pink cheeks, and large strong hands.

'She refused to come up in the lift, my little savage.' Stephan said to us when he brought her in to introduce her. My mother shook hands with her.

'Welcome Comrade, you will soon get used to our ways here,' my mother said. Stephka made a fuss over me:

'What a fine young maiden your daughter is! She'll grow to

be a fine young lady, I am sure.'

'She is only a child,' my mother said. I blushed and wished they would stop talking about me. I wasn't used to this kind of appraisal of my person. Stephka removed her hand from the top of my head, stopped stroking my hair and said:

'How can you live here? All those stairs! I will never look out of those windows – never! I'd rather die. How can you live without a garden here? Where do you get your vegetables?'

'We buy them from the green grocer.'

Stephka turned to her husband: 'Buy vegetables? Never. I'll never spend money on that. In my village, we grow them in the garden.'

'Come on, let's go.' Stephan took her away, looking at her affectionately.

After a few weeks, my mother noticed that the enamel on the edge of the toilet seat was badly scratched. She couldn't think of how this had come about. She told me that she suspected that Stephka had scratched it, using too much scouring powder to clean it. She approached her carefully about it. Stephka laughed and blushed, then confessed that she wasn't used to sitting down while 'doing her necessities' – in the village they crouched, so she climbed on top with her wooden clogs, and crouched!

Chapter Four

My New School – I meet Mimi

On September 1st, I went to my new school. Once again I found myself in a school courtyard where I didn't know anyone; the difference being, that the crowd here was mixed – boys and girls who knew each other, formed little groups. I felt ill at ease in the presence of boys.

The loudspeaker ordered us into formations and then – into the classrooms. I followed my class and sat at an empty double desk at the back of the classroom. Our form teacher accompanied us from the courtyard – into the room; she was a tall thin woman with short salt and pepper hair, no make up, and she wore a plain mid-calf length skirt with square looking low heeled shoes. She sat at her desk which stood on a rostrum, took the register and began calling our names. When called, we had to stand up. She took a good look at each and every one of us, as though to memorise our faces, asked for confirmation of our addresses then, went on to the next name. When this was finished, she stood up and took a long look around, scrutinising some of us, more than others. Finally she said:

'I am going to take you for Geography. I will also be responsible for your behaviour at school and outside it. School uniform is to be worn at all times. Is that clear? Is that clear?'

'Yes ... yes ... a few shy voices came up.

'It better be. What is more, each and every one of you is also responsible for his or her classmates' behaviour. Anyone seeing a pupil outside the school not wearing the uniform, or behaving in such a manner as to disgrace the good name of this school, must report them to me. The punishment will be from a reprimand to expulsion and let me tell you here and now, no pupil of mine will be expelled; that is to say, you will behave in accordance with the honour bestowed upon you as pupils of this very special school.'

She swept the class with her chilling eyes. She looked like a hawk ready to dive at her prey. Somebody moved, somebody cleared their throat. The teacher, who was holding a long slim ruler, slapped it on the desk violently,

'I haven't finished yet' she screwed up her eyes and went on, 'The girls. All hair will be cut short so that the ear lobes are visible. No fancy styles – a straight line around the neck, and the lobe – visible. As of tomorrow. No plucking of eyebrows, no manicuring of finger nails, no fancy stockings or shoes. The boys. Tomorrow all boys will come to school – their heads shaved.' A murmur of discontentment swept the classroom.

'Silence! Shaved, I said; and after that, the hair will be allowed to grow two centimetres all round. No fancy styles.'

Somebody's voice rose above the others and something like: ' ... it's like being in the army ... ' was heard.

'Who said that?' the teacher barked, looking around, waiting for the guilty one to stand up.

'Who said that?' she repeated.

After a short pause, a boy stood up.

'I did.'

'Your name?' She wrote it down.

'This is a joke,' somebody said.

The teacher looked up and her voice shrieked:

'Who was that?'

Another boy stood up.

'It was I in the first place Comrade Teacher. Dimitry here only tried to cover up for me. I was the first one ... I don't know who said that it was a joke.'

Although he hadn't said anything offending, he had managed to imply a light hearted mockery in his voice.

The teacher seemed disconcerted now. She looked around and just then, the bell rang. There was an initial movement of people getting up and the desks rattling, but her voice rose firmly above it:

'Nobody is going to leave or move until we sort this out. If it takes the whole day.'

She sat down and even I at the back of the room, could hear her breathing. I looked around in expectation of further developments. I met a girl's glance; she smiled at me behind the back of the girl in front of her so as not to be seen. I smiled back. She shrugged slightly, meaning: 'don't worry, it isn't serious.' I made a face, trying to say that it looked pretty serious to me. The girl nudged the girl sitting next to her, they looked at each other, then the first girl seemed to point me out to her friend. Then, they both looked at me, smiling.

The teacher's voice startled me and I straightened up:

'I am waiting!'

Some time passed and no one moved. The teacher stood up and said:

'You two – at the Headmaster's office after class! As for the coward who daren't stand up – the whole class will be punished because of him. You will stay here after classes, every day for a week, for a whole hour all of you! You will copy texts without a sound. I will supervise you myself.' She spoke in short sentences.

'You will be punishing yourself too, in that case .... ' somebody whispered loudly enough for all of us to hear, but if the teacher heard him, she didn't react. She stepped down from the rostrum.

'Everybody take your left shoe and sock off. I will see to it that you wash properly.'

'Good lord!' a boy's voice came up from the front rows 'I expect this to be necessary in the Balkan Mountains, but not here. We are civilised here you know.'

The teacher pretended she hadn't heard and I gathered that she was smart enough to realise that she would be driven mad again and lose face, so she concentrated on our feet and while she was at it, she inspected our ears as well. When her inspection was over, she went back to her desk, picked up the register and walked out.

There was a sigh of relief all round. The two girls with whom I had exchanged glances and smiles, came over to me:

'Hi. My name is Mimi, and this is Annie.' said the girl who was the first one I had seen.

'How do you do.' I said.

'You had a real scare, didn't you, coming from the French school, you are not used to these things.'

'Yes, it was a bit ... tough, wasn't it?' I said carefully, just in case they were activists and provocateurs.

'Isn't everything?' Mimi said.

I didn't answer.

'We heard your address when the dragon was reading our names out, you live very near us. If you like we might walk home together.'

That would be nice.' I was pleased that my company was wanted, but also a little dubious as to whether or not I could trust them.

Before the day was out, we met our history and maths teachers, we were given the programme of the weeks' studies, a list of books to purchase, and then dismissed.

'You must be careful whom you befriend.' said my mother when I told her what had happened at school.

I went to have my hair cut in the afternoon. There was a queue of school girls at the hairdresser's who gave all of us the same treatment. I realised that those specifications were not issued specially for our class, or our school, but for all schools .I felt very self conscious with so little hair around my face and its child-like features so exposed, so naked.

'It doesn't make much difference,' my mother said, 'in any case, it will soon grow.'

Back at school the next morning, I found that everybody had done as they were told. The boys' heads shone in the bright light, and the girls' ear-lobes were all clearly visible.

Mimi and Annie came to find me again after class. They asked me about the French school and how I had coped with a foreign language. I learned that, until the closure of all foreign schools, Annie had been attending the Deutsche Schule and Mimi, the American School but they had known each other for a long time, and had been friends even though they went to different schools.

'You must teach us French.' Mimi said.

'With pleasure. And you must teach me English.'

'It's a deal! When do we start? Your place or mine?'

My suspicions were aroused immediately. Who were they really? Why were they so friendly, so interested in me? If it became known at school that my father was detained, I would be expelled immediately. A daughter of a 'reactionary imperialist' wouldn't be accepted in this school – the first one to be modelled on the Soviet Educational system. When filling the entry form I had answered the question: 'Father's occupation?' by: 'office clerk'. Luckily the form didn't enquire as to his employer!

Now on my guard I said carefully:

'Oh, it doesn't really matter only my mother hasn't been very well lately.' They looked at each other.

'I am sorry,' Mimi said, 'we can make it my place.'

The bell rang calling us back into the classroom. Although this was only the second day, we could already tell who the activists were. Once again we were being organised in various 'circles'. A 'circle' for the study of the history of the CP, a 'circle' for the study of advanced dialectics, the philosophy of Karl Marx paralleled with that of Engels etc. etc. Membership fees were being collected, Red Scarves inspected, days for regular meeting of the Stalin Youth Organisation set. I felt sick at the thought of going through all this again. What a restful time I had had at the French school! We were eventually asked for volunteers with drawing abilities to draw slogans and posters for the school's classrooms and outdoor events; I stuck my arm up.

'Are you good at drawing Comrade?' the activist asked and to my surprise a voice came up from behind:

'The best! You ought to see her lettering, oh, boy simply delightful! She is your best choice!'

'OK,' said the activist, 'I think we will have the handicrafts' hall at our disposal every Thursday afternoon. This might be subject to alterations, but you will be notified in good time. In any case, we meet here, next Thursday at 4pm.'

I was very pleased at the way things had turned out; now I could get out of many tedious meetings and lectures. The boy who had spoken in my favour came up to me:

'I haven't a clue what your lettering is like, but I felt you wanted the job and could do with some support.'

'That was very kind of you, thank you very much!' I blushed, wondering why a boy was bothering with me.

'Not at all. My name is Slavy. I know yours, I heard it – very nice.'

'Thank you.' I didn't know what more to say, but couldn't

help feeling elated by the mere fact that I was talking to a boy. The arrival of the teacher put and end to our conversation.

Mimi, Annie and myself walked home after school.

'It's such a nice day today,' said Mimi, 'why don't we all go to the park this afternoon. What do you say?'

'Lovely idea.' said Annie.

I was taken aback but as they expected a reaction from me, I said:

'I don't know … I can't very easily … my mother ….'

'Oh, I am sure she won't mind!' Mimi said, enthusiastically, 'even if she is not well she won't mind!'

'Just for a short while,' Annie added, 'the park is so beautiful this time of year.'

'I'll try.'

'We'll pick you up around three. OK?'

'OK. See you.'

We had reached 'Doctor Long'; they left me outside the door and walked off. They lived in the same Street – Vrabtcha Street, which met Rakovsky at a T junction just opposite 'Dr. Long'.

On my way up, in the lift, I felt that going for a walk in the park was a very attractive idea, but couldn't help being just a little worried. Worried about these girls' interest in me. Up in my room, I could see them still walking down Vrabtcha Street.

'It's impossible!' my mother said, 'You can't be out all day and leave me alone!' I so wanted the girls' friendship and even though I couldn't be certain that this is what they were offering me, I felt disappointed with my mother's refusal. Now I could never really find out. The hours spent at school didn't really matter. That was artificial togetherness.

'OK.' I said. 'I won't go.'

'No, no,' my mother said quickly, 'you can go today because I am going out too, but you mustn't make a habit of it.'

'Oh, mummy! Thank you.'

'You must be home by six though.'

'I will.'

At ten to three I was standing by the window, looking down Vrabtcha Street. I saw Annie leave her house at no.35, stop and ring the bell at no.12; Mimi showed up after a while and they walked together. I saw them talking and laughing. Mimi had a distinctive way of ducking her head and lifting her right hand when something amused her. She was a little taller than me, but 'older' looking (she wore a bra), she was wearing stockings and a chequered skirt which looked positively foreign. Her complexion was fair and she had hazel eyes – I thought she was very beautiful. Annie was even taller than Mimi, but willowy; she had a prominent forehead and large 'bambi' eyes; her nose was small and she had dimples on both cheeks. Her short wavy hair was combed away from her face, which seemed naked, somehow, and vulnerable As they neared, I ran downstairs.

'Hi!'

'Hi!' they greeted me together.

We climbed up Rakovsky Street, turned left, passed Alexander Nevsky where we took the boulevard leading to the park.

The Park, or the Royal Gardens, as it used to be called before the war, was a present from King Boris to the people and children of Sofia. It had a large landscaped area with trees, lawns, flower beds, benches and a large lake; also a fenced in area for children with many games. Further in, the park was left wild with a favourite 'lover's lane' called 'Unter den linden' after some similar place in Berlin.

The sun was high up in the sky. The air was warm and clear, scented with the delicate perfume of the flowers and trees around. I found the feeling of being out with my own friends, with girls my age, very agreeable. Annie and Mimi seemed at ease.

'Do you know what you are going to do when we finish school?' Annie asked me.

'No. Not really. I would like to be an interior decorator, or an architect, but I am hopeless at maths.'

'Don't tell Annie about it – she won't sympathise. She is a genius at maths and thinks everybody can do it.'

'Does this mean you are going to do maths at university?' I asked Annie.

'Not necessarily.'

'Why? If you find it easy?'

'Because I see further than that. Say I did maths. What next? Teach? Can you see me coping with a bunch of kids like us? I'd rather scrub floors.'

'You could lecture at university, that's easier.' Mimi said.

'How about getting married?' I asked.

'Do you think we will?'

'Everybody else seems to.'

'Rubbish! I'll never get married! Cook and scrub and look after lunatic kids for the rest of my life – never!' said Annie.

'I'll get married,' there was conviction in Mimi's voice, 'I want to have children and a home. Look at my mother – she doesn't have to scrub, as you call it, we help her! Annabella and me and mum – we are friends.'

I felt a pinch of jealousy.

'How about your father?' Annie asked.

'You know him. He isn't much good round the house.'

'You see! and you tell me that your mother is happy! – rubbish!'

'But she has us!'

'You don't sleep with her! It's your father she has to sleep with!' Annie insisted. 'To sleep with a man who is no good! Ugh! I'll never get married.'

We had arrived at the park and were now walking down the central path.

'Shall we hire a boat?' Mimi turned to me, 'Can you row?'

'No, I can't and I have never been on a boat, but I'd love to.'

'Come on, then, we will. Annie and I can do the rowing.'

The thought that I couldn't swim passed through my mind, but I wasn't going to miss this excitement, because of a mere detail!

'How much is it?' I asked, remembering that I only had a few pennies in my pocket.

'That's all right. We'll treat you this time, you will be given a chance to pay next time.'

Mimi went into the little hut and came out with a man who led us to one of the boats. He held it while we got on board, then gave us a push. I sat in the middle seat with Mimi and Annie, next to each other, facing me, With even strokes they took the boat out, in the middle of the lake, under the Japanese bridge and along the edge, under the weeping willows ....

'This is so beautiful.' I said.

We rowed in silence for a while, then my two friends decided to rest and stopped the boat under a willow, in the shade.

'You know' said Annie to me 'You are a very interesting girl to us.'

'Me? Why?' I was taken by surprise.

'You give an impression of a real 'femme du monde', but you are quite a child really, aren't you?'

I was confused.

'How do you mean?'

'When I first saw you, I was under the impression that you know a lot more about life and people than you really do. Am I right?'

'I don't know. I don't know what impression I give to people .... '

'Do you do it on purpose?'

'Do I do what, on purpose?'

I was totally disconcerted.

'Give an impression of worldliness?'

'I ... I am not worldly at all ... I am sorry, but I am quite ordinary really. I am sorry to disappoint you. I haven't done anything on purpose, I can assure you!' There was a short pause.

'I wish I were more ... 'femme du monde', as you call it.'

'Do you have a boy-friend?'

'Me? Of course not.'

'Why 'of course' ?' asked Mimi.

'Look at me. Who would bother to take a second look at me.'

'Hmm ... I wouldn't know about that. I saw Slavy eyeing you more than once.'

'I haven't even got my periods yet.'

'What of it! I haven't got it either, but it doesn't worry me.' Annie said

'I have it, but believe me, it's nothing, really.' Mimi was rather shy about it.

'But ... isn't it a fact that one isn't ... doesn't really develop until one has one's periods?' I enquired.

'It may be part of it, but my mother tells me that it's not all; and she should know, she is a chemist.' Annie said.

'I know nothing about it. My mother doesn't talk to me about these things.'

We fell silent for a while. The gentle ripples made by other boats, swayed the boat gently from right to left and the water caught between the flank and the shore, made a soft clinking noise.

'Do you ever go to the 'Promenade'?' Mimi was the first to speak.

'No! But I would love to!' I said quickly.

The avenue at one end of the Alexander Nevsky Cathedral was the meeting place of everybody who considered themselves young and 'with it'. In the early hours of the evening, young people would go there for a 'few rounds' – that is, walk slowly up and down the 500 metres at that spot of the Avenue Royale which constituted 'the promenade'.

They looked at each other, and for a moment all my illusions of friendship were swept away.

'Yes?'

'OK.' Annie took the initiative 'here goes: last summer we went to the Promenade quite regularly. In our wanderings, we noticed a bunch of boys; three to be precise. We saw them more than once, we followed them sometime; they paid no attention to us. They have no girl friends – we are sure of that. They are called Ivan, Vladimir and Rudy. Ivan lives at Doctor Long's.

'He does?' I said quite sheepishly, not quite following what she was driving at.

'Don't you know him?' Mimi asked.

'No … wait a minute, what's his surname?'

'Stoylov.'

'I know his mother! She is friendly with my mother!'

'But you don't know him?'

'No, I am sorry. But it won't be too difficult to arrange, I am sure.'

'OK! You make his acquaintance and then we shall have to think of something.

'This is exciting!'

'Mimi is in love with Ivan.' Annie informed me 'and I – with Rudy.'

'Unusual name' – I was thinking of my own father's name.

'His mother is German. You will have to have Vladimir – he is not a bad looking chap.'

'I don't really want a boy friend, but I will be pleased to do something for you.'

'Don't be such a wet blanket! Of course you want a boy friend!' Annie was adamant.

'When we heard your address in class, you can imagine what we felt.' Mimi said, 'We knew that we had to approach you, and as you didn't seem to be … an activist … '

'No, I am not an activist.'

'We want to be friends with you,' Mimi said again, 'and I want to be honest. Your address may have been the initial motivation we had, but it isn't important any longer.'

'How do you mean?'

'Well … simply that … we like you.' Annie said.

'There is more,' Mimi hurried to say before I could say anything, 'I have to tell you everything, so you can relax and stop being so careful and on your guard all the time,' she paused for a moment, 'My father, you see,' she went on, 'is a pastor, at Dr. Long's.'

I looked at her.

'A Methodist Pastor. He replaces Pastor Ivanov at Doctor Long now – Doctor Long, at the Church.'

'Yes?'

'Mrs. Ivanova has told us about your father – we know her very well; so you see, you don't have to worry, you are among friends, we are on your side.'

A long moment passed while I was taking it all in. I felt exposed and reassured at the same time.

'You are not saying anything.' Annie said, her forehead furrowed. 'Mimi is telling the truth. Are you angry because of the boys … we could … '

'No. I am not angry, not at all. I appreciate your frankness. I want to be your friend.'

'Hurray!' Mimi stood up, dangerously rocking the boat, then sat down and they both began to laugh.

'Now that all is in the open, and we know where we stand, we must work out a line of attack, about the boys, I mean.' said Annie.

'Leave it to me,' I said with a surprising self-confidence, 'by Christmas Ivan and Rudy will be your respective 'boy-friends'.'

Chapter Five

News from Prison – 'Le Malade Imaginaire'

'You can't make a habit of this.' my mother said to me in a quiet voice over dinner. 'These girls have normal homes. Their fathers are at home; can you really enjoy yourself when you know you have left me here alone? It wasn't the case today, but normally, it would be, wouldn't it?'

I had enjoyed myself. I felt guilty.

'Mimi is a nice girl, for the first time you have chosen a nice friend.' My heart filled with happiness at my mother's approval. 'But,' she went on, 'she is not like you. She is a lot more grown-up, shall we say. Her interests are different, you can't go out like this yet.'

In one breath I was acknowledged and wiped out again. I was about to defend myself, when the door bell rang twice. My mother and I looked at each other, frightened.

'Stay here.' my mother said 'I will see who it is.'

'It may only be Mrs. Stoylova.'

'It may be.' She left, and I sat motionless, trying to hear what was going on. I heard a deep male voice and, almost immediately, my mother ushered in what seemed to be a giant. He was unshaven, his hair was long, untidy and dirty, his clothes rough and too small for him. He scared me and I wondered what was my mother doing, asking him in.

'Ah, and this 'ere would be your young 'un.' he said.

'Yes. Please sit down,' my mother invited him, and to me, 'He comes from your father. '

'You make mighty nice cakes, lady. Your ol' man, he gave us all a taste. I never got any parcels, see my ol' woman, she's in the village; she wouldn't find her way in this 'ere city.' he said with a giggle, 'anyways, as I was saying, your ol' man an' me, we were pals. A grand man 'e is, your man, a gentleman. So last week, they transfer us to a new cell an' guess what? The window looks right out on the street. For the first time in months, we saw people, streets, trams and the like, from up there, on the pavement across the road from the 'otel' – that's what we call it – if you look up, you can see your ol' man!'

'I can actually see him?'

'Yes, lady, but be careful. If the guard outside see you, it will be trouble, big trouble.' and as he said this, he passed a finger over his throat, with a meaningful raising of his eyebrows, 'seven months I was there lady an' I am, telling you, it's no holiday.'

'Why were you there?'

'I am stupid, lady. I have a stupid ignorant head. I should know danger when I see it. Me and my ol' woman, we have a small piece of land. Small, but ours, see, it feeds us. God hasn't blessed us with offspring, so with a chicken or two and a pig to fatten for winter, we had enough. And who asks for more, when you have enough?'

At this point, my mother asked me to make coffee and I missed some of his story and his colourful language. He had been imprisoned for having refused to join the village co-operative, work all the land surrounding the village, and only get 'according to his needs'.

'Work all that land, and get what I need for two people, and the others, working the same and get what they need – for four or five people! Is this right? I am asking you? Oh … coffee … well, I don't drink much of the stuff … this is for city people, but if you have a little of the …, ' his thumb pointed to his mouth, ' … a drop maybe. It's been months … '

We had a bottle of slivovitz in the medicine cabinet which we used for winter colds as a medicine. My mother poured him a glass. He downed it in one gulp and put the glass down, smacking his lips.

'Ah! This is life! A bottle of slivovitz and a piece of land and a good woman.' He got up. 'I better go now. My ol' woman will get a good fright when I get there in the middle of the night!'

My mother saw him out.

'Do you believe we will really be able to see dad, from the street?' I asked her as soon as she came back.

'It would seem so,' she said slowly, 'What charming company your father has, in there! Disgraceful!'

'He seemed a nice man.'

'Yes … specially the range of his conversation.' I looked at my mother, not quite knowing whether she was being sarcastic.

'We can go and see him tomorrow.' I said after a while.

'Perhaps.'

'Why? Why, perhaps?'

'What if it's a trap?'

It seemed unlikely to me:

'They must go to terrible lengths to disguise someone like this to set a trap for us.'

'Yes, maybe. All right, we will go tomorrow.'

In the morning, I was much too excited not to tell Mimi about it.

'That's marvellous,' she said, 'not only will you be able to see him but, seeing you will be very good for his morale. It must be terrible being imprisoned.'

'Yes. It must be.'

'If you want, I will go with you sometime. It will be easier for the two of us to pretend that we are just walking around aimlessly, than for you and your mother. Mothers and daughters don't just pace the pavements to and fro, but girls – do. What do you think?'

'You are right Mimi, thank you.'

'You tell me when and I will come with you.'

'Me too.' said Annie.

In the afternoon, I couldn't settle down to do my homework.

'Can we go first?' I asked my mother 'I'll do my work later.'

'All right then, let's.'

There was no tram connection to the Militia Detention Centre, and we walked in the cold autumn afternoon. When we got there, we slowed down and, looking at the building across the road, we counted the floors. As I counted five floors, I scanned the row of windows, all shut and with iron bars across them.

'I can't see a thing,' I said to my mother, 'Can you?'

'No. Let's walk up and down a few times. He must be on the look-out, since he knows the man came to see us last night.'

Suddenly I saw a window pane flash in the pale evening light, the window opened and I saw my father. He was standing a little away from the opened window and waved. I looked ahead, and pretending I had seen someone at a distance, I waved, throwing my arms in the air. My mother made a smaller gesture as she stole glances up at the open window.

It was I who started to cry.

'Poor dad! Behind bars ….'

'Don't be silly!' my mother scolded me, 'or we will be found out!'

'He hasn't done anything to deserve being there! It's awful!' I went on crying. Soon we had to stop waving, all we could do was smile widely at each other, but as our smiles were meant for him – to tell him that we were well and bearing up, that we are with him – we exaggerated our smiles, and with the tears running down our cheeks, we looked like grand guignol puppets.

Ж

My mother's hand, gripping my arm, woke me up.

'Call a doctor …, ' she said in a whisper, 'I am having a heart attack …. '

I switched the light on and looked at her.

'I am afraid,' she went on quickly, 'that I need a doctor this time. It is serious …. '

I put my overcoat on and ran to the door. It occurred to me that I knew no doctor. I looked at the time. It was 2am. Could I wake up Mrs. Stoylova once more and ask her to call a doctor? I knew they were on the phone. I took the keys and skipped down the stairs, being too impatient to wait for the lift. As I skipped down, I remembered having seen a Doctor's plaque at the door of the block across the road.

The cold night air hit me as I walked out of the building and I realised that I had forgotten to put my shoes on. I had never been out in the street at night alone and found it strangely quiet and threatening. I took a deep breath and ran across the road, read the plaque to find out which floor it was, found the front door open – to my surprise, and ran up to the third floor and without hesitation rung the bell. My mother's life depended on it!

I stood shivering on the cold stone landing, jumping from one foot to the other, surrounded by the total silence of the small hours when nothing moves and there is no sound.

It seemed to me that hours had passed since I had rung the bell, and as I was preparing myself to do so again, I felt, rather than heard, a slight movement behind the door. A woman showed her face, mistrustful.

'What is it?'

'The doctor, please, we need the doctor ... my mother is very ill.

'Wait' she said laconically and shut the door again.

My feet were frozen, and I couldn't feel them any longer, but when I jumped from one to the other, they ached. My mother was dying all on her own, and here I was, waiting! I wanted to run back, when the door opened again and the doctor came out. He shut the door carefully behind him and whispered:

'Where is it?'

'At Doctor Long's; across the road. Please hurry Doctor!'

We walked in silence. The lift had never seemed so slow.

My mother lay, pale on her pillows, her eyes shut. I thought that she was dead. The doctor took her wrist and looked at his watch. She moved slightly, her eyelids fluttered.

With infinitely slow gestures, the doctor opened his bag, took out and unfolded the stethoscope. He bent over my mother and listened to her heart; every now and then, he would move the instrument and shut his eyes as he listened. Eventually, he straightened up and began to fold the stethoscope. His eyes scrutinising my mother's face. She sighed and looked at him briefly, then shut her eyes again. He took her blood pressure slowly pumping the rubber ball, then stood up.

'It's just a little nerves.' he said.

Her eyelids acknowledged.

'Take it easy for a while. I will prescribe some tablets; take three every day, for two weeks, preferably after meals. Then come and see me. I will also prescribe some drops.'

He was writing in his prescription pad as he was talking. When he finished writing, he turned to me:

'If your mother feels like this again, you will be able to count twenty of those drops, called Valerian, and give them to her with some water. There is no cause for alarm.'

I nodded.

She mustn't work too hard though and she mustn't worry.' he looked at her again: 'Take a rest, take it easy for a while.'

He picked up his bag from the floor.

My mother lifted herself up on one elbow in a surprisingly vigorous movement.

'My handbag … in the wardrobe … she said to me.

The doctor stopped me with a firm gesture.

'Leave it now. You will be able to settle my fee when you come and visit my surgery in a fortnight.'

'Thank you doctor.' She let herself fall onto her pillows again. I saw the doctor to the door.

'Don't worry too much' he said lightly as he left.

My feet were frozen and I was shaking with cold. I hurried back into the bedroom and found my mother lying, her eyes shut. I climbed into bed to warm up as quickly as I could. I wanted to ask my mother whether she felt better, but her even breath indicated that she was asleep.

I curled up and shut my eyes, expecting sleep to come and carry me into the land of oblivion, but after a short while I realised that I was still awake, felt cold and sweaty; I wanted a drink of water, but as I had forgotten to fill the jug we kept in the bedroom overnight, I was not going to get up, so I pressed my eyelids together in an attempt to go to sleep.

It didn't help. Thoughts imposed themselves upon my mind and I couldn't sleep. How awful it was that my father was a prisoner. What were we going to do to survive? What if my father didn't return? What were we going to do? What could I do? Could I go to work?

I must have fallen asleep for a while when I woke up with a start. I was breathless and sweaty. I had to go to the toilet. I felt hot now and didn't find it too difficult to get up. I was aware of my mother's even, deep breathing next to me. I slid out of bed and noiselessly into the hall. I didn't have to put the light on, to find my way to the toilet and even hesitated a moment whether or not to put the light on in the toilet itself, shivering once again, and not anticipating with pleasure the crude white light. I found the place rather spooky though, and switched the light on; I got a shock at the sight of blood. There was no doubt in my mind that it was blood and my first impulse was to run back to the bedroom and wake my mother. I had obviously injured myself somehow, but as I took a step in the direction of the bedroom, I stopped, had a second look at myself and then it struck me.

It had finally happened. I had become a woman! I took some cotton wool from the cabinet washed the blood off my pyjamas, shivering in the cold night, jubilant and elated. I slid back into bed, quietly. My mother hadn't heard me; she was fast asleep.

I didn't tell her; for three days while it lasted, I kept it as my own private secret. For three days, I had a private, intimate happiness of my own. Then, when it stopped, I told her.

'Good' was all she said.

Ж

On a very cold December day, Mimi and I were going to 'visit' my father. My mother couldn't make it that day and since my father was used by now to seeing at least one of us every day, it was left to my friend and myself. We thought it would be best to go immediately after school, because the days were very short and dusk fell soon after 3pm. Mimi went home to have a bite to eat and was coming to pick me up within half an hour. I finished my lunch and without looking at the time, went downstairs to wait for my friend. I stood outside the front door, shivering with cold and regretting that I hadn't looked out for her before I had hurried down. I even considered going back up, when suddenly Vladimir appeared in front of me, out of the blue, a wide smile on his face. He pressed the bell and as soon as the intercom crackled he said into it:

'I am here old man.'

I looked away, my heart pounding, my mind telling me that this was the golden opportunity and that I was going to let it slip without even making an attempt to 'do something'.

To my great surprise, Vladimir spoke to me:

'Will you find it terribly impertinent of me if I talked to you? he asked, 'It seems very silly the way we see each other all the time, yet we don't know each other don't you think?' His green eyes were smiling at me.

'Yes … of course.'

'Oh, good. I thought it very silly, to pass each other by, after all my best friend lives in the same block as you, yet there was no way in which we could be actually introduced.'

'Yes.' I said again, still embarrassed and surprised, and wishing I could find something more interesting to say. But my mind was blank.

Luckily, Vladimir's wasn't.

'How do you find the State school after the French college?' he asked.

'How did you know I was at the college?'

'I have seen you wearing the black velvet beret with the fleur de lys.'

'Oh, I see.'

'Actually, I wonder if I can ask you for some help.'

'Help? From me? In what way?'

'We are doing a production of 'Le Malade Imaginaire' at the university drama circle, and perhaps you can help us with the interpretation of the characters, if you have studied the play. Have you?'

'As a matter of fact we have, yes. But I have no experience in … '

'There is no need, all we want is to understand the characters, and if you have done it in French, you are best qualified to advise us.'

'I can try …. ' having said that, I realised that it would be impossible for me to help his drama group. I knew that I would let him down if I promised, and tried to get out of it, 'it is very interesting but, I don't … '

'Yes, you do! That's lovely!'

Ivan appeared at the door, and Vladimir said to him:

'Look, it is I, after all, who will introduce you to your own neighbours!'

We shook hands. I mumbled something to the effect that: ' … We have seen each other at times … '

He just smiled.

I saw Mimi appear. She saw us talking; I saw her hand go to her mouth, then she composed herself and crossed the road.

'May I introduce my friend Mimi.' I said.

Hands were shaken all round and smiles exchanged. We were all rather self conscious and embarrassed.

Suddenly there was a clicking noise in the intercom and I heard my name. Everybody looked at the intercom. It was my mother's voice:

'I saw you from the window … if you don't leave immediately, you might as well not go at all.'

'Yes mum, we are on our way.'

I felt the others looking at me and avoided their glances.

'You better' my mother was saying, then the receiver was replaced and the voice disappeared. I looked at Mimi.

'Let's go' she said.

'We'll be in touch,' said Vladimir, 'perhaps Mimi would like to join in with the drama group?'

'I'll tell her all about it,' I said as we walked away, 'bye for now.'

'Ciao.'

We walked down the street in silence but as soon as we turned round the corner I let my enthusiasm go wild.

'Oh, Mimi, isn't it wonderful! It's finally happened! We met them finally, and we spoke to them, now things will be happening for you and Annie.'

Mimi appeared her usual calm self.

'Aren't you pleased?' I asked her.

'Of course I am pleased.'

'Come on, Mimi!' I took her arm. 'You don't sound it, what happened?'

'Nothing. Don't be so childish.'

'I am not!'

'Yes, you are. You may not be aware of it, but you are jumping up and down like a kid.'

'I was pleased that you finally met Ivan, that's all.'

'I hope that Annie will be pleased, she will get to meet Rudy.' Mimi sounded distant.

Wouldn't it be interesting though, to join a university theatre group.'

'You don't mean to say you believed him do you?'

'How do you mean? Of course … shouldn't I?'

'You really believed that they are doing a play?'

'Yes.'

'You did. You know something? You are incredible!'

We had arrived now and I looked up to see my father. It was

very cold and my teeth were chattering.

'Are you saying that Vladimir lied? That maybe they too were looking for a pretext to meet us?'

'What I think is, simply, that Vladimir is crazy about you.'

This was the last thing I had expected to hear. I was fighting the cold, trying to stop my body from shivering; my thoughts didn't seem to be very clear but I most certainly didn't agree with Mimi's speculation.

My father had spotted us by now and smiling broadly, waving a towel, pretending to be drying himself in case there were spies in the building opposite in which case he would be spotted and accused of sending signals. Even from that distance I could see that he was very thin. Perhaps he was ill. I kept smiling as broadly as I possibly could and nodded towards, Mimi, for my father to interpret that everything was all right with us. My legs ached and I couldn't feel my feet with cold. A sharp pain pierced my chest when I took a breath.

'What's the matter with you?' Mimi asked 'you are shaking all over, don't tell me it's the emotion and surprise?'

'What surprise?'

'Vladimir's attraction to you. I saw him; he was looking at you with wide eyes.'

'You see what you want to see. I can't see why he would take any notice of me.'

'Let's go up once more and then go home. It's freezing.' Mimi suggested.

'All right.'

'You may not know it, but you are quite a nice looking girl.' Mimi went back to our topic.

'Shut up, will you!'

'I am cold,' she said, 'and I have no patience to argue with you. You are as obstinate as a mule.'

I waved my father 'good-bye' looking ahead of me to avoid detection and we sped down the road. The pain in my chest was still there, piercing me each time I breathed.

'Are you sure you're all right? You are so pale.' Mimi said.

'I have a pain in my chest when I breathe, it's very unpleasant. I must have caught a chill or something.'

Poor dad, I thought, is his cell heated? I doubted it very much.

'Annie will be thrilled to bits tomorrow when we tell her.' Mimi said.

'I should hope so.'

We parted outside Doctor Long's and I went up.'

Chapter Six

I Am Seriously Ill – A Summons to State Security

My mother had just come home from an appointment with some official still trying to find out the reason for my father's detention.

'How did you get on?' I asked her and sat down by the stove which was emitting very little warmth.

She was morose.

'I didn't get on at all. Something quite dreadful happened. You don't know of Herzl, do you?'

I searched my memory.

'Yes, I do. It was in Moskovitch Mansions, wasn't it, you hid him one night, Aunt Rachel asked you to. The Nazis were looking for him.'

'So you knew. Yes, that's him. Well, I was sitting there in the waiting room when he came out of one of the offices. I went up to him thinking that finally I had found someone who would be sympathetic. And you know what? – he pretended he didn't know me! Me! who saved his life! God, they call themselves communists, humanitarians. Rats, that's what they are, rats!' she sat down, and now calmer, asked me: 'did you see your father?'

'Yes. He seemed all right.' I was having difficulties breathing. My mother noticed.

'What's the matter with you?'

'I don't know. I think I have a cold or something. I don't feel very well.'

'Come here.'

I did. She put her warm dry hand on my forehead.

'Get into bed.' she said, and as I did, she placed the ice-cold thermometer in my arm pit. I leant back on the pillow and shut my eyes, I felt very tired.

Next thing I knew, my mother was holding me up and was trying to change my pyjamas. It was broad daylight – about noon, the following day.

'What happened?' I asked, helping with the pyjamas.

'The doctor will be here soon and you were all soaked with perspiration.'

'What's all the fuss about, I only have a cold or flu.'

'I am not so sure.'

'What else could it be?'

'I don't like this pain in your chest for one, and with 39.5 C, we better have a doctor round.'

The doctor was a short middle aged man with a broad friendly face. He examined me with his freezing cold stethoscope, patted my back and chest with his freezing cold hands, then went away to talk to my mother.

In the afternoon I was dressed and wrapped up like a mummy, then taken in a taxi for X-rays and blood tests. Two days later the doctor came in with the X-rays in his hands and, having talked for a long time with my mother in the kitchen, he came in and sat on the bed. He took my hand in a friendly gesture and spoke to me in his deep warm voice:

'You see, my child, you have ... an inflamed ... gland in ... the lung.'

He made long pauses between each word, as though to emphasise its importance.

I looked straight into his friendly eyes.

'What is that doctor?'

'It means, that your body is growing faster than you can cope with and that it hasn't got enough materials to grow on. Do you understand? It's like a plant that hasn't got enough sunshine and water – it grows limp. You are short of materials – vitamins. Now. Your mother tells me that you don't, as a rule, like food. You don't like to eat. I am afraid I will have to ask you to think very seriously about this because in the condition you are in now, you will have to eat. I will help you at the beginning with injections .... '

I cringed.

'It can't be avoided I am afraid, they will give you a kick-start, but it is food you need, otherwise ... '

'Otherwise – what?'

'Well, in view of the fact that it is the lung we are talking about, you might get ... TB.'

'TB?'

'I am afraid so. Don't worry, you are far from it now, but you can't afford to neglect yourself any longer, not a day longer.'

I didn't want TB. It was an awful disease and I was afraid of it.

'No, no, no,' the doctor said, probably reading my thoughts, 'we are going to fight – and win – together. I will help you, but the main effort will have to come from you. Do you understand that?'

I nodded.

'Good. Now, this is what I want. I will come every day and give you injections. Every day a combination of calcium and vitamin C – in the vein, and every other day – liver extract, in the bottom. It will hurt, but it is necessary. For one month only. I want you to take some food every two hours. Not much – but often. I want you to stay in bed, the idea being that you will not spend any of the energy we will be pouring into you. You won't even read in bed – it's tiring. I want you to sleep, eat, listen to the radio a while – and nothing else. I don't want you to get up except for the toilet. Do you think you will be able to do it?'

'If it is necessary and you say it is, I will do it.'

'That's my girl! Roll up your sleeve, we start now.'

At eight o'clock every morning, my mother gave me my breakfast and then every two hours after that, she would deposit a tray by my side and leave the room. I didn't know whether she left me alone because the doctor had advised her to do so, but I was grateful for this privacy. I couldn't bear to have anybody witness my struggles. My temperature stayed high, I was nauseous and each mouthful that I had to swallow brought a violent revolt from my stomach, which I fought, tears in my eyes, but I was determined to win. I ate everything that was on the tray. It didn't matter much what it was, since I had no appetite whatever, nor could I taste anything; it all seemed the same. Eating usually exhausted me and I fell asleep afterwards.

The doctor came every day to give me my injections. It was soon established that I 'had no veins', and he had to prod my skin and twist the needle inside for a long time before the drop of blood, confirming that the needle had penetrated the vein, appeared in the syringe. Soon, my arms became swollen and blue-green bruises appeared. The doctor searched for veins elsewhere and found one, quite prominent and easy to inject into, on my ankle. The liver injections presented a different kind of ordeal. The liquid was thick and no matter how slowly he injected it, it hurt very much; also the area remained painful and after four or five injections, I couldn't sit. Not that I was allowed to, but I had to take my meals propped up on my elbow, lying on my side.

The temperature remained high and sometimes I despaired of ever getting better. The pain in the chest was there all the time when I breathed in. Then, suddenly, in the fourth week, there was a general improvement. The temperature began to fall a little every day, I felt better, the pain eased off and I even felt hungry from time to time. When the temperature reached 37.5 C, I thought I was cured, just a half a degree to get rid of, but that half a degree took a whole month to get down.

From where I lay, I could see the grey winter sky. When it snowed I watched the large snow flakes floating cheerfully, free to land when and where they chose. When it stormed, the wind would blow the flakes against the window pane where they remained and froze into beautiful patterns. I lay, hour after hour, day after day, sometimes hopeful of my recovery, sometimes despairing, suspecting that perhaps I would stay as I was, ill forever, and they weren't telling me.

My mother went out a lot, but she always made sure I had my meals in time, and if she was going out, she would ask one of the neighbours to bring me my tray. She never once told me off during the whole period, nor did she have an attack during the night.

Mr. Stoylov came to visit us, quite unexpectedly one evening. I wasn't allowed visitors at the time, but he said he would only stay a few minutes, in fact, he wanted to ask a favour, he said.

'Would you be so kind as to agree to store some of our coal in your cellar? We have our own ration and my sister in law's, and now Ivan has a separate ration – we have no room for it.'

'With pleasure' said my mother 'I will let you have the key to the cellar, it's half empty anyway.''Ah, this is very' kind of you. Thank you. By the way, you can use some of it if you like. We couldn't possibly use it all in one season, and next year you can return it to us,' Mr. Stoylov said quickly, 'I must go now, keep well.'

My mother saw him out and came back quickly:

'Do you think what he says it true?' she asked me.

'No. I believe they are trying to help us.' I felt maudlin, 'Such good people mum, how can we ever thank them!' I began to cry.

'What are you crying for? Stop it, your temperature will go up again. They know I am broke, they know I won't accept any money from them, so isn't this fantastic. No one in my family would have done this for me.'

'Such good people!' I sobbed.

By the end of February, I was allowed to get up for an hour a day, and also receive short visits. Of course, Mimi was the first to come and see me. I was excited and happy at the prospect of seeing my friend again.

'Hi! Good to see you up, how do you feel?' Mimi said as she walked in and although she was calm and composed, I detected concealed emotion. I was sitting by the stove, my mother had gone to take my father his weekly food parcel.

'It's good to see you too, Mimi. I am better. Tell me about you and school and everything!'

Mimi looked at me, as though she hadn't heard my question.

'Stand up a minute,' she said, 'you … look different.'

I stood up.

'You have grown. This is incredible, in such a short time! Not only grown, but changed. You look … you are a young woman! Honestly. Your features have changed.'

I was baffled.

'Do you really think so?'

'I am sure so! How could you grow so fast?'

'I wondered why the doctor kept watering my feet every day, now I know.'

She laughed.

'You devil!'

'Tell me, have the boys been in touch at all?'

'Umm. I told you, it was Vladimir who was after you. Besides, it's been a hard winter. It wasn't easy to hang around in the street, trying to 'bump' into people.' She paused for a moment, then, looking away, she added: 'I am not interested in them any more.'

'Oh, but why?'

'There is a reason. But I rather not talk about it. Don't take it personally, but I fear that if I talk about it, it won't come true.'

'All right. If that's what you want. But this is ... superstition.'

'I can't help the way I am.'

'All right.'

'Thank you. Tell me about yourself now, how did you pass the time, what did you do?'

'I wasn't allowed to do anything, not even read. I just lay here and looked at the sky and slept and thought. I wasn't bored.'

'What did you think about?'

'Oh, things. Some cheerful, some gloomy.'

'Tell me about them.'

'Well, for a while I thought I'll never get better again, then when I got better, I thought about different things. The future. It holds nothing good for me. To be realistic, I know I will never get a place at university. If my father gets out, my parents will want to emigrate. I don't relish the thought.'

'I agree with you about university. But why not be pleased that you do have this opportunity to get out of here!'

'We haven't got the opportunity yet. My father is still 'in'. But you are right, it would be the first time that being Jewish might prove advantageous.'

'Gosh, your thoughts are gloomy, aren't they? People in Israel are given an opportunity of a new life. Every new thing is hard, every beginning is difficult, but you must have faith and you will make it.'

'Oh, yes, faith. Aren't you lucky to have it. Something to hold on to. And I have none. Nothing to hold on to, but my parents.'

'No, yourself.'

'I don't have faith in myself. I don't know much ... or maybe, I don't understand much.'

My mother walked in at that moment. She was breathless; shut the door behind her and leant on it to recover.

'What is it, what happened mum?'

'He isn't there, your father ... isn't there any longer ... I ran, I hoped that he might ... have been released ...? '

Both Mimi and I shook our heads. Mimi got up and offered my mother her chair. My mother untied the scarf from under her chin and unbuttoned her coat.

'I took the parcel in, as usual but the man said:

'He isn't here'.

'I insisted, I said that I had been coming every week but he said he wasn't on the list. She broke into tears.'

'Where could they have sent him?'

'Is there another Detention Centre in Sofia?' asked Mimi.

'There are many possibilities, but why? Why?' my mother was sobbing bitterly in her handkerchief. I went to her and put my arm round her shoulders. She felt small and frail.

'What are you doing still up!' she tore away from me, 'One hour, that's all you are allowed, back into bed, quickly.'

'It's hardly been longer, mum, don't worry.'

Mimi stirred.

'I must go now. Please let me know if there is anything I can do.'

'Thank you Mimi, this is kind of you,' my mother said.

'May I come tomorrow?' Mimi asked me, but then turned to my mother,'If that's all right with you Mrs Ashkenazy?'

'Certainly. For an hour only – doctor's orders.'

Mimi left, I went back to bed and my mother – to the kitchen. I felt quite exhausted and the question as to my father's fate hung limp and disconcerting in my mind. Eventually, my mother brought my tray in and as usual, left me to it.

'I'll pay a short visit to the Stoylovs.' she said.

The nausea had disappeared now, and although I had no appetite to speak of, eating wasn't so trying any longer. I sat up, despite the pain in my buttocks. In the last few weeks, the top of my pyjamas had began to swell slightly and I liked the feeling of the soft cotton fabric against my breasts. There was no mirror readily available in the room and often, when I was alone, I stood by the window and looked at my reflection in it. I swung from left to right and searched over and over again for the curve in a semi-profile position.

Yes, I had most certainly changed. 'Grown' Mimi called it or 'developed'; a few centimetres in height, perhaps, but the real change was a lot deeper and intimate. There was a new roundness to my cheeks, a new shadow in my eyes and something different in the curve of my mouth. I very strongly wished my mother to notice it, to see the difference and acknowledge it; to treat me more like an adult. But she seemed totally unaware, and except for Mimi's remarks, the only person to whom it made any difference, was myself. Even though I worried about my father, our financial situation, my mother's emotional state, there was a deep-set feeling of personal, intimate happiness which prevailed.

My mother came back, her brow darkened with worry.

'Mr. Stoylov says that he might have been sent to a concentration camp. He knows of a case, an acquaintance of theirs, where the man was detained with no conviction for a few months and then he was sent to a concentration camp. His family received a post card from him.'

'How awful! Are there any concentration camps here, in Bulgaria? Wasn't that a Nazi thing?'

'There are plenty of them here, like there are in Russia, gulags, they call them.' my mother said sadly.

'But what can they hope to achieve by taking away people's freedom in this way? Surely in the end people might rebel.'

'No one will rebel, don't worry. They make sure of that.

They preach one thing but practice something completely different. At least the Nazis didn't do that. I am weary. I have no more strength.'

We didn't speak for a while. I wondered what did people do in those camps, but didn't want to talk about it; it would distress her and wouldn't help me understand any better.

'All this because of the Americans.'

In the morning, having given me my breakfast, my mother went out shopping. She returned a few minutes later, holding a small brown envelope. She was pale and shaking like a leaf.

'What is it mum? What happened?' I asked, looking at the envelope and thinking that my father was dead.

'It's from the State ... Security ... it's for me ... they are calling me ... tomorrow.' I went up to my mother and led her to a chair.

'This is where political detainees are held, isn't is?'

'Yes,' her hands lay limp on her lap. She shook her head, 'now we know ... it is political after all ... somehow I had hoped that ..., ' and she shrugged, ' ... what's the point of hoping ... there is no hope .... '

She got up with difficulty as though her body was too heavy for her to carry. 'I'll have to go to Albert's and ask them to come here ... tomorrow afternoon ... in case I ... '

'In case – what, mum?'

'In case ... I don't come back.' She left the room before I could say anything. She came back soon, gave me my 10am tray and left before I could say something to her. I wanted to say something, to reassure her, but there was nothing I could have said. I knew it, and she knew it.

Stephka came to keep me company for a while; Mrs Stoylova brought me my lunch at noon; the doctor came to give me my injections, which were spaced to three times per week now; and finally Mimi arrived.

When my mother came home, they had all gone.

'Albert says it's just a formality. A few routine questions then they will let me go. But I don't believe him.' Her voice denoted fatigue and lassitude. 'He doesn't believe it either, she went on, 'but he has to say something. Anyway, they will both come here after their lectures. Who knows, I might come home even before they get here.'

I felt that these words were meant to reassure me, but didn't comment.

In the morning, my mother left home at half past seven, to allow herself enough time to get there. She didn't want to be late. I assured her that I was well enough to make my own breakfast, but she wouldn't have it; she had made it herself, earlier.

The hours passed slowly. I was allowed to read in bed now, but my mind wandered from my book. I looked out at the bright early spring day. The sun was shining, the trees along the road were budding, the air was clear and soft. How could so much unhappiness exist under so much beauty? Why was there so much suffering for us, so much punishment without a glimmer of an end, a clearing. Why was it that our sky kept clouding over and over until I could see nothing else?

Mrs. Stoylova came in, carrying the inevitable tray.

'How are you?' she asked.

'OK.'

'Any news?'

'No; not yet.'

'Well it is a little too soon … '

'Yes, it is.' I took the tray from her hands. 'Thank you so much Mrs. Stoylova, I can make it myself, really, don't bother any more.'

'I promised your mother. I must go now, I'll pop in later.'

'Thank you.'

My doctor came in later. I was surprised to see him, because it was not his day.

'I was in the area, and just thought I'd look in. How are you, any news?'

'No, no news. I am well. Very kind of you to come, really!'

'Why you are my girl. I am very proud of you and I care what happens to you.'

I blushed.

'Thank you.'

'You are my model patient. It was your own efforts that cured you, I only helped a little.'

'Am I cured then?'

'Yes. Still we will have to wait and see the X-rays next week, but for all intents and purposes, you are cured. And you have grown. You see, we gave you the necessary materials to grow on, and you did. I must go now. How is your mother?'

I burst into tears. I hadn't expected to do so, and trying to control my sobs, I couldn't speak. Eventually I calmed down and told him where my mother was.

He paced up and down a while, then said:

'I will come tomorrow for your regular injection. I trust your mother will be here and the whole thing will be forgotten.'

'Thank you doctor.'

He left and I sobbed in my handkerchief, allowing for a while my worry to surface, but then, taking hold of myself, I decided not to cry any longer. If my mother didn't come home, if she were detained as well, then, I thought, I will have plenty to cry about.

Stephka came in again; she was knitting baby's clothes and kept talking about her village and the people there.

Albert and Mary arrived just after five o'clock. They were hungry and Mary went straight into the kitchen to prepare the supper.

'No news.' Albert said to me; it was more a statement than a question. I shook my head.

We ate in silence. It was the first time in months that I sat on a chair, in the kitchen. I tried to ignore the discomfort that the sitting position caused me, and concentrate on the meal. We cleared the table and went back into the bedroom. Albert put some more coal in the stove and paced around until Mary asked him to stop. He sat down; then she got up and looked out through the window.

At eight o'clock Albert suggested that I should get dressed and go home with them.

'I am not going anywhere.' I said firmly 'I shall stay here, my mother might return at any time and I don't want her to find our home deserted.'

'She has a point.' Mary said.

'Yes, I am aware of that, but how will she cope? And also, I will be worried not knowing what's going on.'

'You won't know any more if I am with you, will you?' I said to him.

'Yes, but at least I won't worry about you.'

'Don't be silly, she is not a child any longer, she can cope.' Mary said. Albert nodded, his brow still furrowed. We sat quietly for a while longer. Each of us sunk in our own thoughts.

'I am very tired' Mary said after some time.

'Let's wait another half hour. Then we will have to go.' Albert looked apologetically at me.

'Don't worry about me.'

Once more silence fell over us. Even Maria next door wasn't noisy that evening. All we could hear was the occasional car zooming by in the street. I tried to visualise my mother's whereabouts at this moment, was she being interrogated? Tortured? What could they ask of her?

She arrived just before 10 o'clock. She walked in, holding the panels of her coat to her body, as though it would warm her better that way; she had large dark circles around her eyes. I was in her arms in one leap, sobbing.

'It's all right,' she whispered in my ear, 'I'm back.'

'Do you have to … go back?' Albert asked almost as if he didn't want to hear the answer.

My mother shook her head and sat down still holding her coat to her.

'What happened?' Mary asked and Albert made a gesture as if to scold her for asking. My mother, looking at some indefinite point on the wall, said in a dead, flat voice:

'Frightening.'

'Are you all right?' Albert asked.

'Yes.' her voice still disembodied.

'We must go now.'

'Yes, thank you.'

'We will come to see you tomorrow.'

'Yes.'

They left. It was only then , that my mother began swinging from side to side, on her chair, lamenting in this frightening, dead voice of hers: ' … how much more can I take … how much … how much …. ' I knelt by her knees:

'Mummy, mummy, please tell me what happened?'

She stood up in a sudden movement, nearly throwing me on the floor:

'I can't tell you anything,' she shouted, 'anything! Didn't you see that Albert knew? He didn't ask, did he? He knows. I had to sign a paper swearing that I will never, so long as I live, tell a soul what I saw there, what I was questioned about, or to whom I spoke. Do you hear? I can't talk, I can't tell you anything. Don't ask me any questions, do you hear!'

Many years later, she told us what had happened. She had presented herself to the officer on duty, showing him the letter. He had ushered her into a room where she was told to wait. The room was totally bare, not even a chair, so she stood in one corner trying not to show any signs of nervousness in case she was being observed. After about an hour, a man came in and took her along many corridors and stairs, into another office, where a man asked her some questions; mainly about my father and his work at the American Military Mission. The questions were very strange, or so my mother found them: 'How much was he paid for his services? What extras did he get? How often did he visit the Pastor? During the questioning she had been left standing. On a few occasions the man had left the office but had left the door open and she felt observed and at the same time could overhear odd words, like 'Doctor Long ... rent free ... subsidies ... from the States .... ' She wanted to tell them that we weren't living rent free, that there was no such thing as subsidies ... but she hadn't dared.

She was joined by three men later; they all asked questions from all directions, trying to confuse her, to get her to contradict herself. She was taken to another office; more corridors, more stairs, some going up, some going down, such that she didn't know any longer which floor she was on. The windows were opaque and she couldn't see through them. She was left alone , then questioned again, and again the same questions were fired at her.

Finally a man handed her a piece of paper, telling her to show it to the officer on duty at the entrance, he would let her out. She found herself in a corridor; there wasn't a sound, as though the whole building was deserted. She turned to the left, then to the right, she walked down some stairs, then up – it all looked the same. Then she thought that it was a trick, they hadn't freed her at all, this was to intimidate and confuse her. She was in tears. She hadn't eaten or had a drop of water all day. Eventually, a woman came out into the corridor as my mother was passing by, and asked her what she was doing there. My mother told her that she was looking for the way out, not really believing that the woman would help her, but to her great surprise, the woman escorted her all the way down and showed her out.

When I was allowed to get up, I went into my room for the

first time in over three months. The radio with the green eye was not on its dainty table, the two Persian rugs had gone and the floor was bare. I stared at the room, stunned and hurt; it seemed to me more like the mutilation of a sanctuary than anything else. I realised that the objects had been sold. It was done quietly, my mother had never mentioned anything to me. I joined her in the kitchen, on the verge of tears.

'Mum … I didn't know … the radio and … '

'Where did you think the money for your treatment came from?' she was angry, 'It cost a bomb.'

'Yes, of course. Only … I didn't know, that's all.'

'Next – the last rug goes; then my rings and after that – well we will just have to stop eating!'

'I will get a job.' I said.

My mother looked at me and I read in her eyes: *what can you possibly do?*

'I wish there was something I could do!' I said.

My mother's face was closed. She looked down, at her lap, then put her arms around herself in a tight, weird embrace and began to sway from side to side. She got up suddenly, with a wild determination, went swiftly to the bedroom I followed her. She went straight in the middle of the bed on her knees, her arms clasped tightly around her, moving now in a round motion, like a wound up mechanism. Her head had fallen onto her chest, and a deep almost inhuman whine escaped from her throat. I joined her in an attempt to interrupt her swaying, unlock her arms, bring her back from this trance-like state. At the same time, I was afraid of her. I thought that she might strike me, or push me on to the floor; I was aware of the physical strength that accompanied the state she was in. I struggled and pleaded with her, I begged her to stop, I implored her to look at me, to talk to me. Suddenly she stopped swaying, pushed me away with a violent, sharp gesture:

'Go away! Leave me alone!'

I had never seen so much hatred in anyone's eyes. I moved away and got off the bed, then walked backward towards the door, looking at her all the time, my eyes blurred with tears, my heart pounding. Before I left the room, my mother threw herself on the bed, and I saw her body convulsing in sobs. I went into the toilet, locked myself in, and cried. I cried because I was afraid, because I felt lonely and hurt, rejected by my mother who insisted on suffering by herself. I went back after a while and found my mother asleep where I had left her, lying on her side in the middle of the bed. I covered her with a blanket and tip-toed out.

I went for a walk towards Alexander Nevsky, walked around the square, felt too restless to sit on a bench, so I turned back concerned that something might happen to my mother. I didn't know what; just something. I found dinner ready. We ate silently. I stole a glance towards her a few times, but couldn't summon up the courage to tell her what I felt and thought.

Her face was serene. There was no trace of the afternoon's scene. The hostility had gone from her voice when she addressed me, but still, it was cold and distant.

I took a long time to go to sleep. My mother's eyes, her whine, her swaying wouldn't leave me; then, suddenly, I felt her hand on me, shaking me and asking for the doctor.

'I'll give you some of the drops, mum. Don't worry.' I said gently.

'No ... it's serious ... I am afraid ... this time ... it's serious .... '

I jumped out of bed and went for the doctor. He came, somewhat reluctantly, examined my mother and gave her some drops. 'This is all I can do for you my dear,' he said to her, 'you mustn't be afraid, your heart is not ill, your nerves are a little shaken, that's all.'

I saw him to the door.

'Doctor, please tell me, what is the matter with my mother, is she seriously ill?'

'No, she is not seriously ill,' he whispered in the dark. 'Sometimes it happens to women her age that their nerves get a little shaken, that's all. How old is she, by the way?'

I didn't know. I made a quick calculation and said:

'Probably just under forty, forty or forty one.'

'Hmm. In any case, there is nothing to worry about. She needs attention.'

My mother's eye lids fluttered when I came back, but she didn't open her eyes. I understood that she wasn't asleep, but she didn't want to talk. What did he mean, 'she needs attention' I thought all my attention was concentrated towards her. Perhaps I gave too much to my friends, and school. But she rejected me. Perhaps because I was clumsy, inadequate. I must try harder.

I switched the light out.

Ж

I returned to school after the Easter holidays. I was pleasantly surprised at the warm welcome I got from everybody in my class. Even 'the dragon' welcomed me back.

I was asked to go and see the Headmaster after class. Mimi and Annie went home without me, and I knocked on the door of the Headmaster's office.

'Come in.'

'Good Afternoon, Comrade Headmaster.'

'Good Afternoon. Come in, sit down.'

I handed him the letter from my doctor. He looked at it briefly.

'I am pleased you are back, and in good form.'

'Thank you. It's good to be back.'

'You are aware, Comrade, that you have missed a whole term. Usually, in such cases, we keep the pupils back a term. We don't know you very well. It's only your first term with us, but from the reports I see, I believe we can allow you to continue in the same class, but you will have to pass examinations on all material the class has done during your absence. Do you understand?'

'Yes. I am sure I can, given a little time.'

'You will have to cope with the current material at the same time.'

'I will, I don't want to go back, please.'

'All right, you can give it a try. Can you get ready within a month?'

'Yes, I think I can.'

'So be it then. A month. Good luck, Comrade.'

'Thank you very much Comrade Headmaster. I appreciate your help.'

He smiled and nodded. The interview was finished. He wasn't so frightening after all.

I walked out into the street across the now deserted courtyard. It was a clear warm afternoon, the air carried a scent of blossom, a fragrance of spring; the breeze brushing my bare arms and my cheeks gave me an unfamiliar thrilling sensation. Suddenly I was aware that somebody, having passed me by, had stopped a few paces behind me, and was looking at me. I thought that it was somebody I knew and had omitted to acknowledge, I turned round and saw a man, a total stranger, standing on the pavement, looking me up and down, his eyes glaring. He whistled. I turned away quickly and ran; eventually, when I thought I was far enough away, I slowed down and continued walking home. A little self conscious, flushed with this novelty.

Chapter Seven

The Promenade – A Live Witness

I passed successfully all my examinations, and the term was now drawing to its end. Annie, Mimi and myself got together every afternoon in my room because of my mother's objection to my going out. She left us alone there, probably thinking that we were busy solving logarithmic problems, or theorems, which we did for a while, but our main topic was 'the boys'.

One afternoon Mimi arrived first and we sat on my settee, the sun streaming in through the open window.

'Now that it's all over, I can tell you about it.' Mimi said.

'What do you mean? What is over?'

'Do you remember I refused to talk about something when I came to see you? You were ill at the time.'

'Yes, I remember, you being superstitious about something.'

'Call it what you like. That's the way I am.'

'I am sorry, I didn't mean to .... '

'That's all right. Anyway, it was just before Christmas. My father told me that he had a new family coming to his congregation, and he wanted me to meet their son. We were invited to their home, for lunch on Christmas day. He was a fabulous looking guy. Last year at Medical school and all that. I went out with him ... '

'You did! How exciting'. Tell me about it, please!'

'Nothing to tell really. We just ... had nothing to say to each other. I found him very dull company. That's all there is to it.'

'I think this is fantastic! You have actually been out with a boy, the excitement of a date! Oh, it must be wonderful. What did you do, where did you go?'

'We went to the cinema. I didn't enjoy myself. If I tell you that I was really bored, you wouldn't believe me. Well, I was.'

'It's not on, then?'

'No.'

'You know what I find most incredible, Mimi?'

' What? '

'That it was your father who actually wanted to introduce you to a boy. Who encouraged you to go out, with a boy. I don't know, but there is something very odd with my parents, as far as boys, or generally my going out, is concerned. My father isn't here now, but a few years ago, they let me go to a Jewish 'do' with a girl friend. I was 20 minutes late coming home. You should have seen the row. It was murder. They just about locked me in afterwards.'

'Maybe you were too young at the time.'

'Maybe I was. But even now, I can't go anywhere.'

'It's different now. Your mother needs you now.'

'If only I had the conviction that you are right, but you see, she doesn't; she has no use for me. I just have to be in, that's all; I don't ... I can't even find the words to say it, but I feel so left out. She doesn't take me in, you see, she lives it all by herself.'

'You are imagining things. It's your adolescent blues.'

'How do you know?'

'My mother told me about it, when I had it.'

Annie arrived at that point.

'It's a lovely day, let's go for a round at the 'promenade'. Everybody seems to be going that way.'

'You go. I'll stay home.' I said.

Mimi got up:

'I'll ask your mother.'

I heard her knock on the bedroom door, where my mother was. Soon she returned :

'You've got until six o'clock,' she said, 'come on, let's go.'

It was five o'clock. I went to say 'good bye' to my mother and thank her.

'No later than six,' she said.

We went out quickly.

'Rudy is wearing a navy and white sweater,' Annie said, 'you can't miss him.'

'How do you know?' I asked.

'She had seen them going out, didn't you guess from the start?' Mimi asked.

'No, I didn't.'

Annie leant towards Mimi and said to her:

'She is sweetly naive.'

People on the 'promenade' walked ten or twelve abreast, in a pell-mell fashion, occupying the whole pavement and half the road. The traffic wasn't very dense in those days; still there were cars hooting, trying to get by. The opposite pavement was for the elderly in other words anybody over 23.

'Here they are!' Annie spotted the boys as soon as we got there, and we positioned ourselves, such that we would meet them 'accidentally'. I felt embarrassed and since I was in the middle, I drew the two of them together and hid behind them. This sudden shyness of mine made them laugh; they struggled to free themselves and get me out into the open, then all of a sudden I saw Vladimir, a Cheshire cat's smile on his face.

'Finally we meet!' he said and his remark seemed to be addressed to me, I mumbled:

'I don't think you have met our friend Annie … '

They all shook hands. Ivan turned to me:

'How do you feel now? You were ill, my old woman kept talking about it.'

'Oh, I am fine now, thank you.'

Rudy was looking on, a bored expression on his face.

'Do you came here often?' Vladimir asked me.

'No, not really. Do you?'

'Very seldom. Too much work to do.'

'We are stopping the flow, shall we walk?' Ivan suggested.

I found myself walking with Vladimir. Mimi and Ivan were in front of us, and Annie and Rudy were somewhere to the right. It had worked out just as my friends had planned it. I was certain that Annie was happy; I couldn't tell about Mimi.

'Is university very hard work then, Vladimir?'

'My friends call me Vlady.'

'OK, Vlady.'

'It is and it isn't. It's more up to you, you need discipline. Are you thinking of going to university yourself?'

'Yes. I am thinking all right. But thinking is not quite enough these days.' I immediately regretted this careless statement. What if he were a provocateur?

'No. It isn't,' Vlady said, 'it was easier, two years ago, when I got in, but now they search as far back as your grandparents.'

I didn't answer for fear of getting deeper into a dangerous area.

'Do you swim?' he asked.

'I am afraid not.'

'Shame. Still you could come to the swimming pool and enjoy the sunshine, school will be over soon.'

'Oh, I don't know …. '

'Oh, please say you will come, it's such fun, and a sun tan would suit you very much.'

He must have thought that I was playing 'hard to get'. All I had in mind was my mother. I didn't even own a swimming suit. Having thought about my mother, I asked what the time was.

'Ten to six.'

'I am sorry, I must go home now.' I looked around for my friends. Soon they all joined us and we made a little group in the middle of the throng.

'I am afraid it's time for me to go home.' I said apologetically.

'I am going too.' Annie said.

'Me too.' Mimi joined in.

'This is a conspiracy!' Vlady said. 'Just when we are enjoying good company, they are leaving us all alone.'

'Yes, don't go yet, it's early!' Ivan pleaded.

'I am sorry, I must.'

'But we will see you again won't we?' Rudy asked.

'Yes. Of course.'

We walked off. I was in the middle again.

'So?' I asked. 'Tell me, don't keep me in suspense.'

'Nothing to say.' said Mimi.

'Oh, we know you! You would be talking to the king and it would be 'nothing' to you! How about you Annie?'

'He is fabulous … ' she said in a dreamy voice ' but he is going … I better start forgetting him now.'

'Why? Where is he going?'

'West Germany, his mother is German.'

'Shame.'

'I will see him again, though.'

We had reached Doctor Long's.

'Are you coming up?'

'No.' they said together.

'See you tomorrow then.'

'See you.'

They walked off and I went home.

Ж

The summer brought warmth and sunshine, but nothing to brighten up our life.

We still didn't know where my father was, or even if he were alive at all. The last Persian rug had been sold and some of my mother's jewellery. Soon, we would run out of things to sell.

My mother continued relentlessly to try and get to see and speak to officials. She always got appointments, but they seldom actually took place; the person being 'suddenly called on official business', or if she were received she never got any answers to her questions. She often had her attacks at night but I learned to cope with them. I gave her twenty drops of the brown liquid called Valerian, rubbed her wrists and chest with a cloth damp with a solution of cold water and vinegar.

Mimi had gone to the country; Annie and I saw each other; sometimes we went to the cinema in the afternoon – usually when my mother was out herself. I had two more years of school ahead of me and tried not to think beyond that.

Early one morning, my mother and I were having breakfast in the kitchen, when there was a gentle knock on the door. Almost immediately Stephan looked in:

'May I come in?' he said, shutting the door behind him. He laid the morning paper on the table. 'I think,' he went on, 'that there is something you ought to see. Don't worry it isn't bad news.'

Our eyes glued to his face at first, now went over to the newspaper, where the front page headlines read in thick black letters:

'A GANG OF SPIES HIDING UNDER THE AUSPICES OF THE METHODIST CHURCH EXPOSED.

15 PASTORS, SUBSIDISED BY THE UNITED STATES TO STAND TRIAL FOR HIGH TREASON.'

We read the headlines, trying to understand why Stephan made such a fuss. 'Poor Mrs. Ivanova,' my mother said, 'This is what you meant, isn't it Stephan?' my mother asked.

'No, lady, look here.' we followed his finger as it ran down the middle column. It pointed to a sub-title: 'Witnesses' and then ran further down the list of names and stopped. It was my father's name he was pointing at.

'Oh, my god! A witness to a … show trial … a high treason trial … he'll never see the light of day again! Never.'

'But can't you see, lady if he is going to be a witness, he is alive. He must be somewhere in town.'

'Yes, yes … you are right … but where could he be?'

'As far as I know, they keep these cases in a special wing of the prison, the Central Prison.'

'Good lord.' my mother sat down, stunned.

'I must go now, I thought I'd let you know.'

'Oh, Stephan, thank you so much!'

Stephan left.

'I wonder whether Mrs. Ivanova knows, if she has seen the paper?' I said.

'He is right you know. We are going to the prison this afternoon! Your father is most probably there.'

The Central Prison was in the outskirts of Sofia and, having enquired about the visiting hours, we took the long tram journey through town. Slowly, as we reached the outskirts, the only passengers left, were women, some carrying children, on their way to visit prisoners. The gates of the prison were shut and we had to wait outside. Trams kept arriving every few minutes, pouring out a new load of visitors. Children were crying; some of the women were crying too.

Eventually the heavy iron gates swung open and we rushed

in, swept along by the others. There was a small office immediately inside, on the right. It's door was shut, but there was a little window, protected by iron bars, behind which one could just discern the features of a man. A line was formed and women, as they passed by the window, said something, probably the name of the person they wished to visit, then went on towards another structure further down the cobble-stone yard.

When our turn came, my mother whispered my father's name, the man looked down at an invisible, to us, list. His lips formed the words as he read to himself, like someone who isn't used to reading too much. Finally, without looking up, he shouted:

'Not here. Next!'

'You will go to the prison tomorrow morning,' said my mother, 'You will demand to see the Director and you will demand from him, to see your father!'

I looked at her, stunned.

'I have tried enough!' she went on 'no one can deny that. I have tried and tried; I have knocked on all doors, all closed. It is time you did something for your father!' Her voice didn't allow for any argument.

'Yes, mummy, I will.'

The walk from the tram to the prison gates was, I suppose, the worst experience of the following day. The walls, in whose shadow I walked, seemed somehow taller than the day before, where I had come with my mother, and the watch-towers, each like a fortress, dominating and menacing. The eyes and guns pointing at me from up there, weighed heavily on my shoulders, even though I was aware that they were there to prevent people from behind those barred windows getting out.

There were less women in the little office today, and I waited until they were all admitted to visit their relatives. I waited merely because I didn't know what to do.

'Comrade! Hey, you there! What do you want?' The man in

the 'hole in the wall' was pressing his nose against the iron bars addressing me. His eyes, his voice, his uniform frightened me; I couldn't move, I felt stuck to the floor, and felt unable to utter a sound. I must have looked a pretty pathetic sight, because the man suddenly appeared at the door which separated the room where I was, from his 'hole in the wall' area.

' 'oo 'ave you come to see?' he asked.

'The Director' I said, not moving from where I stood.

The man laughed. Then, having stopped, he looked at me as though I had to find a better excuse for being here.

'My father … he is here … he is very ill … he himself doesn't know how ill he is … ' I said quickly. ' … we got word that he might be sent home … that's how ill he is! But you see … now my mum is also ill and I must see the Comrade Director.'

I broke into tears now, probably because I ran out of lies, but I knew for a fact that if, through interrogation a prisoner was dying, they made sure he was sent home just before.

'All right, all right. Stop crying now,' my tears embarrassed him, 'you, wait here,' he pointed at a chair in a corner of his office, and disappeared through a door. I sat on the edge of the chair and sobbed quietly in my handkerchief, not knowing what would happen next.

The door opened, the man peeped in and said with some urgency in his voice:

'Come on, follow me!'

We walked along a long bare corridor, passed a few doors, he then stopped and knocked at one of them. A voice from inside said:

'Come!'

My first impression was that of awe when I faced the man sitting behind what seemed to be an enormous walnut desk. His arms rested on it, over a blotter and his hands held a pen. His eyes, having dismissed the man who escorted me, came to rest on my face now and to my surprise I found them kind and their weight, not too heavy. I sighed.

'Come in and sit down, and tell me what is this all about,' he said in a quiet voice, and I knew immediately that I could not lie to him. The walk from the door to the armchair seemed very long. I was aware of the blinds being drawn, of the horizontal light and shade, of the wind outside playing with the trees' branches making moving patterns on the walls and furniture.

'Sit down, Comrade. I won't bite you.' His eyes were smiling at me. His face was clean shaven. I recognised the material of his suit – one of the two kinds 'distributed' for men, but rather than the rough, 'potato sack' look it had on other men, my school master for instance, on the prison director, it looked like a real garment, a suit.

'What have you come to ask for?' he said when I was seated.

'How do you know I have come to ask for something?' I asked back, realising the impertinence of my question.

'People always do. Come on I haven't got all day.'

I told him the whole story, the whole truth. The man listened patiently to my story. His long hands played with the pen all the time. I was mesmerised by them, and just kept on talking. When I had finished, a long silence fell between us; I had nothing more to add, no more pleading, no more imploring.

So I looked at him and waited. He put the pen in the pen-holder and rested his chin on his hands, now clasped together.

'You cannot see your father,' he said slowly, 'this is a prison, not a rest-home. But I can tell you that he is alive and that he is well. Go home now and stop wasting my time.'

I got up, as if propelled by a spring. How could I tell my mother that I had failed my mission?

'Can't I, just for a moment just see him without him even knowing? If only to reassure my mother.' I said quickly, expecting him to physically throw me out now.

'You have asked for things I cannot do. You have asked for

things I cannot say. You are taking too many liberties with my patience!'

He hadn't raised his voice, but his anger was frightening. I must have looked like a trapped mouse, because he added, his voice softening, 'What made you come here anyway?'

'We thought that … my father is dead … we haven't heard from him for months now ….' I was crying now, at the thought that it might be true. 'For months, you see … and if he is dead … my mother, who is so ill … she might die too … and we thought that he might … just might … be here …. '

The man stood up. I remember his dark blue eyes looking down at me:

'Prison Directors aren't all powerful, little girl. Go home and tell your mother that your father is alive. That's all I can say.'

He sat down, his long hands picked the pen from its holder and I understood that the interview was finished. He hadn't shouted the last words, but in the way he had said them I felt that they were not just a meaningless reassurance, but a true piece of information.

'Thank you' I said, 'thank you very much … and please forgive me … ' and I found myself outside, perspiration running down the middle of my back.

My mother made me repeat my story over and over again and then said:

'Nonsense. He only told you all that to get rid of you. You should have insisted more! Been more positive!'

Chapter Eight

The Pastors' Trial – The Village Dance

Maria had gone to her home town to have her baby and her husband was away at sea; the flat was a lot quieter. Stephka was also going to go to her village to have her baby, but as Stephan was not allowed any leave, she was postponing her departure until the last minute.

September was nearing, and with it the Trial and the beginning of school.

Mrs. Ivanova, the Pastor's wife, had been contacted by the State Security and asked to bring her husband's best suit. Throughout these months, she had kept her smile, but her face had grown paler and drawn. We heard her singing psalms, accompanying herself on the organ, downstairs.

There were rumours that Mimi's father, who had taken over Pastor Ivanov's congregation, was the spy among the pastors. I refused to listen to the name of my best friend being reviled; my mother's argument was quite strong: if fifteen pastors of the Methodist church were being accused of high treason, how come 'they' allowed the church to continue its existence and functions? Why wasn't the church, along with so many foreign institutions closed down by the authorities? The question remained unanswered, like so many others.

Comrade Rashkov, our landing spy, continued his early evening visits; he hardly bothered to disguise them any longer and Stephan would often lose his temper:

'Come on, come in, then and have a good look! This bread here, comes from the oven – our own – my good wife baked it and the flour came from our own village!'

'Hold your tongue Stephan!' my mother would scold him, 'This temper of yours won't bring you anything good!'

Stephka on the other hand, expressed her concern in a more colourful language:

'You fool! Have you eaten your brains? Can't you swallow your tongue too!'

I laughed, and was scolded accordingly; Stephan also laughed:

'My little ignorant mouse!' He put a protective hand on his wife's head.

One afternoon, I went round to Mimi's. It was four o'clock, and since I was allowed out until six, I didn't hurry. I enjoyed the afternoon sun, the sheen on the flawless blue sky when I realised that the person coming towards me from the opposite direction was Vlady. He stopped and was smiling at me:

'Hi!' he said, 'Where were you? In cloud cuckoo land?'

'No, why?'

'I have been looking at you for a while; you seemed immersed in your thoughts, your feet were not touching the ground, you were floating in mid air. Tell, me what was it you were thinking about?'

'I wasn't … nothing, probably. And if I were, I wasn't aware … '

'How are you?'

'Very well. And you?'

'OK. Listen, I am throwing a little party at my place on

Sunday, would the three of you be free to come over?'

'I think so. As far as I know, we are not doing anything special.' We never did, I thought.

'Lovely, see you on Sunday then, around six. Do you know where I live?'

'No.' I did, but I didn't want to say so.

'Along the same street,' he pointed behind him, 'at No 27. Ciao.'

'See you then, ciao.'

I hurried to report the good news to Mimi.

'I bet you showed all your enthusiasm.' she said when I told her.

'Not as much as you think, but I expressed my thanks. Aren't you pleased?'

'Of course I am pleased, silly, only one mustn't show it.'

'Well. I wasn't exactly jumping up and down, but I showed a certain amount of pleasure.'

'It doesn't work that way, you silly girl. You can express your joy and pleasure to me, never to boys! If a boy realises you are interested, he'll take advantage.'

My mother had spoken on occasions in the same terms.

'If somebody likes me enough to want my company, it is only polite to express gratitude, even joy, if I like him as well. I can't very well see how he can take advantage of me, if I don't want him to.'

We telephoned Annie to tell her the good news; it was decided that they will both come up to the flat, and we will all go from there. When I got home, I found my mother in a bad mood.

'You can come home a little earlier, you know.' she said in reply to my greeting.

'It's only just six o'clock mum … '

'Never mind that. You could show some consideration and come home before the hour that I set, and keep me company.

I am left all alone here, for hours.'

'I am sorry.'

It was impossible to talk about the party now and as I was setting the table for dinner I realised what a fool I had been to think for a moment that I would be allowed to go. We were eating, as usually in silence, when the door opened and Stephan came in without knocking. He seemed upset, short of breath. His hair, wet with perspiration, fell over his face.

'I've had it,' he whispered. 'I got into a fight with the big boss's chauffeur, not only that, but in the middle of the fight I called him a 'dirty commie'. I am surprised I am still free. I will be taking Stephka to our village in the morning, if I am free. If she sees me being arrested, we will lose the child, I am sure. I will try to see you again, before they come for me. This is the end of me.'

He left without awaiting any reply from us. In any case there was very little one could say. If he got arrested during the night, at least we would know what was going on, and we had to see to Stephka ourselves.

I gathered the plates, and as I began washing up, the bell rang, freezing us both, in the positions we were in. These were the only times when my mother and I looked directly into each other's eyes, not knowing what to expect.

By the way the bell rang, it couldn't have been anyone we knew. It was a prolonged ring, not long enough to replace the two short ones our visitors used for us, nor long and persistent enough for the Militia men. Also it wasn't the time of day when they called:

'I'll go.' I said.'

A tall fat man stood outside holding a bundle under his arm, leaning on the wall.

'I want to see the Ashkenazy woman.' he said.

My mother emerged from behind me and took over. She ushered him, into the kitchen.

'I come from your man.' he said, as he sat down.

'Make some coffee' my mother said to me, and to the man: 'Will you have a bite to eat as well?'

'I won't say no, lady, it's a long way to my village.' He was rolling a cigarette. 'My name is Vassili Mirov, but they call me 'The Fox'. His thick calloused fingers still handling the cigarette. He passed a pointed red tongue on the edge of the thin paper, secured it, then lit the cigarette, drawing deeply and inhaling the smoke. We were watching him, expecting to hear what he had to tell us.

'They call me The Fox' he went on, 'because I never fail a job.' He looked at us triumphantly. 'No safe of any kind or door – locked or bolted – resists The Fox!'

'Where have you come from?' my mother asked as I put his coffee in front of him.

'The nick. Three years I did for my last job, but it was worth it. A clean job it was and they never found what they were looking for!'

He took a large mouthful of bread and jam that my mother had put on the table, sipped noisily his coffee and went on, smacking his lips as he ate.

'Your man is well. He has been in solitary, – a long time. That's no good for a man. Two weeks or so ago, they brought him to our wing. He is better off with us, I tell you lady. We are better people. Miserable lot they are, the politicals. We fed him a little. As thin as a tobacco leaf he is; the wife sends food, from the village, like.'

'Did he tell you when he will be coming home?'

'Politicals – they don't talk lady. He asked me to tell you that he is well and alive, well – alive and well, he can't be well and dead, can he!' A guttural laughter accompanied these words, which turned into a bronchial cough. Both my mother and I found this joke in poor taste, we looked at each other and waited for the man to stop coughing.

'A nice man, you know lady,' he went on, 'he knows the world, speaks softly, sweetly. Nice man.'

My mother was crying.

'Hey, lady! He is well, he is alive, he will be home soon.'

'When, home soon? I can't take much more of this!'

'You should know better than talk old wives' talk! If he is alive – he'll come home.'

He got up, picked up his bundle from the floor where he had left it, straightened up painfully and said:

'I'll be on my way now.'

My mother saw him out and came back, mopping her eyes.

'What Company he is in, hard core criminals, my God, how low can one sink.'

'At least he is not in solitary any longer,' I said, 'It must be terrible to be locked up, all alone in a cell.'

She continued to cry while I tidied up. Then we went to bed.

When the light was out, I thought about being locked up, alone for days on end, months perhaps. I wasn't allowed out much and I found it difficult sometimes, but what was it like to be totally locked in, and all alone. At least he was alive, that was comforting. Then I remembered my visit to the prison, and what the Director had told me. He hadn't lied to me! He hadn't just said anything to me, just to get rid of me, as my mother had suggested. No! He had told me the truth!

In the morning, Stephka came to say goodbye to us before she left for the village. She was very big with the baby now; her face had become completely round and strange brown marks had appeared on her upper lip and forehead.

'You have been like a sister to me,' she said to my mother, 'please come to our village with Stephan! What a welcoming we will give you! And please, look after my Stephan, he is like a child.'

'I will, don't you worry, I will,' my mother reassured her.

'And I hope your husband comes home soon.' Stephka said.

'Come on woman! I have a job to go to.' Stephan called from behind her.

They left and we went to have our breakfast. After last night's good news from my father, well 'good' in so far as we now knew he was alive, I thought I could mention Sunday's party and ask for permission to go. She listened for a while, then said:

'How low can you sink! A boy … a nobody you have met in the street. What will he think of you? That you are an easy girl who … ' The contempt in her voice, the way she put the whole thing took me by surprise; obviously my judgement had been totally wrong. Still, I tried to explain:

'But mum, Vlady is Ivan's best friend – Ivan is … '

'What of it?'

' … the Stoylovs' son and they are your only friends … surely … wouldn't you be offended if she said things like that about me … your daughter, wouldn't you think that she would trust my friends through … '

'Don't answer back!' my mother interrupted me angrily. 'There is a lot of shopping to do. I have to go to the Court and obtain a pass for the trial. You have to pull your weight.'

I took the shopping list, the purse and the shopping bag and made for the front door.

'How can you think of amusing yourself at times like these?'

She was right. I was a monster.

I took my place in the queue and plunged into my book. When the vegetables arrived and my turn came, I ended up with turnips, cabbage and the inevitable green peppers. All I had on my list was a kilo of tomatoes and cucumbers. I went to queue at the grocers' next, but mentally I was in Paris, following the heroes of Erich Maria Remarque's book 'The Arch of Triumph'.

My mother came home later in the afternoon. She had obtained a pass for the three days the witnesses were going to be heard. They knew in advance which days those were going to be – like any good production, here too, the sets and the props were carefully arranged in advance. The pass was for only one person who had to be related to the prisoner. Suddenly we heard the front door open and loud male voices in the passage. My mother took the pass from my hand, stuck it in my book and told me to sit down and not say a word. She put her handbag behind her chair, sat down and took the newspaper from the shopping bag.

After a little while, the door opened. Stephan looked in, his face as white as a sheet. A Militia man was standing right behind him. Stephan's eyes said: 'This is it. I've had it.'

Slowly and politely he said:

'I am going away for a while … I don't know how long I will be, so I better return the book you lent me. I did like it.' My mother took the large volume from his shaking hand. It was my Maxim Gorky. 'Bye for now.'

'Bye bye Stephan, look after yourself and don't worry about a thing.'

He disappeared. We sat quietly until we heard them leave the flat.

'They have arrested him.' I whispered.

My mother took the book from the table:

'I wonder what this is all about,' she said, 'I never lent him a book.'

She leafed through the pages. A small folded piece of paper fell from it.

My mother unfolded it and read it to herself. I watched her in expectation to hear what it was.

'He wants me to write and tell Stephka. How can I do that?'

'He thinks that perhaps he won't be able to communicate with her … so he … '

'Yes, but why me?'

'I wonder what will happen to him.' I said.

My mother just looked at me and didn't say anything.

That night, my mother had one of her attacks. She woke me up, and as I was going for her drops, she asked me to go and bring 'someone' because she thought 'it' was really bad this time. I went for Mrs. Stoylova.

She opened the door, her shawl already wrapped around her shoulders, ready to come up. She went through the now routine gestures – the rubbing of the wrists, temples and chest, and her soothing low voice:

'Don't worry my dear, you will be all right ....'

My mother's eye lids fluttered for a while, her chest went up and down very fast, then eventually, it slowed down, she opened her eyes and smiled, the same Mona Lisa smile:

'It would seem that I have made it again ....' she whispered.

'Yes, my dear, you are very brave.'

'Thank you.' her hand lay limply on the covers.

Mrs. Stoylova sat on the chair by the bed.

'I hear our youngsters are getting together this week end.'

I didn't believe my ears at first, then I made gestures to her to stop, I shook my head, but she didn't seem to take any notice of me. 'After all, now is their time.'

My mother opened her eyes and I stopped making signals.

'You will come and have supper with us, won't you?' Mrs. Stoylova went on.

'Yes. If I feel well enough .... '

'Of course, and let's hope that you do.' she stood up.

'I am tired, I will go now. Sleep well and take it easy tomorrow, won't you.'

My mother nodded.

I saw Mrs. Stoylova to the front door.

'You wouldn't have been allowed to go, would you?' she said to me in the dark.

I was afraid that she might have been offended that her son's friends were called 'boys of the street' even though I knew that she couldn't have known.

'Never mind,' Mrs. Stoylova went on, 'your mother will come round, she'll get used to the idea that you are growing up. Don't worry.'

'Thank you so much!' I mumbled, but she was already in the lift.

On Sunday, I was feverishly excited the whole day. Albert and Mary came for lunch. They had just returned from a summer holiday in Shoumen, and over lunch told us how the Jewish quarter was now empty of its previous inhabitants, with few exceptions, Uncle Marco and Aunt Victoria, of course, among them. The houses were now inhabited by Armenians or Turks from the adjoining quarters. Everybody, who was not a communist had emigrated to Israel.

Ж

I brushed and ironed my blue dress. I had to take the hem down, because I had grown; this put the waistline much too high and out of place, but I tried to cover this up with the belt. I looked at myself in the mirror. The coarse fabric squashed whatever shape my chest had acquired into a shapeless bulge. I washed my hair and tried to curl it with the old metal tongs my mother had. I heated them on the electric ring but not knowing how to handle them, I burned my fingers, my skull and singed some hair. I gave up. Brushed my hair and left it at that, without looking in the mirror.

Annie and Mimi arrived at about three o'clock. Mimi, as usual wore the best clothes. A magnificent tartan skirt with a white lace blouse. She said that the lace wasn't real lace, but some new American material called nylon. It looked lovely.

Annie wore a dress her mother had made for her out of this season's fabric allowance. She looked very nice.

My mother made some approving remarks about my friends' appearance and told me to be home by six o'clock.

Mimi took it upon herself to explain that we were invited for six.

'All right then, make it seven.' said my mother and left without awaiting an answer.

The time seemed long, as we sat, speculating as to who would be there and what the party would be like. At six o'clock, we saw Ivan leave the house and decided that we could turn up at 6.15.

Vlady opened the door as soon as I rang the bell. He lived in a town house on three floors, sandwiched between two blocks of flats. We followed him into the lounge where we had to screw up our eyes, in order to see – it was so dark. Ivan and Rudy were sitting on the floor. They got up and came to greet us. Ivan put an arm round Mimi's shoulders, and led her away. Rudy took Annie by the hand and they sat on the floor. Vlady went to see to the record player and I sat on the settee.

A record sleeve was put over the only lamp in the room; the thick velvet curtains were drawn and there was no one else but us. I went over to Vlady and looked on as he was piling up the records on the turn table.

'That's an interesting record player! I have never seen one like it.'

'It's automatic. Quite old actually.'

'It changes records, just like that, automatically, without any assistance?'

'Yes, it does. Come, let's dance.'

He put his arms round me quite naturally and held me close. A languid male voice was singing a romantic song as we moved slowly to its rhythm. The nearness of Vlady's body, his strong grip, took me by surprise. My heart was racing and I felt a little dizzy. The sensation was that of pleasurable excitement, mixed with bewilderment. Vlady moved away slightly, our eyes met and he smiled at me, then he swung his head to one side and kissed me. I felt his whole body pressed against me, I felt his mouth, his tongue searching into mine, sending waves of hitherto unexperienced sensations through me. I felt my whole body vibrating, swept by his passion; then, slowly, as he was pressing my head backwards, my mother's face filtered through my whirring mind and immediately I freed myself from his arms, from him. He didn't persist. He moved away at my very first reaction. He smiled warmly:

'You taste so good!' then looking closely at me, he said: 'What's the matter, are you all right?'

'Yes, yes. I am.'

The record had stopped and Vlady went to see to it. I sat back on the settee. The room around me slowly came into focus, became coherent again. I became aware of the others. They seemed the same; the room seemed the same. Rudy handed me a drink. Mimi was laughing. No, they hadn't noticed anything. I seemed to be the only one to whom 'this' had happened. My mother was right, I was no good. I had to be kept in check all the time. I was most probably pregnant.

Vlady sat next to me.

'Have you seen the last jazz show, I say last, because it's pretty certain they are going to be closed after this one.'

I couldn't talk; I felt awful. Vlady looked closely at me:

'Are you all right?'

I looked down.

'Yes,' I whispered.

'Did I frighten you?'

I nodded.

'Was it the first time?'

I nodded, looking down at my clasped hands.

'I should have known! I am sorry. Please forgive me! I

should have controlled myself. Will you forgive me? Say you do!'

He took my hand, 'Do you?'

'I don't know really. I don't know what it all really means.'

'How old are you?'

'Nearly sixteen.'

'You are very young. But you see, you are a young woman,' he said softly. 'You felt things you didn't know existed in you, didn't you?'

'Yes, I did. It's, all so wrong. I want to go home, please.'

'You have done nothing wrong, please believe me that much.'

'I do, but please let me go home.'

'As you wish. May I walk you home?'

'No, no. I prefer to be on my own.'

'Please don't be angry with me. I will never frighten you again. I promise.'

'OK.'

Mimi was talking to Ivan.

'I am going home.' I said.

'Is it time already?'

'It's gone seven.' said Annie.

'All right, let's go.'

We thanked them for the party and left.

'Late again!' my mother said as soon as I walked into the kitchen. I had hoped that she might be at the Stoylovs.

'I am sorry mum .... ' How I wanted to tell her what had happened, how I wanted to know from her, what it was that I had felt, and was it so wrong? How I needed to hear from her that really it wasn't wrong. I didn't dare.

'I am sorry mum,' this is all I seemed to be able to say.

Ж

School began as usual, on the first day of September. It was good to go back to the routine that took me away from home for most of the day; away from my mother's changing moods. The front pages of all the newspapers were busying themselves with the forthcoming Pastors' Trial. On the opening day, we learned that no foreign reporters would be allowed in the courtroom, only a few local reporters and immediate relatives of the accused. As soon as the trial began, and we read the reports in the papers, we realised that they could just as well have been written in advance. Familiar strings of meaningless phrases. The Pastors who were referred to as 'agents of the foreign imperialist powers', 'reactionaries, who spread the poison of the West and its decadence among our people' etc. ... etc. ... ad nauseum.

The Pastors were said to be looking well, composed and straight faced when confronted with their acts of 'high treason'. On the tenth day of the trial, the Court began hearing the witnesses. They were going to be heard over a period of three days, which my mother's pass covered. We didn't know exactly when my father would be called. I had secret hopes that my father would be freed as soon as he had given evidence. I was wrong.

My father was the third witness to be called on the very first day. My mother had managed to sit on the end of a row, near the door through which, she gathered, the witnesses would be ushered in. When my father's name was called, she leant sideways, looking back towards the door. My father appeared and saw her immediately. He smiled and winked at her as he passed her by in steady bold strides towards the witness box.

'He looks like an old man,' my mother sobbed as she was telling me about it in the afternoon. 'His hair is completely gray, and he is so thin, I wouldn't be surprised if he has tuberculosis. He was wearing the same clothes! The same clothes he wore when they arrested him and it seemed that he hasn't worn them since. God knows what rags he has been wearing all those months.'

'What did, they ask him? What did he say?'

'What do you expect. He was there no longer than five minutes. They asked him how well he knew Pastor Ivanov, and he said: 'By sight only', then they asked him if he knew any of the other pastors, and of course he knows the curate – Mr. Andreyev, who, as you know lives in the church with his mother, so he said that. Then they asked him if, in his capacity as an official at the American Military Mission – official, indeed! – anyway, whether he had had any special privileges.'

'What does that mean?'

'I don't know, overtime payments, that sort of thing. He said 'no', and I was sure they were going to bring up our stay at the villa that Christmas, but to my surprise they didn't … to think that this was two years ago now … and your father has been away for nearly a year and a half … I have a splitting headache ….'

'Are you going again tomorrow?'

'What's the point. They won't call him again.' She took the aspirin that I handed her.

'I had hoped to find him outside the Palace of Justice, or perhaps, here ….'

'I had hoped for that too.'

'They will send him to a labour camp now, you mark my word.'

'But why? He wasn't accused of anything!'

'They don't free people just like that, you wait and see.'

Mary and Albert came later in the afternoon to find out what had happened. My mother went over the story again and expressed her fear that he would be sent to a labour camp. In those days, the labour camps weren't very numerous, nor too full, not as yet anyway, and many communists preferred to think of them as rumours, so Albert denied the possibility vehemently.

'Most certainly not! He will be released in due course.'

When they had gone, my mother said:

'Poor Albert, he has to defend his party and his regime. It has always been his ideal, he can't as yet admit that they are not living up to his expectations.'

Even though we knew it was unreasonable, we went on expecting my father to turn up at the front door. We even went as far as trying not to leave the flat, because he didn't have a key. When he didn't come back at the end of the week, my mother said:

'Now, I shall have to look for him again. But where shall I go? I have been everywhere, knocked on all doors.'

In the morning, we received a postcard. It was in my father's handwriting and came from Dobroudga – a large arid area in the north-east of the country, bordering the Danube Delta in the north and the Black Sea in the east. My father wrote that he was well; that we could write to him – one post card per month, containing no more than ten lines. The address: 'Labour Re-Educational Co-Operative'. We could also visit him once a month. That was wonderful!

My mother made immediate enquiries and, it became clear to us that these visits were impossible. To get there on a given day and on a fixed hour (between 2-4pm), we had to travel ten hours by train to the nearest village which was twenty kilometres from the camp. There, we had to find someone with a cart, horse or mule, or even donkey, who would agree to take us to the camp and wait there, to take us back. Then we had to find accommodation for the night, because there was only one train per day. For accommodation, we had to rely on the peasants' hospitality – it was a folly to imagine that anything resembling a hotel or an inn could be found in those parts – but the peasants had been warned to have nothing to do with the camp, its inmates, or any visitors. We had to make do with post cards, which after all, was contact with him and a lot more than we had had until then.

Ж

We received a long, sad letter from Stephka, written in a large, inclined, child-like handwriting. She told us that she had had a card from Stephan and that he was in a labour re-education co-operative, somewhere in the South, near the Turkish border. Now she knew she was going to have her baby on her own, and that Stephan would not know his child. In the end, she said that her elder sister and her husband were coming to occupy their room. Her brother in law had a job as a porter or watchman in one of the official buildings.

That same week, Anastasia and Dimitry arrived. She was an older version of Stephka: robust, angular, with an easy broad smile. The couple had no children.

Maria our CP secretary co-sharer, returned from her home town with her baby girl and her husband returned from sea. The flat was, once more, full. I loved Maria's baby and whenever I could I went to see her and asked to look after her. Maria took advantage of my offer and hurried out to do her shopping.

On a cold night, early in December, Anastasia came to our room.

'Do you mind if I sit with you for while. My Dimitry is on night duty and I am not used to sitting on my own doing nothing.'

We sat around the black shiny stove. It spread an even,

pleasant warmth provided one sat quite near it. The reason was simply that we didn't have enough coal to fill it up.

'I've been thinking.' said Anastasia, 'You know we are going home for Christmas, well, I would like to invite your daughter to come with us, like. She's never seen a real village, has she? Also, what I mean to say is, you could go out and about a bit, see some friends, like.'

'Oh, isn't this lovely!' I enthused 'I would love to see a real village!'

'You should know better than to suggest such things, Anastasia!' my mother scolded her, 'You know I don't go out, and what will I do, all alone here?'

'But you ought to go out! Look at you, you are drying up like a tobacco leaf!'

'So is my husband.'

'Let her come. We have a dance in the village hall, and a play. She'll like our lads. Also, this time of year, all the students would be back from Sofia. The educated lads, like yourselves.'

'My sister-in-law is coming for a few days, from Shoumen, I am sure my daughter would like to see her.'

'Who is coming? Aunt Victoria?' I was surprised. My mother hadn't told me about it.

'Yes.'

'Oh. But I still want to go! You see, mum, if Aunt Victoria will be here, you won't be alone!'

'I don't know. We'll see,' my mother said in a voice which closed the discussion of the subject.

'We never sit like this in our village, doing nothing.' Anastasia said.

'What is it you do?' I asked.

'Oh, many things. We weave, we knit, we spin wool. There is a lot to be done in the evening. But being alone is the worst.'

'Who is with you then, when Dimitry isn't at home?'

'My mother. She is an old woman, but she is still very useful.

She bakes the bread, she looks after the house. She can still spin like a young girl with her old fingers.'

'Do you work in the field?'

'Sure I do. Dimitry can't cope on his own. We plough together and we sow the grain in the spring.' Anastasia took a deep breath; her voice broke and her eyes full of nostalgia, she went on: 'we would walk along the furrows and spread the grain, and Dimitry would sing. A fine voice he has, my Dimitry.'

'Why did you leave the village, Anastasia?'

Her face was sad now, and I noticed large dark circles around her eyes. She sighed:

'I don't know. I don't know. They came to the house and asked him to go to the city. To be a watchman in their Party Administration. I don't even know what it means. My poor Dimitry, locked up in a building for the best part of his life. And my little sister; we left her alone with my old mother, and she heavy with child.' She broke into tears. It was painful to see her strong, square shoulders shaking with sobs, like a child's.

'Don't worry Anastasia,' my mother said to her, 'Stephka will be all right. You will see her soon, at Christmas and you will see for yourself that your mother and she are all right.'

'They want to take Stephka into a hospital. We are not used to these things. I haven't been blessed with children; this will be the first grandchild my mother will have and … we are used to children being born at home, she wants to look after Stephka … my mother she has had five children, she knows. What do they know about us in those hospitals …. '

'Oh, but they do, I can assure you. They go to special schools for many years, and they learn how to do everything.'

'Do you think so, Mrs. Ashkenazy? Do you really think so?

'Of course I do!'

Anastasia blew her nose and wiped her eyes:

'I must tell Stephka and mum. You see, all our lives we look after each other; my father, bless his soul, – taught us everything. Now they come and everything has to be different, why?'

'These are difficult things to understand. Politicians say it's for our own good. Who are we to understand?' my mother was talking like to a child.

'How can they know what is good for us? They don't know us?'

'I don't know. I am in no better position than yourself, Anastasia.'

Anastasia shook her head:

'I don't understand anything any more. I am not very educated. I went to school for four years; I can read and write. I read the newspaper, sometimes. Still I don't understand. You know, before the war like, when the King was still alive, God bless his soul, it was … different. I mean, who ever heard anything about government and all that, in our village. We just … lived and worked … and we were happy. It isn't our business to get mixed up in all this. We are simple peasants, we know how to work the land. Then the war came, and everybody tells us that the Russians are our enemy; then some boys from the village, they run away from home and into the bush, the mountains like and they tell their mothers when they come home at night for bread and the like, that the Russians are our friends. And the police, they hunt them like foxes. They were our boys, so we helped them, we hid them. Now the Russians are here; and where are we? No more land, no nothing. Our Stephka's husband taken away, and us, sent here – to the city, and Dimitry sitting doing nothing, like an old man for whom there is no more use. I don't understand it. Do you?'

We were all sobbing now.

'No I don't.' said my mother.

'You have been to school more, you know the world like … didn't they teach you?'

'All I can say, is that the Communists say they want to change our lives for the better.'

'For the better! I don't know about you City people, but us peasants – they have taken our land away from us, and this is all we have, I mean – our land.' she wiped her eyes again, 'I am ashamed of myself, I didn't mean to cry. A full grown woman and crying like an old woman.'

'It's all right, Anastasia, we all have something to cry about.'

'The trouble is, Dimitry tells me not to talk to no one. Otherwise we will have problems, and he might be sent away as well. How can I live without telling what's on my heart?'

'He is right, you shouldn't talk. You can talk to me, because I am in the same situation Stephka is in – my husband has also been sent away. But never tell your thoughts to anybody else.'

'No, I won't.' she stood up, pulling at the rough material of her skirt, 'as I said, let her come for Christmas.'

'We shall see. Good night Anastasia.'

'Good night.'

Ж

Aunt Victoria arrived a few days before we broke up for the 'New Year' vacation. This is what the Christmas holidays were called now. With her intervention I was allowed to go to Dragovo, Anastasia's village. We left Sofia four days before Christmas, the Orthodox Christmas, two days into the new year – 1950. I had packed a small bag with a towel, my tooth brush and a piece of soap. I wore my eternal blue dress – but I had new shoes. The old ones had become too short, and my mother had to buy me a new pair on the winter ration. It was a very plain pair of black shoes; everybody wore the same style, in black or brown, but the sensation of wearing something new was exciting.

Stephka was waiting for us on the windy platform of the village station. She was huge now, and I saw her wobble on her feet, as she hurried towards us. She was smiling and tears ran down her cheeks. She kissed her sister, her brother in law and then me. She took her sister's heavy bag off her hands, and I made a move to take it myself, but Anastasia, realising what I was trying to do, turned round and stopped me:

'In our ways, this is a respect a younger sister pays to her elders.'

We walked in a single file. It was very cold and the sky hung, heavy and gray above us. There were small, white-washed bungalows scattered around us in no particular order. Cheerful red and white chequered curtains hung over the windows. The roofs were low and red-tiled or thatched. All the spaces between the bungalows were covered in mud, which the cold had frozen in deep uneven folds. We crossed what appeared to be the village square.

'This is where we hold our summer dances and fêtes,' Dimitry explained, 'It doesn't look much now, but it's lovely in the summer.'

A few hens walked around, displaying their colourful feathers, jerking their necks towards us and as though meaning to appear busy, pecked the dry mud every now and then. A few dogs walked placidly around, gave us a look as we passed them by and, obviously not finding us very interesting, went on their way.

Eventually Stephka stopped, put the bag on the ground and opened a low wooden door.

'Here we are, welcome to our home.'

An old woman appeared, a toothless smile on her wrinkled face, her deep blue eyes sparkling with joy. Anastasia and Dimitry bent down to kiss her hand as they walked in; I followed suit. They had all taken their shoes off at the entrance, and I did the same.

'Come in, come in and warm up by the fire.'

We followed her into a spotlessly clean small room where large logs were burning cheerfully in the fireplace. The wooden floors were polished to a mirror-like shine. Colourful, most probably hand woven kelims were spread over the main walking areas. There were two mattresses on the floor, on either side of the fireplace, with colourful cushions spread over them. We all sat down and Anastasia began giving her mother an account of her City life. Every now and then she would look at her husband who would confirm her words with a nod,

'That's it, that's how it is'.

When she had finished, Anastasia asked her sister what was the news from her husband. Stephka got up with surprising agility and came back, holding a few post cards. I recognised them immediately. She handed them to her sister:

'This is all I get. One a month. I can write one a month too. Look, they are all the same. He always says the same things.'

Stephka was crying desperately. The cards were passed on by Anastasia to her husband. I was surprised that no one did anything, or said anything to reassure poor Stephka. She went on sobbing for a while; I wondered whether I shouldn't try and say something comforting to her when I realised that there wasn't anything comforting that one could say. That whatever would be said, would be just empty words, that in reality, there was no hope, that these people knew it, and that they didn't play games.

Eventually, the old woman spoke:

'We must look after our young guest.'

I could hardly understand what she was saying, since she had no teeth.

'Come and freshen up.' Stephka said.

'May I go to the toilet, please?'

'Come, I'll show you.'

A door through the kitchen, led to a back yard. Stephka pointed at a few pairs of clogs:

'Here, put on some of these.'

I followed her out, to a small hut at the bottom of the yard.

'This is it,' she said, and turned back.

The door of the hut was held by a piece of string onto a nail. I took that off and the door screeched open. To my great amazement, there was nothing inside, but a hole in the middle of the wooden floor, there was a bucket of water in the corner and a bunch of neatly cut newspaper rectangles on a brick. I had never seen anything like it before.

Later,we all sat around the kitchen table. The Mother said grace, and Anastasia dished out the stew. Dimitry took the large round loaf of bread, put it against his chest and with a sharp knife, cut long, even slices.

I slept on one of the mattresses by the fireplace, and Stephka's mother slept on the other. I heard her get up a few times during the night to put some logs on the fire to keep it going. When I woke up in the morning she was no longer in her bed; the house was full of the appetising smell of freshly baked bread. We had fresh milk with our breakfast, that Stephka had just milked from their cow; butter, that they had made, home made jam and bacon.

The whole of the next day was spent in tidying up, cooking, and talking about the dance. Finally, it was time to go. The village school, where the dance was held, was in the village square. We went into the gym, where there was a stage over which hung a curtain – a little too short, and too narrow, but nonetheless, a curtain. Rows of metal chairs filled the gym.

'This is our theatre.' whispered Anastasia, 'Now we are going to see a play. The teacher is very clever. She teaches them all what to say. It's a Nativity play. Here, look,' whispered Anastasia to her sister 'Isn't that Tonya's boy? He is looking at our guest, his eyes are popping!'

'Yes, it is him. Hasn't he grown. He'll have to wait, won't he?'

'I should say.'

A woman came up to us, she spoke to Anastasia:

'I see you have city girl with you, a guest is she?' and without awaiting an answer, she turned to me, 'our lads are all waiting to dance with you. I hope you enjoy it here.'

'Thank you, thank you very much. I am sure I will.' I mumbled, embarrassed.

The woman walked away. Anastasia looked after her, and again, whispered to her sister:

'She's got to poke her nose everywhere, doesn't she.'

Dimitry, who hadn't said a word the while, scolded her:

'Hold your tongue, woman!'

Eventually, the lights went out and the curtain was pulled jerkily to one side. It was a most lovable, naive Nativity play, where the actors obviously missed their cues, forgot their lines, and got individual acclaims from their family as they came on stage. It made me think of the Christmas festivities in my French school. All gone now, behind me.

When the play ended, after a lot of cheering, clapping and shouting, the curtain was pulled again, the chairs were re-arranged into rows alongside the walls of the gym to allow for dancing space, then the curtain was pulled once more and the orchestra was revealed. Immediately, they broke into a tango.

A young man came up to us, bowed to Anastasia who was obviously considered as my chaperone, and said:

'Do you allow me to dance with your guest?'

Anastasia looked him up and down:

'You are Andrew's boy, aren't you?' she seemed to be enjoying herself.

'Yes, I am, the elder.'

'All right. You can dance.'

And so it went. They would come to her, ask her permission, she would enquire whose boy they were, and would grant the dance. She refused only once. She allowed only one boy to have two dances. The boys were all very polite; some asked me what my name was, others just went through the dance without saying a word. The dance finished, they would take me back and thank Anastasia. I was greatly amused and didn't even once think that the village girls must have hated my guts.

When we got home – well after 1am. – the first late night in my life, I was tired and went straight to bed. I thanked my hosts, Anastasia expressed her satisfaction that the village boys had liked me and she added:

'It isn't finished yet' whimsically.

'What isn't finished?' I asked, my curiosity aroused.

'I am not saying. You'll see.'

I fell asleep as soon as she left the room. In my deep sleep, I became aware of music being played before I was really awake. Slowly I pushed the covers from over my head and heard it clearly. I saw the mother standing by the window, peeping out, but trying to conceal her face behind the curtain.

'What is it?' I asked her.

'They are serenading you.' The old woman came away from the window, giggling. Surprised I got up and went towards the window, but she pulled me back:

'No! You mustn't show yourself. Or they'll think you're willing.'

'Willing – what?'

At this point Anastasia came in. I could see a wry smile on her face in the light of the glowing logs.

'You see, I told you!' she whispered, 'I'll give them some wine.'

'Why? Why wine? What time is it?'

'It's two o'clock. Wine is customary. He'll understand.'

'Understand – what?'

'That he can't court you, you silly girl.'

I sat down, incredulous of what was going on around me. I was being serenaded. I thought of Cyrano de Bergerac. Did the boy outside have a long nose? It was so romantic!

I was made to go back to bed. The mother put another log on the fire. Eventually the music stopped and I heard Anastasia go back to their room.

Chapter Nine

'Who is there to love, if not our parents?'

My mother was standing at the far end of the corridor. From where I saw her, outside my classroom, she seemed to be leaning against the wall, as though she would fall down if she weren't. I hurried towards her, wondering what new disaster had befallen us now. As I came near her, and before I could say a word, she said quickly:

'It's your father. He has come home.'

Had I only been listening to her voice, I would have thought that she had just announced his death. The meaning of her words sank in.

'At home? Free? When? Mummy, that's wonderful!'

'He wants to see you; come on, let's go I have asked your headmaster's permission.'

We walked quickly down the corridor.'

'How is he, mummy?'

'You'll see.'

We walked in silence, hurriedly. I was desperately searching my memory for a picture of my father's face, but no image appeared. That was awful! I had forgotten what my own father looked like! We found him, standing in the middle of the kitchen in his long johns, surrounded by a pile of rags.

'My girl!' he said, 'My little girl!' and tears were running down his cheeks. I took a pace towards him, but he stopped me, his hand extended in a 'halt' gesture, 'No! don't. I am full of lice. Your mother will sort me out.' and his eyes, red-rimmed, the eyes of a lost child, looked at my mother, 'What do I do next?' he asked.

'Go and take a bath. I shall burn all these in the stove.'

My father made his way, passed us, to the bathroom. He was small and very thin; his body almost that of a boy, only his hair was completely gray, and he couldn't stop crying.

I was sent to do some shopping while my father was having his bath. My mother, also crying, wanted to cook one of his favourite dishes.

My father had returned home. After almost two years – he had been in various prisons, in a labour camp; some of the time we hadn't even known whether he was dead or alive, and now – he was home, alive and all I could feel was sadness. No joy, or happiness – just sadness. I didn't even know whether I loved him. I was pleased that I had to queue for a while, to allow myself time to collect my thoughts, or find some answers, which, of course I didn't.

I found my mother in the kitchen, crying.

'What happened? Where is he? They haven't come for him again, have they?'

I panicked.

'He is asleep.' she said flatly.

'Oh, mummy please don't cry ... he is back, he is with us once again, isn't that the main thing?'

'Yes, it is ..., ' she sobbed, 'he ... went to sleep on the floor ... he is not used to a bed any longer .... '

I put the shopping bag on the table and sat down. My

father's clothes were burning in the stove, spreading an unpleasant smell. I observed my mother's closed, preoccupied face.

'Did he tell you anything … what happened to him … all this time?' I asked

'How could he? He too has signed a paper; and when they make you sign that paper, they make sure you are scared to death to even think about it, let alone, talk about it.'

'He is terribly thin.'

'Yes.'

'I wonder if he isn't …? '

'Yes, I know.'

'Rest and food will help, don't you think mum?'

'Perhaps. If it's not too late. I'll have the doctor round tomorrow to give him a check up.'

She was busy over the sink, her back turned to me.

'Of course,' she went on, 'the only thing for us to do now, is to emigrate as soon as we can.'

My heart sank. I had dreaded that the subject would be raised some time. I didn't want to emigrate. I didn't know why, but I didn't. I was frightened of what seemed a journey towards the unknown.

'Why?' I asked.

'You are silly! What can he do now? His record isn't exactly clean, as far as they are concerned, is it?'

'Maybe Uncle Marco will be able to help?'

'Nobody helps no one now, haven't you noticed

We were quiet for a while.

'Go to your room and get on with your homework.' my mother said.

'Oh, mum, please let me stay with you!'

'No! Go to your room. Do as you are told!'

I went to my room. It was chilly. I sat on the settee and looked around. I hadn't been in my room all winter. I thought that I had to take my things from my parents' wardrobe and put them back into my cupboard. I was pleased at the thought of regaining my autonomy at night. I would, once again, read in bed. The radio with the green eye wasn't there any longer, but I thought that there would be no necessity for hiding; after all, I was a lot older now.

Mimi arrived towards the end of the afternoon.

'What happened? Is your mother all right? Why did she come for you?'

'My father is back.'

'Oh, how wonderful! This is really good news. Is he all right?'

'I don't know ... he is so thin ... ' I broke into tears. Mimi put her arm round my shoulders.

'There ... there .... Don't you see, everything will be all right now! Your mother won't be alone any longer ... you will be free .... '

I hadn't thought about that.

'You know something, Mimi, something quite terrible. He is my own father, and I don't know him. On the way home from school, I couldn't remember his face. I feel nothing at all, isn't it terrible?'

'It's the surprise, the shock. After all, it has been ... such a long time, and you were only a kid when ... never mind. It will pass. Everything will be back to normal within a few days, you'll see. As for feelings, I can tell you here and now, if I haven't told you already, that I don't particularly like my father.' Mimi concluded.

'I remember my father telling me, when I was a lot younger,' I said, 'that he can't make me love him, but that I had to respect him, because he was my father.'

'They might demand what they want, they can't command your feelings. We can't just love them blindly, because they are our parents.'

'What are you saying? Who is there to love, if not our parents?'

'My father is a bully. My mother is lovely and soft.'

'I have forgotten about my father. He can be a bully sometimes. And sometimes he used to be quite nice. As for my mother … I don't know. She does strange things … sometimes, but I love her.'

'You will soon find out about your father, now that he is back and you are old enough to judge.'

'You talk about parents as though you know them. I don't think I do know them, I have always thought that parents … are parents.'

'If you are saying that parents are beyond criticism or judgement, you are wrong.'

'Am I?'

'Yes. I am not going to allow my father to tell me what to do with my life! I don't respect his opinions nor his judgements, so why should I listen to him? I have my own opinions.'

'But … he is your father … surely he knows best, doesn't he?'

'Not necessarily, not for me.'

I sighed. I really didn't know what was right and what was wrong. All I knew was that respecting one's parents was one of my father's mottos.

'Here,' Mimi said in a lighter tone, 'I brought you today's notes.'

'Thanks.'

'Cheer up, it'll be OK, you'll see.'

'Yes.'

I saw Mimi out and joined my mother in the kitchen.

'I am exhausted.' she said, 'The food is ready, I'll go and get him up. He must eat something.'

I lay the table. My mother returned with my father who had wrapped a blanket over himself, over his pyjamas. His eyes were puffed with sleep. He came to me and kissed me. I threw my arms around him, wanting to feel more than I actually did. My father resisted my impulse; pushed me gently away:

'You're a big girl now. How much you have grown! How are you doing at school?'

I thought that he meant that because I was a big girl, I shouldn't embrace him, but I wanted his warmth, his caress! Disappointed, I answered his question about school:

'OK.'

'How do you mean 'OK'? Aren't you top of the class?'

I remembered another one of his obsessions – being top.

'Well, I … not really …. '

'And why is that?' A lump came up to my throat. I recognised the cold, unfriendly, strict voice.

'Let's eat.' my mother said and turned to my father, 'You must remember that things haven't been exactly easy for us, here. She has done her best under the circumstances.'

I was grateful for my mother's intervention.

'She was ill,' my mother went on, 'she was ill for three months last year.'

'Was that the time she stopped coming outside the Militia Detention Centre?'

'Yes.'

'Who were the girls who used to come with you?'

'My friends, Mimi and Annie; you will meet them soon.'

'Very nice of them to have accompanied you. Are they Jewish?'

'No. Does it matter?'

My father seemed to have difficulties in swallowing. He chewed his food laboriously, then swallowed as though it was very hard and dry. It was painful to watch.

'How did you manage with money?' he asked my mother.

'I sold things … how else?'

'What did you sell?'

'The Persian rugs, my rings, the radios …. '

'And you managed! Well done.'

'It took a lot of planning and sacrifice.'

'I am sure. Now I am back, you won't have anything to worry about any longer. '

'The doctor cost a lot .... '

'Tomorrow I am going to go wherever it is that one goes, and apply for an emigration visa. A new life awaits us in Israel.'

I was listening, my heart full of misery. I said nothing about my apprehension which was, I thought, most probably, unfounded. Nonetheless, it was there. They spoke about emigration without a moment's thought that I would have to interrupt my education, in the middle of my last year. Yet, my father wanted me to be top of the class!

'I'll have to write to Isaac.' my father said.

'Yes.'

'Have you any news from the others, how are they doing?'

'Very few letters from Amelia containing little information. It would seem that all women work, they have become daily helps, while their husbands study Hebrew. My sister, Clara, who grew up with a German nanny is a daily help!'

My mother looked as though she was going to cry.

'Don't you worry about a thing.' my father said. 'I speak numerous other languages. While I am alive, you won't have to go to work! And you – you will go to university, you'll see, even if I have to sweep the streets.'

'Girls go to the Army in Israel.' I said.

'You won't.'

'It's the Law, everybody does.'

'We'll see about that. Isaac will advise me what is the best thing to do, how to start in order to settle down. Did you know you have cousins in Tel Aviv?' my father asked me.

'Yes, I do. Your brother Isaac, and his wife ... Aunt ... and their two children.'

'Aunt Rebecca' my father told me the names of these faceless people, 'and your cousin Esther – a little older than you, and her young brother Uri.'

After dinner, I transferred my things – clothes and books – from my parents' bedroom into my own. My father decided to try on some of his old clothes. They hung pitifully on him. He had to hold up the trousers because they were far too big. He gave up, sat down and took a cigarette. He inhaled the smoke with great delight; he hadn't smoked in two years; but his face turned yellow, he put the cigarette in the ash-tray, held his stomach and ran to the toilet.

We heard him being sick. He came back, his face frighteningly white.

'It's nothing,' he said, 'I am not used to cooked meals. It will pass.'

Contrary to his plans, my father didn't leave the flat for over a week. He was being sick, or feeling sick all the time. He had to get used to sleeping in a bed again; to going to sleep after 7 pm and getting up later than 5am, he had to get used to wearing shoes, to eating cooked meals. The doctor came to examine him and found nothing wrong. He prescribed rest, food and more rest.

During that period, I often heard my mother telling him about our lives during his detention. About her constant attempts to see officials, about her relentless 'knocking on all possible doors' to try to get them to free him, or obtain information about the reason for his detention, about her 'heart condition', her solitude, her difficulty in having to cope with a child.

I felt embarrassed. I was sure that whatever had happened to us, was in no way comparable to his ordeal, yet he was not allowed to talk about it, to tell us what solitary confinement had been like and what it had done to him. These questions bothered me. One day I made an attempt to reassure him about my mother's condition, like the doctor had, at the time, reassured me. But my father rebuffed me:

'You mustn't interfere. You are too young to understand,

and it's not for you to talk about it.'

When he felt better, my father went and applied for a permit to emigrate.

'I went to the Jewish Community Centre,' my father said to my mother when he came back. 'It seems that there aren't too many Jews left in Sofia at all.'

I was doing my homework in my room, but the door was ajar and I could hear every word. I was about to close the door, because I wanted to concentrate, when I heard my father say:

'I want her to frequent Jewish people.'

'Where is she going to find them?' my mother asked.

I now stood by the door and listened.

'I want her to join one of the Jewish organisations. I made enquiries, she can go to Maccabi.'

'She has a lot of work and little time to spare.'

Once more, I was grateful to my mother for coming to my defence.

The door bell rang just then and I closed my door quickly. I heard my mother ushering Albert and Mary in. I got on with my work.

Eventually, loud voices coming from my parents' room imposed themselves upon my conscious mind, I looked up from the book I had been engrossed in, and listened.

My father was shouting at the top of his voice: ' … not socialism, but despotism, destruction of human rights, destruction of human dignity! Humiliation to the core … to the quick … to where there is no more …. That's what you and the likes of you stand for! You are hypocrites, murderers! Do you know what they do to people in there? But you must know, you are one of them. Dogs! That's what you all are, dogs!' I heard my father's fast steps down the hall, then the front door opened and slammed shut. I looked into the hall; there was no one. I went into my parents' room. My mother was crying, Albert was trying to calm her down, Mary looked scared.

'How am I going to live with this man …? Tell me how …? ' my mother cried.

'He has been through a lot, you must be patient with him.' Albert was saying.

'To shout like this at the only person who ever cared for me when I was alone!'

'I started it …. '

'No, it was him!'

'Even so, I should not have replied. I made a mistake and I hope that he will forgive me. We mustn't forget the fact that he was interned … badly treated …. '

'We better go now, so he doesn't find us here when he comes back.'

'If he comes back,' my mother said as though she wished he wouldn't.

'He will. Don't worry.'

'Who's worried?'

I was worried.

Albert and Mary left and my mother told me to go back to my room. I couldn't do any more work. I paced around; I went to the window and looked down. Eventually I saw my father turn round the corner. Poor father! I went to wait for him in the hall, I wanted to say something … I didn't know what, to tell him that … I loved him, perhaps, or that I cared.

He walked in, and I embraced him in the dark, cool hall.

'Dad please, you are not … '

His hands went to my arms, and undid my embrace.

'You mustn't do these things any longer. You are a big girl now. Behave like one.'

He went straight into their room. I went into mine, sat on a chair, my arms hanging limply down. Was I ever going to understand adults?

Over supper, I felt that my mother was being 'difficult' and my father – 'accommodating'.

Two weeks later we received a negative reply to our application to emigrate. My father re-applied immediately and went out to look for a job.

Upon his release from the 're-education co-operative', he had been issued with a paper which he had to present to any prospective employer. It stated that he had served his time and had not run away and, that he was an 'undesirable element'. My father soon realised that the only work he could get was that of a labourer.

He found a job in a leather workshop. His job consisted of bashing with a mallet a metal mould, placed over several layers of leather, thus cutting the ends which were then sewn onto braces. At first his arm hurt, then it became swollen and my mother had to apply cold compresses at night. Eventually the swelling disappeared, he stopped complaining of pain and even began producing more cuttings than the norm per day. This meant that on the May Day and the 9th of September Parades, he would march with the proud 'over the norm' men in industry, a special red sash across their chests.

The Pastors' trial had, by then ended, with four of them, our neighbour among them, getting life imprisonment, nine – 30 years and two – among those, the curate who had lived in the church – 15 years. All their families were deported to different remote villages, where no one could reach them and where they lived in most primitive conditions, having to report daily to the local Militia Station. Mrs. Ivanova came to see us before she left with her two sons. She had grown thinner, the circles around her eyes – darker and deeper, but she smiled:

'God, the Lord is with us,' she said, 'He spared my husband's life. We must be grateful. God bless you, I will pray for you.'

A few years later, Pastor Ivanov died in prison.

Ж

The spring was quickly turning into summer; Mimi and I often went for a walk, usually to the Alexander Nevsky garden, to air our heads after hours of study. We chatted endlessly; there was always more to talk about, and we found it difficult to part. My 'curfew' – 7pm was the decisive factor.

One afternoon, we were parting outside our front door, when it swung open and Vlady came out.

'Hullo! How are you? I haven't seen you for ages.'

I realised that Mimi wasn't going to talk; I answered:

'Very well, and you?'

'Fed up with studies, otherwise – intact! What are you doing with yourselves these days?'

'Nothing much … we … '

'I must be on my way,' Mimi interrupted, 'I am expected home and am late already.' And she walked off.

'Do you like the cinema?' Vlady asked me.

'Yes, very much.'

'Would you like to go sometime?'

How was I to tell him that all my movements had to be approved by my parents?

'Well … I … ' I just didn't know what to say, and I didn't want him to think that I didn't want to go with him.

'It can wait. You must have a lot on with your finals and so do I.'

'Yes, that's it.' I sighed with relief.

'Look, may I ask you for a favour? I need a French/Bulgarian dictionary for a paper I am writing, do you have one that I can borrow?'

'Yes, certainly, come up with me, I'll let you have it now.'

We went up in the lift, and as we went into the flat, I saw my father peep through the kitchen door which he shut immediately.

'Come this way.' I asked Vlady to my room and took the heavy volume from the shelf. My father's angry voice startled me, coming from the kitchen the door of which he had obviously opened:

'You are late for supper! And whoever is there with you should know better that come in at supper time! Come here at once!'

I wanted the floor to cave in, and swallow me forever! I was so stunned and embarrassed that I could not say a word. I felt all my pores open and perspiration run down all my body and face.

Vlady put a reassuring hand on my arm and smiled:

'Don't worry .... '

'I ... I am so sorry ... ' I mumbled.

'I understand. I hope he won't be too hard on you ... do you want me to talk to him ... apologise or something?'

'Apologise for what? No, no, I'll talk to him,' I said it knowing full well that I would not be given a chance to do it.

'Would you rather I didn't take the Dictionary?'

'No, please take it.'

I saw him out, went straight to the bathroom and sat there until I calmed down. To my surprise, my father didn't say another word; had he done so I would have had a chance to defend myself, but his silence made it impossible for me to start an argument; it would mean that I had to attack, rather than defend myself; and that, I didn't know how to do.

I went to my room after dinner and soon heard my father's voice. I opened my door and listened. They were in their room:

' ... tell your daughter to stop frequenting 'goyim', do you hear! or I'll wring her neck! I won't allow any loose behaviour and I want her to go to a Jewish organisation, do you hear!'

My mother's voice was quiet and I couldn't hear her reply; but I heard my father's voice again:

' ... if she brings home another 'goy', I'll kill her!'

I shut my door. I didn't want to hear any more. Why didn't he tell me these things? Why was he calling me 'your daughter'? Wasn't I his daughter too? Couldn't he tell me face to face what he felt? How could he reject a person he hadn't even met, just because he wasn't Jewish? How narrow minded and prejudiced that was! Besides, where was I going to find Jewish friends? Hadn't he, only a few years back, denied me any contact with organisations, Jewish or otherwise? I cried bitterly in my pillow.

'You mustn't judge him too severely.' said my mother, when I raised the subject with her on the following day. 'He is concerned for your future, it's for your own good.'

'What future? I gave the boy a dictionary, that's all.'

'That's how it starts. Your father will never forgive you if you fell in love and wanted to marry a non-Jew.'

'Who is getting married? I am sixteen! I lent him a book!' I was beside myself; couldn't she see how ridiculous it all was? 'Also,' I went on, 'why not talk to me? Why not tell me about his feelings? Or am I too daft for him?'

'Don't be silly. He thinks these matters are better discussed between mother and daughter.'

'What's wrong with father and daughter? Or aren't I his daughter?'

'Don't be silly.'

'I don't know, he kept mentioning me as 'your daughter'.'

'It's his 'façon de parler' and you know it. You are too young ....'

'Yes, and I don't want to be! If young means that even my own father won't trust me, then I don't want youth, I want to be old!'

'You are dramatising. Leave me now. I am tired.'

After supper, my mother handed me the address of the Maccabi Youth Organisation.

'Apparently,' she said, 'they meet twice weekly. You can go

and enrol on Monday, at 5pm.'

On Monday afternoon I went to the Maccabi Club which was about ten minutes brisk walk from home. It occupied a few rooms on the fifth floor of an otherwise disused building. Empty corridors and doorless rooms gaped at me as I walked up the stairs – the lift was not in use. The fifth floor was bustling with life. I walked into the 'Office', paid my membership fee to the girl at the desk and was issued with a membership card.

'Here,' she said, 'you will join the Hannah Senesh Group; they have just begun their meeting, you will see the name on the door.'

I made my way among the chatting youths to the door marked 'Hannah Senesh', knocked, heard a loud 'come in!', and opened the door. About fifteen boys and girls sat on chairs, scattered around, facing a young man who was standing up. They all looked at me.

'A new member?' the young man, obviously the leader, asked.

'Yes, I have just ... '

He extended his hand and I understood that he wanted proof of my enrolment. I handed him the receipt which was wrapped around the membership card. He read my name aloud and said:

'Come and sit down. Welcome to our group. We meet on Mondays for a class, and on Thursdays for gymnastics. You need shorts, a tee-shirt and plimsolls. If you haven't got the gear, don't bother to come to gymnastics. We start promptly at 5pm, and finish at 7pm. OK?'

I nodded, and he resumed his lecture:

'As I was saying, the kibbutz Guinossar is situated on the shores of the Sea of Galilee, it was founded in .... '

His delivery was very good and quickly I was absorbed in the subject, pleased that after all, the experience was not going to be a total bore.

When the meeting was finished, a tall blond girl came up to me:

'Hi, my name is Lilian.'

'Hi.'

'Did you like him?'

'Yes, I did – I mean his delivery. Didn't you?'

She shrugged.

'Are you going to emigrate?' she asked.

'My parents want to, I am not so keen.'

'My parents can do what they like,' she said aggressively 'I am staying, I am a communist and I like it here.'

'Oh, I see. Look I must run, see you on Thursday!' I said quickly and ran off.

'See you!' she shouted after me.

I ran down the stairs, thinking to myself that *they* were everywhere!

'Where the hell have you been!' my father's angry voice greeted me as soon as I walked through the front door.

'Maccabi … the club … don't you remember ….' I was taken by surprise, uncomprehending.

'Do you know what the time is? Have you no sense of responsibility? I work like a slave for you, the least you can do is to come home for supper! And supper is at seven! Not at ten to, not at ten past, but at seven. And you, you will be here on time!'

'But dad … '

'No 'but'.'

'The club meets at … '

'Don't answer back! You'll be here for supper if I have to lock you in!'

I stood clumsily by the door.

'What are you waiting for, sit down!'

'Yes, dad.'

This injustice made my blood boil over, but I had to contain myself. I knew I wouldn't get anywhere with him. I decided to take the matter up with my mother.

'Mum,' I said to her when I came back from school on the following day, 'the club meets from five till seven. How can I be at home at seven, you tell me?'

'You know your father is strict about supper.'

'Yes, I understand, but he sent me to this wretched club, he wants me to go, how can I get up and leave in the middle of a lecture because my father wants me home at seven and not ten minutes later. You must agree with me … '

'Will you stop arguing! Leave me alone!'

I tried, again, with my father in the evening. But as soon as he realised what I was going to talk about he said: 'We eat at seven. That's all.'

As soon as I walked into the Club on the following Monday, I bumped into Lilian who seemed to have been waiting for me.

'Why didn't you come on Thursday?' she asked, 'Were you not well, or something?'

'I didn't have the necessary gear for gym. I don't know where to find plimsolls.'

'I can get them for you; we have them at the factory store.'

'Factory store?'

'Yes, didn't I tell you, I work in a factory.'

This statement was said with a great degree of pride.

'What sort of factory?'

'We make various tin receptacles.'

'What can you do in such a factory?'

'I operate an enormous machine. It's fascinating. Do you want to come and see, sometime?'

'I'd love to, perhaps during the summer holidays. I have never met a girl who works in a factory. What about school?'

'I have finished that, silly! I am twenty years old!'

'Twenty! How wonderful. I wish I were twenty.' I said dreamily.

'Why, what's so special about being twenty?'

'Because if you are older, people take more notice of you.'

'Oh, I don't know about that. Tell me, what do you think of our leader/lecturer? Did you know that he is a doctor, specialising in gynaecology?'

I didn't exactly know what that was, but I knew that gynaecologists were women's doctors, and that they examined you 'there'.

'Fancy that!'

'I, personally, don't like him at all. He is bigoted. I only came out of curiosity. You see, my father is a green grocer and all he wants for me is to marry a Jewish green grocer, have a flock of Jewish kids and be a nice Jewish housewife. Well, I want more from life than that!' I listened to her, intrigued, interested.

'How about you?' Lilian asked.'

'I don't know what my father wants for me. Sometimes he says that I should become his secretary and carry his brief case and type his letters.'

'That's not much of a future for you! And what do you want?'

'I think I would like to go to university.'

'Yes, you would do,' Lilian looked at me, 'you are an academic. If you ask me, it's a waste of time. While you waste your youth buried in books, which are soul destroying anyway, the world is making large strides forward, great things are happening, and you – you are left behind. You emerge at the end of your studies, pale from sitting in dusty libraries, bespectacled, with greasy hair and unable to cope with the events that just pass you by.'

I had never heard anybody saying anything remotely similar in all my life. I felt that she had a good point, which I knew I couldn't tackle. I said hesitantly:

'You want to … be involved with … progress?'

'Yes! And I am contributing directly to the development of our country.

We will have heavy industry before long and won't have to depend on the rich nations any longer, on the contrary – they will be purchasing our produce and we will be benefiting from the foreign currency which, in turn will be used for further development.'

This sounded like a lot of communist propaganda to me; quite stirring though, but I was afraid to argue, in case she was a provocateur. In any case, it was time to go in for our lecture .The lecture was on the structure of the Israeli Government; unfortunately, I could only half listen because my mind was on the clock. At a quarter to seven, I plucked up courage, got up and making my way towards the door whispered, looking furtively at Moshe, the lecturer:

'Sorry ... have to ... ' and shrugging, in an attempt to indicate that there was nothing I could do, I left.

'Very good!' said my father, looking at his watch. 'Very good indeed, you see that you can do it if you want to!'

'I interrupted very rudely .... '

'It doesn't matter how you did it – you did it, and it is possible.'

I gave up.

I told Mimi and Annie about my sudden Jewish activities, as I called them, with a degree of embarrassment, which I tried to conceal by being light hearted about it. Mimi knew me too well.

'You are not enjoying it one bit!'

'Well, it has its interests.'

'I know, your father made you do it. Don't worry!' she said quickly before I could say anything.

'My father is the same. Why do you think he introduced me last year to that boy I mentioned? Because they were Methodists, that's why. Parents are like that. Don't take any notice.'

'How can you say that? How can one not take any notice, when my whole life is decided by them without as much as a thought about my own wishes!'

'Come on, if it were that bad, you wouldn't have gone.'

'Quite frankly anything that takes me away from home is acceptable to me.'

We didn't discuss the subject any longer.

Chapter Ten

Summertime

Now that the warm days were back, Mimi, Annie and sometimes Mimi's sister and her mother, all went to the swimming pool. I wanted to go with them, but my mother wouldn't let me.

'First of all, you have to study for exams and secondly, only loose women go to those places. Once the term finishes, you will be able to go out with your friends from Maccabi, I promise.'

One afternoon, Mimi and I came back from a short walk at the Alexander Nevsky garden and we had, as usual, stopped outside Doctor Long for a final chat. The sun was still high in the sky and suddenly, I took a decision.

'Mimi,' I asked her, 'do you have an old swimming costume?'

'Yes I do. Why?'

'Would you lend it to me?'

'But it's … far too big for you. No, wait on, I have another one, an older one, when I was … smaller. Why?'

'Let's go to the swimming pool tomorrow! Please!'

'With pleasure, but it is an old suit!

'I don't care, provided I wear something.'

'What will you tell your mother?'

'I'll tell her that you and I are spending the afternoon at Annie's.'

'Fine. What time will you come?'

I thought for a moment.

'I better tell my mother that we are spending the morning until early afternoon together, what do you say?'

'This sounds better, it will allow us longer.'

'Right. I'll be at your place at 10am.'

'Fabulous, see you!'

Mimi's old swimming suit fitted perfectly, and that was because it was of the type criss-crossed with elastic thread – it would fit anyone. It is true, though, that the elastic wasn't put to too much of a test on me.

The swimming pool was a half hour's tram journey and it was called Diana Baths. We paid at the entrance and went into the section marked 'Ladies'.

'They haven't changed that to 'Comrades'!' I said and we laughed – there is no masculine and feminine to 'Comrade'. We were given a cubicle each and a key on an elastic band. I undressed and met Mimi outside. She had slung the elastic band with the key around her ankle. It looked very 'with it' and I did the same. I felt terribly self-conscious, being half naked like that, in front of other people, but Mimi's self-confidence, and the fact that no one was actually staring at me, put me at ease. We walked out and found ourselves on a terrace overlooking the pools. The view was magnificent. There were three pools whose perfectly blue water scintillated in the sun. A young man was getting ready to jump from what seemed to me a tremendous height, into the water. I watched his slender body, wearing the briefest of briefs, compose itself, his arms extend, become completely immobile for a few seconds, then with a leap he did a beautiful somersault and dived in, in a perfect vertical line, his arms extended. I gasped.

Mimi pulled me out of my reverie:

'Come on, let's find ourselves a nice spot.'

The pools were surrounded by a tiled area, but further away, it was all green lawns and trees.

'I prefer the grass myself, or maybe you want a deck chair?' Mimi asked.

'No, no, the grass is fine for me.'

We found a spot, somewhat distant from the pools, Mimi spread her large towel, we sat down and she handed me a bottle of sun tan lotion:

'Here, put some on, otherwise you will get burnt. You are as white as milk.'

I did as she told me, then she did my back and I did hers as she lay down on her stomach, but I remained seated, watching avidly everything that was going on.

People, many people, some young, and some, not so young, children, men, women, jumping into the water, splashing, laughing. Didn't they have worries? Were they all loose? But how about the people with children, surely they were respectable? Mimi got me out of my reflections:

'Come on, let's go in and cool off a bit.'

'I can't swim.'

'You don't have to. You can stay in the shallow end and just play around, it's relaxing and fun.'

The water seemed very cold at first. I held the rail and Mimi showed me how to let my body float. It was a fantastic sensation – the cool water on my skin, the weightlessness of my body, the warmth of the sun on my face, as I shut my eyes.

Mimi had gone away to swim, eventually she came back, stood by me, removing her rubber swimming hat, a little breathless:

'Hi, you seem to have enjoyed yourself!'

'Yes, I have. You?'

'Of course, but I am used to it. You seem to have come to life, look at you! your cheeks have acquired a little colour and your eyes are sparkling. You don't know what a miserable soul you are sometimes.'

She started to climb up the steps, and I followed her.

'What pains me, you see, is that it isn't you ... what I am trying to say is ... you are not a sad person by nature .... '

I understood where she was leading and didn't want the subject to develop.

'I know. Lets leave it at that, shall we.'

Mimi dried herself without saying a word. My parents came to my mind, I thought of the time.

'Should we go back?'

'As you wish.'

We arrived back at Mimi's at about two o'clock in the afternoon. I stayed a while, to put a mental distance between this morning's escapade and the time to face my mother. I went home before four o'clock. Luckily, my mother wasn't in; I went into my room and took the unfinished second volume of 'War and Peace' which we had to read for next term. I was quite immersed in it when the door opened and my mother came in.

'Hullo mum!' I said cheerfully, having, for an instant, genuinely forgotten that I was going to lie to her. She didn't answer; she took a step towards me. I put my book away, not realising that I was being scrutinised.

'Do you want me to help you with something?' I asked.

'Where have you been!' she didn't ask, she shouted, her jaws clenched. I got up, as she was getting nearer and bending over me. I was afraid she was going to hit me.

'Nowhere .... What do you mean ...?'

She straightened up.

'You,' she said, screwing up her eyes, 'you have been to the swimming pool!' Her hand extended quickly towards me and pulled my blouse away from my neck. I just stood there, incapable of moving or talking.

'You are all red! You have been to the swimming pool with that slut!' I took a step back. She went on: 'Speak up! You slut!'

'We ... we sat in the park for a while ... my lie was too week, even I could tell.

'Take your clothes off! Go on, quickly!'

I didn't move.

'Do as you are told! and if you are lying to me, I will wring your neck! You should know better than lie to me!'

Tears burned my eye-lids as I undid the buttons of my blouse. I took it off slowly, baring my arms and shoulders. I took my skirt off, as she motioned me to do so. The sun had outlined the swimming suit, I was as red as an oyster. The truth was all there. I felt defeated, humiliated.

'You, you lied!'

I looked at her. So much venom, so much hatred. Then, unexpectedly, I felt something inside me stirring, revolting.

'You made me lie,' I shouted at her, 'You wouldn't let me go, you don't let me do anything. I don't want to lie to you! You make me!'

'You are getting more and more impertinent with every passing day. We will have to wait and see what your father will have to say about it.'

'Mum, it's such a nice place! Why shouldn't we go together, like other people? It's so enjoyable, so carefree!'

'Indecent, that's what it is!'

'But families go there together – husbands and wives and children!'

'Expose their bodies, naked, in front of each other, disgusting!' She went towards the door, 'Don't think that this will pass without punishment! You will learn and remember to obey and do as you are told. I know better than you. I am your mother!'

She walked out, slamming the door.

Chapter Eleven

Are we going to Emigrate?

During the summer, we received two more negative replies to my father's applications for emigration. With each refusal, I felt reassured and rather pleased at my father's defeats. A topic my parents often discussed at table was Uncle Isaac and his failure to reply to my father's numerous letters, neither did any of the other members of the family give my parents information about how they had settled down, or what would be in store for us.

Mimi and Annie went to the country for a few weeks and my only social life was narrowed down to the visits to the Club. The Club met in the usual way with the added Sunday meetings for recreation at members' homes. I was not allowed to go out on Sundays without my parents. I pleaded with them, reminded them of their own promise and in the end they agreed to let me go from four until six. The Club didn't meet until five. I didn't tell them that, and went out at four and spent that hour sometimes on my own, in the garden square, enjoying the sun and the trees and the birds; sometimes Lilian met me and we chatted for an hour before we went to wherever the Club was meeting. I wasn't particularly sorry that I could only spend an hour with the group, because I didn't like them particularly. I found the girls spoilt and vain, and the boys dull.

Two days before the school term was due to start, our permission to emigrate arrived. Having received six refusals in seven months, the permission took me by surprise. My father, jubilant, made immediate enquiries and found out that a ship was leaving Varna for Haifa in three weeks' time, taking cargo and emigrants on board. My father decided that we would be on that ship. We were allowed 100 kilos luggage between the three of us, and we could send as much as we wanted by freight.

I tried to conceal my feelings from my parents, because I realised that I was being selfish. I went to tell Mimi.

'You lucky sod!' she said.

She had just come back from the country looking tanned and lovely. Her mother came to talk to us:

'Why do you feel so bad emigrating?' she asked me, 'What future can you hope for here?'

'I know it is stupid, I know I can't expect my father to accept being a labourer all his life; I don't know what frightens me, but I feel frightened.'

'It's a new country,' Mimi's mother said, 'with new people, and new opportunities. You will learn Hebrew in no time and then – the world is yours! University, jobs, you name it – it's a free world! You don't remember life before the war, you don't know what being free means. There – you will be free. Emigration is difficult at the best of times, you will feel at the beginning like an uprooted plant. But you are young, you will soon grow new roots …I was crying. How wonderful it was to be spoken to, told things. I got up and kissed her. She patted my cheek, 'It's the insecurity of your age, it will pass. After all, you are not alone, are you?'

I shook my head.

'You will write and tell us, won't you?' said Mimi.

'If I can afford the stamps.'

I walked up to the Alexander Nevsky square. I sat on a bench and looked around. The linden trees were crowned with luxuriant foliage, but some rusty leaves, dried and crumbled chased each other along the pavements, gently pushed by the evening breeze. The sun was setting behind the Cathedral, lighting as it did, its golden domes and stained glass windows with a thousand lights. I squinted at the view, took a deep breath in, in an attempt to enhance the image by taking in its scent, and engrave it on my memory; the scent of the linden trees in blossom, belonging to the spring, which I would not be here next year to see and smell; I had to imagine it now, in the fall, to complete my picture and take it away with me.

The days that followed were full of feverish preparations. My father purchased three kit bags which were to contain our personal belongings to be taken with us on the voyage. He had two enormous crates made for our furniture to be sent by freight. They were placed in the back yard, near the church entrance. One of them was literally as large as a room, the other, although smaller, could still take two people standing in it.

'How are you going to address those, dad? 'Tel Aviv beach'?'

'Don't be silly, by the time they will arrive we will have a home.'

'How? With what money?'

'Leave this to me.'

I went to school. It seemed impossible to me that in less than three weeks I would not be here any longer; I would be gone, forever perhaps.

'You are mad!' people kept telling me at school, 'why waste your time here?'

Eventually, time became shorter, and I realised that I wanted to see everybody who had been a part of my life, just see them … say 'good bye'. After all, I was leaving a part of me behind too.

I rang up Vlady.

'Hi!' he greeted me in his casual, jovial way. 'How are you?'

'I don't know, a little mixed up I suppose. Listen, remember that film you mentioned once, do you still want to go?'

'Yessssirrreeee! When? Tomorrow?'

'Could it be on Sunday?'

'Sunday it is! Anything special you want to see?'

'I leave the choice to you. I am easy.'

'You don't sound right. Is anything the matter?'

'Well, it is and it isn't. I am leaving … emigrating …. '

'When?'

'Soon. In ten days' time I think.'

'So, there is just one Sunday?'

'Yes. I can only go to an afternoon show, my parents … '

'Yes, I know. Listen, I'll meet you around 2pm, at the Nevsky garden on Sunday.'

'Yes.'

'See you then.'

'See you.'

I had it all worked out. As far as my parents were concerned, I was being taken out by my friends, Mimi and Annie, as a farewell treat. I was sure I could rely on my friends, besides, I somehow didn't care too much if I were found out. This was what I wanted to do and I was going to do it.

When I mentioned my plans for the following Sunday to Mimi, she told me that the class were preparing a farewell party for me. I was surprised.

'For me?' I asked rather stupidly.

'Yes, for you.'

'As though anyone would miss me.'

'Oh, spare me the insecurity bit, will you!' then she added in a softer tone, 'I will miss you.'

'I will miss you too.' I said, 'To think that it all started because of the boys.'

'Yes.'

'Did you know that in Israel girls go to the Army?' I asked.

'Yes. That would be something, wouldn't it?'

'Yes. And my father will have no say in it!'

'Yes.'

'I have never seen the sea.'

'Oh, you will love it. I have only seen our Black Sea, but you will go over the Bosphorus and the Aegean and the Med! I am sure you will love it!'

I wanted to see Lilian before I left, but didn't feel like going to the Club and went to her home instead. I told my mother I was going to the Club, surprising myself at the ease with which I lied.

Lilian had just come home from work.

'You! How lovely to see you! Wait until I wash my hands, then we can go and sit in the garden. Have you got time?'

'Yes. Don't worry.'

She ushered me in the lounge. It was full of photographs slid under the glass on the table top; clay ornaments, which I found rather amusing and realised that my mother would call them 'common'.

'Come on, I am ready.' Lilian appeared, refreshed and changed into a light cotton dress. She tucked her arm under mine, and began talking quickly:

'You have no idea what's happened to me! I am dying to tell you. I am in love! I am the happiest girl in the whole world. I have a lover!'

'Is this true? Who is he?'

'The most wonderful person you have ever met! And he loves me so! He carries me as though I am weightless!'

'Are you going to get married?'

'My poor little girl, how old fashioned you are! I am happy, he has made a woman out of me, a real woman! Oh, if you knew what it feels like! But I am shocking you …. '

'No, not at all.'

'Yes, I am. Tell me about you, how are you?'

'I just came to say good bye.'

'What do you mean?'

'We are emigrating.'

'When?'

'Too soon.'

'I am so sorry to lose you … I kept chatting away … excuse me … oh, I am sorry. Are you ready?'

'Ready for what?'

'Ready to leave all this, to start a new life?'

'No, I don't think I am. Lilly, I can be frank with you now, I am not a communist and I hate it here, I honestly do, but Israel … it seems so far away … so unknown … and I know I will hate it too!'

'I am not much of a communist myself, so you mustn't worry. It was just to spite my father, I suppose … come to think of it, I might emigrate as well.'

'I must be on my way now.'

Lilian came with me to the tram stop.

'I wish you all the happiness in the world, you deserve it.'

'Thanks, Lilly, same to you and your … lover.'

I got on the tram and she waved:

'Take care!'

The tram turned round the corner and she disappeared from my view.

Ж

I left at ten minutes to two on Sunday afternoon. It was no

more than a three minutes' walk to Mimi's. I took as long as I could, walked into the front door, in case my parents were looking at me through our windows. I knew that Mimi and her family had gone to the country and there was no point going upstairs.

I walked out through the back, into the narrow street, turned left and up, towards Nevsky Square. A voice, next to me, startled me:

'Hullo!' It was Vlady, he had just caught up with me.

'Hi!'

'Good to see you. I got us some theatre seats. I hope you don't mind it's not the cinema.'

'Not at all, on the contrary. What are we going to see?'

'The Seagull, at the National. It's a matinee, it starts at three.'

'Great, I haven't seen it, but I have read it.'

'We have plenty of time, shall we go for a walk?'

'Yes. Let's.'

We walked up towards the now deserted 'promenade', and down the Avenue towards the Park.

'How are your preparations going?' Vlady asked.

'Don't remind me. My parents are busy with that, it's their department. I am still going to school.'

'You are mad.'

'I know.'

'Say, are you going to be a soldier? A chap from our college emigrated last year; from what I can tell from his letters – he is very happy. He is in the Army and, he says, they have girls there too!'

'Yes. This is probably the only thing I am looking forward to.'

'Obviously, you know very little about armies.'

'Why?'

'Because the army is not a boarding school you know. In the Army, you get up at the crack of dawn, there is training to exhaustion, and rigorous discipline.'

'Any discipline would be better than my parents'.'

'Is it as bad as that?'

'Pretty bad.'

'You mustn't take too much to heart. Let them 'bla-bla' and you do your own thing.'

'Easier said than done.'

'Let's turn back. We have quite a walk to the theatre.'

'OK.'

I had been to the National Theatre many times. Ever since I was a young child; my mother used to take me to Sunday morning children's performances. I had also been to the Opera many times. But now, it was different. I wasn't being taken to be educated, but to be entertained. I wasn't being taken here, because I couldn't be left alone at home, but because my company was wanted. And what a difference that made! The plush seats, the red carpets, the gilded mouldings over the tapestry-like wallpapers weren't intimidating. They were there to please me, to enrich my experience of the afternoon, to embellish my entertainment.

I took Vlady's arm.

'I am going to enjoy this very much' I said.

We found our seats. Vlady lowered mine and waited for me to sit down, then sat next to me.

'Can you see?' he asked. It was only the 'safety curtain', but I could see fine!

The actors took many curtain calls at the end, and I clapped tirelessly. Outside, we found it was still daylight. It was a quarter to six.

'Shall we go for a walk, or is your time limited?' Vlady asked me.

'It is limited, I am leaving in a week's time!'

'Do you want to go to the park?'

Only now, I realised that my remark might have sounded

flippant.

'What's the matter?' asked Vlady, 'are you having second thoughts?'

Was I so transparent?

'I haven't even had first thoughts!'

'Look,' he suggested, 'lets go and sit at Nevsky's for as long as you wish, OK?'

'Let's.'

We walked quietly for a while.

'I am very sorry you are leaving the country.' Vlady said.

'I don't want to go.'

'Then – stay!'

'How can I! On my own? They'll never let me.'

Vlady looked at me intently and I couldn't sustain his glance.

'You are very … you are a very frightened young girl, aren't you?'

'What makes you say that?'

'A few things. For instance, just then, when I suggested a walk in the park, it was as though I had made some indecent proposition to you; and then … when I kissed you, remember?'

'Yes.' I whispered, 'as though I could ever forget!' I thought, but he didn't know.

'Well, tell me, what is it that frightens you in this way? Do you know?'

'Are you really asking me?'

'Yes, I am.'

'To tell the truth … I don't really know … it's all very confusing; besides, I don't really understand why you want to bother with me.'

'Are you really asking me?' he mimicked me.

'Yes, I am.'

'Because you are worth bothering with; at least to me you are.' He paused a moment and added: 'I had hoped that you enjoyed my kissing you …. '

'You still haven't told me why I am worth bothering with?'

'Because you are! You are … different, you are witty and you have brains and … I'll give you an instance; when you rang me, you openly asked me what you wanted to ask me. You didn't beat around the bush, so to say, you didn't invent stories awaiting for me to ask you …. '

'Why should I do that?'

'Because it's you! All other girls do it! And another thing, you came on time. Girls never do. They just don't. They can leave a chap waiting for hours, on purpose, just for the … well, I don't know what kick it gives them, that's how girls are.'

'Really?'

'Really. You are so honest,' he looked at me; there was real warmth in his eyes, and affection, 'I don't profess to know much,' he went on, 'but I think that … you must allow yourself to feel things more. You are so afraid! You are on your guard all the time.'

'Yes, perhaps you are right, but isn't it also true that boys take advantage of girls. That given half a chance they will squeeze a girl in a dark corner and … '

'Not if she doesn't want it!' Vlady interrupted, 'At least I don't do it, and most certainly not with you. Because you see, while other girls pretend not to want it, all they do is – delay; they want to be begged, forced even, provided it doesn't appear that it's their decision, their own doing. It isn't so with you. I am sure that when the time comes, and you will want to, you will go ahead and do it, whatever it is.' He lifted his hand to stop me interrupting, 'I am not talking only about sex. I am talking about everything. To go back to my suggestion to go to the park. I didn't have any schemes in mind. I like the park, I want to go there with you. I also want to hold you, and kiss you and – don't run away – make love to you. But I wouldn't dream of doing anything unless you wanted it too.'

I stood up.

'I don't want it. I want to go home.'

'You are so frightened. Sit down, I am not going to touch you.'

I sat down, a little away from him.

'Tell me, 'he went on 'why are you so frightened? What frightens you so much?'

I relaxed. I felt that I could speak truthfully, I trusted him.

'I honestly don't know. I can't even think it through, I don't know where to start. I am lost ... my parents don't tell me what is right and what is wrong – not to speak of the reasons why some things are right and others wrong – they just forbid me everything, 'en bloc'. It's so disconcerting. I don't want to make mistakes, but I know so little, I ... you told me, remember, when you kissed me ... that I was frightened of myself. You were right, you didn't frighten me! I got frightened of my own feelings ... I don't know what they mean.'

Vlady took my hand.

'I wish you weren't leaving.'

I shrugged.' I suppose I better go home now.'

'Thank you very much for spending this afternoon with me.' Vlady said.

'I enjoyed it too.'

'I wish you lots of luck in your new country.'

'Thank you.'

'I don't suppose there is a slim chance of you ever coming back again?'

'If there is, I can't see it at the moment.'

'May I kiss you good bye?'

'Yes.'

He kissed me gently on the cheek. I kissed him too.

'Be happy.' he said.

'You too.'

I walked off, then turned and waved. Vlady stayed there, looking at me, and waving, until I turned round the corner.

Ж

Annie, Mimi, all the Stoylovs, Maria with the baby, Anastasia, and to our great surprise Comrade Rashkov (he insisted), all came to see us off at the Railway Station. We were getting an afternoon train to Varna, where we would board the cargo ship 'Bulgaria' in the morning. We would reach Haifa six days later. The crates, containing nearly all our belongings had been sent by freight, all we had with us were three tall, cumbersome kit-bags and a holdall for the immediately necessary toiletries.

We all lost each other on the tram, because there was a terrible crowd, but found each other again at the Railway Station. The men were carrying the kit-bags in a single file, with my father leading, to the platform, where people were already getting on the train.

The moment to say 'goodbye' had arrived. Everybody began kissing us in turn. I was aware of being kissed and words whispered in my ear. From where I stood, I could see the large clock on the wall, with it's large milky white face, yellowing at the edges; the elaborately carved huge hands were spread out at a quarter to three.

' … won't you? … won't you?' I realised that Mrs. Stoylova was talking to me. The longer hand of the clock made a little nervous jump, just above her head, and the perfect 180° spread was broken. It was a fourteen minutes to three now.

'Yes, I will.' I said to her, not having a clue as to what she had said. Everybody was crying, except the men and myself.

'You will write and tell us all about it, won't you?' Annie said.

'Yes, yes, tell us about the boys there.'

'I will.'

I heard a whistle.

'Come on! On board!' said my father. It was thirteen minutes to three now. I jumped back into Mimi's arms, held her tightly and finally began to cry.

'I don't want to go ... I don't want to go!' I sobbed into her shoulder.

'It will be all right once you are there .... ' Mimi said, but she was crying as well, and didn't sound convincing at all.

At this point, Comrade Rashkov took me in his arms:

'Look, we know you love this country, it is your country, and you love us, because we are your friends, and we love you; but you ought to believe me when I say to you that there is no future for you here. None whatever.'

I nodded. I regretted the salt and pepper I had put in his coffee.

'Come on!' my father shouted from the window of the carriage.

'I trust you won't repeat what I have just told you to no one. You know what awaits me if you do. On board ship, all the way to Israel – you will still be on Bulgarian territory – so watch it.'

'Come on!' my father reiterated.

I ran from one to the other, kissed them all once more and then got on the train. There was another whistle and the train began to move slowly, very slowly. I looked at my friends on the platform. They waved and I waved back. My eyes caught sight of the clock; it's hands were at a right angle now. It was exactly three o'clock.

A moment later the outskirts of Sofia were parading outside the window. I tried to lean out and see, once more, the City, but the train had taken a turning and all I saw were a few houses and endless fields.

We reached Varna at sunrise, our hips stiff from the long train journey and the uncomfortable positions we had slept in. We couldn't afford the 'wagon-lits'

From the station, we took a cab to the port. Once there, we

realised that most of the passengers on the train, were fellow emigrants. At the port, we were told that we couldn't embark yet. We were asked to come back at noon. We were standing in a large hangar type building, and through a wide opening, behind the man who was talking to my father, I had my first glimpse of the sea. It wasn't blue, as I had seen it in the pictures. It was gray-green and its surface, in its constant movement, seemed more like solid matter, than a large expanse of water.

It was a cold November morning. The wind was blowing from the sea, carrying a smell of sea-weed and a taste of salt. We found an open café and had breakfast. We visited the Marine Museum and Gardens; we saw the pier at the end of which, my father informed us, there had been a casino before. It was closed now.

We met another emigrant family that my parents knew.

'Let's go to the Golden Sands.' the man suggested.

'It's risky.' my father said. 'We might miss the ship.'

The family had a son, a huge boy, probably 18 or 19 years old. 'Let's go for a swim.' he said to me.

I disliked his tone, his familiarity and generally – him.

'Youngsters, will be youngsters.' said his mother condescendingly.

'I don't feel like it, thank you.' I said before my father could intervene.

We walked off.

At noon, we returned to the port.

'Come back at four.' we were told.

'We could go to the Golden Sands.' I said. I had heard that it was a most beautiful spot

We sat on our kit-bags. I had a book in my holdall.

At four o'clock we were turned away again. No explanation was given. We kept returning to the port three times a day for the following four days. We stayed at a nearby hotel; so did all the other would be passengers. Rumours had it, that there was a movement of Soviet ships in the port, and that they didn't want anybody to see them. Every day, I wrote long letters to Mimi and Annie.

'One would think that you are in love with them!' mocked my father.

On the fifth day, we were allowed to embark. After long and tedious checks at the customs', all 150 or so of us finally climbed aboard the 'Bulgaria'. As we crowded the deck, a sailor shouted:

'Follow me!'

We followed him down narrow iron stairs, struggling with the kit-bags. The descent seemed endless. Finally he stopped and shouted:

'All women – here. The men – follow me!'

We found ourselves in a large hall, more like a hangar. There were three tiers of bunk bedss set snugly against the walls. On a pillar in the middle there was a notice: 'Fourth floor'.

'I'll come back as soon as I can.' said my father and followed the men.

We dragged one of the kit-bags (my father was struggling with the other two) as quickly as we could, to get a first and second tier bunk. I climbed above my mother's.

'Mum, does this mean that we are actually four floors down, under water?'

She looked around.

'It would seem so.'

'This is frightening.'

'It is.'

'Why didn't they put the cargo down here and give us more human conditions?'

'Emigrating isn't cruising.'

'You can say that again.'

My father arrived, his forehead furrowed, 'Are you all right?' he knew how frightened of water my mother was.

'If you can call this all right ... then, we are.' she said.

'Don't worry my darling. It will soon be over, and we will be free.'

My mother shrugged.

There was an upsurge of voices and movement around us.

'I will need my pyjamas a towel and my tooth brush.' said my father. 'Let's go upstairs and see Varna again!' someone shouted.

Preoccupied with my immediate surroundings, I had forgotten that we would move away any moment now.

'Let's go up, please!' I asked of my parents.

'All right, all right. No need to get all worked up.'

It was completely dark now. The lights twinkled in a haphazard pattern. Sometimes, one could follow the lights on a road. People were rushing around on the deck, some waving to relatives whom they couldn't possibly see, on shore. Somebody was singing a Hebrew song. Somebody was singing the Bulgarian national anthem. Someone shouted 'Hullo freedom!' and a voice retorted in the dark: 'You are still on Bulgarian territory mate, watch it!'

The ship's siren sounded. Powerful, deafening. It covered all other sounds. I put my hands over my ears. The town's lights began to recede; slowly at first, then faster and faster, until they became as small and distant as the stars in the clear autumn sky. The siren stopped as suddenly as it had started and for a moment the silence that followed seemed to be total, until voices, once again, imposed themselves, voices, and the dull thump of the engines. We had left Bulgaria.

I thought that I will never again see my friends, never sit, on a fine spring day, on a bench in the Alexander Nevsky garden and inhale the delicate scent of the linden trees in blossom; I shall never stroll past my former schools, never have anyone with whom to remember.

I ran downstairs blinded by tears, found my bunk, buried my face in the coarse gray blankets and cried bitterly.

BOOK THREE

Chapter One

We were Speaking a Foreign Language

The khaki lorry staggered along the streets of Haifa, its suspension stretched to the limit. There were two men up front, in the cabin and about fifty of us at the back, weary and exhausted, swayed to and fro as the lorry lurched from side to side. I was half sitting, half leaning on one of our kit-bags.

Tiredness prevented me from taking in the street scene but I couldn't help noticing every now and then, down a side street – the sunset. We were obviously travelling along a street parallel to the sea front. The street lights were coming on one by one and twilight was settling over the town.

Eventually we were out of town, and now to my right the sun – a fiery red ball – was about to dive into the sea, lighting it, as it did, with a million lights.

We had arrived at dawn, and now, after a long and exhausting day, we were being driven in a convoy of four lorries to a quarantine camp. To my left, above the Carmel mountain, the night had already begun to invade the sky. The dusk air was surprisingly warm and carried an unfamiliar delicate, scent.

Soon I saw row upon row of peculiar, rather small structures, which, as we came closer, I realised – were tents. They were in the same khaki colour that so many things seemed to be in. Surrounding the whole area where the tents were, was a tall barbed wire perimeter fence. The convoy slowed down and I saw the first lorry turn left into a dirt road. We passed through a gate and drove for another hundred metres or so, and one after the other, the lorries came to a noisy and shaky stop, raising clouds of dust.

The driver came round and opened the flap for us to jump out. Kit bags were passed down, women screamed, children cried, older people complained of aching limbs.

'Here we are,' said my mother once we had assembled our kit-bags and were awaiting further instructions, 'behind barbed wire. Just like the Nazi camps. We have to come to Israel, to experience this.'

'It's only quarantine. They have to make sure that no disease is brought into the country. You heard what the man said this morning.' my father said.

'Forty days! Imprisoned behind barbed wire!'

'I have been behind barbed wire a lot longer than that!'

'No need to rub it in, I wasn't exactly on holiday then!'

The man who had accompanied us from the port, tried to impose his voice over the noise:

'Form a queue, please! Form a single file queue. Otherwise we will never be able to sort you out!'

My parents stopped arguing and got into the line. I stood behind my mother; my father stood behind me. Each of us in charge of a kit-bag, holding it by its strings. Eventually there was an orderly queue, and the 'sorting out' began.

Men were rushing around, gesticulating, talking loudly, laughing. Such laughter! I had never heard such laughter, or if I had, I couldn't recall anyone laughing quite like them: loudly, freely, almost indecently. They looked so strange, so alike, in their knee-length khaki shorts, thick khaki socks folded at the knees, and they all appeared to have generous pot bellies about which they seemed totally uninhibited, and receding hair-lines, although I didn't think they were very old.

Finally our turn came. A tall younger man, whom I hadn't seen before stood in the doorway of the office:

'Three of you is it?' he asked in Bulgarian.

'You speak Bulgarian!' my father said, surprised.

'I am Bulgarian, like yourselves. Three of you – is it?'

'Yes.'

He turned to someone inside and said something in Hebrew and then added to my father in Bulgarian:

'Follow this chap, he will take you to your tent. The beds are there already.'

The chap emerged through a side door, three thin mattresses on his back.

We followed him, my father carrying two kit-bags; my mother and I struggling with the third.

'Here!' the man said, entering a tent and dumping the mattresses on one of the beds.

'Are you all Bulgarians here?' my father enquired.

'We only come to the camp when there is a ship from Bulgaria, to help out with the new immigrants. It would take ages otherwise. Two things you have to learn from the start in this country: time is money, and – be patient. See ya.'

The tent was shaped like a four sided pyramid and at the pointed top where its walls met, a paraffin-oil lamp hung on a hook. My father lit it. There were three metal beds – two next to each other and the third at their feet, leaving a narrow passage in between. We could easily stand up in the middle of the tent, but if we went towards the sides, we had to bend down. My father returned to the office for the blankets.

'Stop gaping and help me make the beds.' my mother said curtly.

I helped her put a mattress on each bed; we then extracted some sheets from one of the kit bags.

'See how right I was to take some sheets along.' my mother said. I didn't remember making any objections, but perhaps my father had, wanting to keep the kit-bags lighter. Anyway, the sheets were welcome now. My father returned with the blankets.

'We have to go to the 'kitchen' for dinner.'

He placed two blankets on each bed.

'It's only until eight o'clock and we will miss it. I am starving.'

'How can we leave here without locking up?'

'Oh, for Christ's sake!

The tent had two flaps and a couple of sets of strings. My father tied them.

'There is a special diet 'kitchen'.' he informed my mother as we walked in the semi-darkness.

'What sort of special diet? I might need a special diet. My stomach aches all the time.'

'I'll get you some food from there.'

'I must know what sort of a diet it is, don't you understand?'

'I'll ask. It may be for diabetics.'

'You ask.'

The 'kitchen' looked like a huge corrugated metal barrel, sawn in half length-wise and flattened onto the sand; two oval openings at each end, for doors, and a few port-holes on its sides for windows. Inside, two rows of tables and benches and a few people having their dinner. At the far end, there was a counter where we joined a queue for our food.

'I want a 'special diet' food.' my mother repeated.

'OK, you go and sit down, I'll fetch you a tray. I am sure they will allow me.'

'Ask what it is though. I don't want any old diet.'

My father returned with a tray, put it in front of my mother and sat down.

We had tea, margarine, green olives, a rather watery white

cheese and a boiled egg each. My mother had some boiled vegetables and a meat ball.

'There are two 'special diets' – one for diabetics and one for ulcers. I got you the ulcers' one.'

'All right.'

'It looks rather better than ours.'

'You ought to taste it.'

'What do you want! It's all cooked, served on a tray, special diet as well, and what is more – free! and you grumble! Women!'

Two tables away from us, a large family were talking loudly in a foreign language.

'What language is that?' I asked.

'Arabic.'

'But, I thought that there are no Arabs here …? '

'They are Jews, silly.'

'Arab Jews?'

'Aren't we Bulgarian Jews?'

It dawned on me, that we too, were speaking a foreign language! Our dinner finished, we left the 'kitchen' and headed for our tent.

The lorries had gone and the camp was relatively quiet. Tall lamp posts spread strong electric light over the whole area; the air was strangely still and the sky, now ink-blue was covered with stars. I had never seen so many stars and they seemed so near!

'Do you know what this scent is?' I asked, 'It's so delicate.'

'Orange blossom. It's probably the season now.'

'It's beautiful.'

I would have lost my way. All the tents were identical each row of the same length, but my father found the way. We didn't bother to light the lamp since we had to undress in the dark anyway. I put my pyjamas on and slid quickly under the blankets. Once the flaps were down, the air in the tent grew very stuffy with the heavy smell of tar. The mattress, through the sheet, smelled of straw and the blankets – of disinfectant.

I felt very tired; my whole body ached but I couldn't fall asleep. Scenes of the day flashed through my mind; the various smells, the voices and faces; the first sight of Haifa, spread over the mountain as seen from the sea.

The long queue at the end of which people seemed to vanish into a cubicle. Every now and then a man would look through the opening and shout:

'Next!'

When my turn finally came I was pulled behind a screen by a woman and before I had a chance to say a word she sprayed my hair, under my skirt, down the front and back of my blouse, some horrible white powder with a tin fly-tox type instrument. I learned later that it was a disinfectant called DDT.

I was pushed out through the opposite side of the cubicle where I found my mother waiting for me, shaking her skirt and sneezing. The queue went on from there, to, a desk, set in the middle of the deck, representing the immigration office, where we were issued with the necessary papers.

I listened for the camp's noises, but apart from some grass-hoppers and the very gentle murmur of the sea, I heard nothing. I tried to remember Haifa, but all I could summon up, was the flashing sunset and the flat roofs.

We were going to stay here for forty days. What would happen then? Where were we going to go? What did this country hold in store for us?

Mimi, Annie, Vlady, my school, Sofia – it was all so far away, as though in a different age, and even, had I believed in it – a different incarnation. I felt suspended between that distant past which I couldn't hold on to, and the present – so alien, I could hold on to it even less.

I must have fallen asleep because a scream, a child's scream, woke me up. I sat up and listened. The scream died away only to be renewed, high pitched and whining. My stomach contracted painfully.

'Why are they letting that child scream like this?'

'Sh … sh … go to sleep.' my father said quietly. 'It's not a child. It's a jackal. Don't be afraid.'

I lay back on my bed. I remembered the drawing in my Natural Science book and the information that went with it.

'Don't worry,' my father went on, 'it doesn't attack people. It only eats the dead.'

'I know.'

I tucked my head under the blankets and shut my eyes, but it was a long time before eventually I fell asleep.

In the morning, the blazing sun had intensified the smell of tar in the tent and we all woke up with headaches. In the white light that filtered in through the gaps, we realised that the tent had flaps all along its bottom edges. They could be folded and tied up, thus letting air in, but at the same time exposing our feet to the gaze of people outside.

'Turn away,' my father told me, 'I'll tie these things up.'

'Where can we get some water? I want to take an aspirin.' my mother moaned.

'I'll find you some water.' my father said.

After a while, having estimated that he must have finished buttoning his trousers, I turned back; he was tying the flaps up one by one and we could feel immediately the influx of fresh air and bright light.

'While you two get dressed,' said my father when he had finished, 'I'll investigate about having a wash. I'll also bring you some water for your aspirin.'

My dress was at the foot of my bed. It was all creased and soiled. My socks were dirty and I decided against wearing them, so I put my bare feet into my shoes which I found full of sand. My mother had dressed in the meantime and began making the beds. I went outside to have a look around.

Two tents away, I saw a woman in her bra and pants. I had never seen anyone so carelessly naked.

'Mum, mum,' I peeped into our tent, 'come and see – a woman in her bra and pants!'

My mother looked out and followed my glance:

'She must be Romanian. They are very loose women. Disgusting!'

My father came back.

'See those corrugated iron cubicles?' he pointed at the rows of cabins at the edge of the lines of tents. 'The white ones are toilets, the green ones – showers.'

'Is there any hot water?' my mother enquired.

'No, not yet, but they say that by mid-day the water gets very hot because the pipes run on the surface and the sun heats them.'

'Let's go for a wash and then – breakfast. I am hungry, an unhealthy kind of hunger.'

My mother handed us each a towel and we went towards the cabins.

There were more people in the 'kitchen' now, than we had seen the previous night and we realised that there were immigrants from many more different countries than we had imagined. The 'kitchen' was bubbling with the sound of languages, some of which I could recognise: Polish, Czech, Yugoslav dialects, French, German, Russian – and many others that I could not recognise but my father did: Arabic, Yiddish, Romanian. It was incredible!

'What a mixture of people! All those languages, all those countries!' I was fascinated.

'They don't necessarily come from the country you think they do.' explained my father, 'For instance, all the French spoken, I am sure is by immigrants from North African countries, others … '

'I am hungry.' my mother interrupted.

My father went to bring her, her special diet breakfast; when he came back, we went to queue up for ours. Soft boiled eggs, green olives, white cheese and tea.

On the tables there were bowls with oranges and grapefruit. The younger Bulgarian man we had met last night was there, supervising. He came up to us:

'How are you settling down?' he asked politely.

'OK.' answered my father.

'If you like to go to Town, tell me; I'll fix it for you.'

'But ... we are in quarantine. We are not supposed to ... '

'Rules and regulations are made to be broken.'

'No, thank you. We will do as we are told.'

'Anyway, should you change your mind, don't hesitate to ask me. The policeman at the gate owes me a favour.'

'Thank you, but no.'

The young man laughed. That carefree laughter.

'How are things in Bulgaria? I left two years ago.'

'Very good.' said my father quietly, having first looked over his shoulder.

The young man sat down on the bench, next to him and said softly:

'You are free now. You can talk. This is a free country, a democracy. You can curse the Government, if you wish, you can tell 'what for' even to Ben Gurion; nobody will take any notice. Nobody cares.'

'This will take some getting used to.' said my father, swallowing with difficulty.

'Life here is wild, wonderful. You can get anything you want if you are prepared to work for it, and you are free.' he got up, then looked at me: 'Perhaps I can show you Haifa some time.'

'No!' my father said quickly, 'she stays where her parents are!'

The young man turned to go away, and with a smile and a shrug said:

'You won't be able to accompany her to the Army though.'

'What sort of a quarantine is this, if it is so easy to get out.' my mother commented.

'Rubbish! He was just showing off.' said my father angrily.

After breakfast, we went back to the tent. It was nine o'clock and the sun was getting hot.

'If it is so hot in November, what will it be like in August?' said my mother.'

'I want to explore a little.' my father said.

'Don't be long I have a terrible stomach ache; I might need you.'

'Keep your mother company. I won't be long.' he wandered off.

'Let's get the clothes out of the kit-bags and air them.' my mother turned to me.

'What's the point, we will have to put them back in again.'

'Do as you are told.'

Sand had found its way onto the beds. We swept it away the best we could, then emptied the kit-bags on the beds.

Some children were playing outside the tent, making a terrible noise. Suddenly a rubber ball landed on the floor in the tent and splashed sand all over the place.

'Take that ball! Tell them to get lost!'

'Mother, I can't speak their language.'

Three small children, dressed in underpants and vests came running in, shouting loudly in some unfamiliar language, obviously asking for their ball.

'Don't give it to them! Let their mother come for it, let's see who she is!'

The small brown bodies looked dirty and their jet black, curly hair, sticky and unwashed.

'Don't they look strange.'

'They are Arabs.'

'They can't be. They must be Jews.'

The children were shouting; one of them started to climb up on one of the beds to look for his ball.

'Stop him! Give him his ball! Get rid of them!'

I gave the kid the ball; he grabbed it, poked out his tongue at me and then, they all ran.

'Bloody impertinent kids. How are we going to live with all these Eastern people, I fail to see.'

'Come on, mum, they are only kids.'

'Kids, kids! Their behaviour tells you what families they come from!' she sighed, 'Let's go back to our work.'

We shook everything before putting it back into the kit-bags, but we found that sand had got everywhere. It was so fine, that no matter how much we shook an item, there always seemed to be more coming out.

When we had finished and the strings were once more tied on the kit-bags, my mother sat on her bed.

'I have nausea.' she was holding her stomach.

My father returned.

'I have a surprise for you! Guess who I found – working here, at the camp?'

'I don't care, I feel sick.'

'I am sorry. Is there anything I can do?'

'What can you do. Whom have you found?'

'Sarah! Sarah Solomon, she works in the 'kitchen.'

'In the 'kitchen'? Doing what?'

'Washing up.'

'You are joking.'

'I am not. Come and see for yourself. They live in Haifa, and she works here.'

'What does Erica do?' I asked.

'Erica is on a kibbutz, studying Hebrew. And the young one goes to school, in Haifa.'

'What is he doing? Isn't he working at all?'

'Yes. He is a … sales assistant … at a grocer's shop. He doesn't speak Hebrew, well, not properly. Therefore he can't do anything else.'

'Working in a 'kitchen' …, ' my mother said thoughtfully, 'is this what we have come here to …? '

'Of course not. Not us anyway. Come on, she is waiting to see you.'

My mother, again, was reluctant to leave the tent because she couldn't 'lock' it. She had to give in eventually, for there was nothing else to do other than let the side-flaps down and tie the strings on the 'door'.

We went to the opposite end of the 'kitchen' where, through a large door we could see the actual cooking area. A few people were busy over the large stoves and sinks, their faces flushed with the heat. Mrs Solomon appeared at the door a wide smile on her face, wiping her hands on her blue apron.

'Thank God you are here! It's so good to see you!' She walked down the two steps and took my mother in her arms, kissed her on both cheeks talking all the time, 'We were so worried, leaving you all alone there how did you manage, God only knows .... '

Then it was my turn to be kissed.

'What a lovely young girl you have grown into!' she looked me up and down, holding me by my shoulders away from herself, 'a young woman! Good God!'

She had doubled in size. Her face was round and fleshy with two generous chins and her apron only covered the middle of her prominent belly.

'All's well that ends well!' she said now, realising that my mother was about to start crying.

'But Sarah ... you ... working – here?' my mother said, her throat tight.

'Oh, yes, I work here and my old man, who can't learn Hebrew because his brains are even smaller than mine, works in a grocer's shop, but we are making out all right. We are very happy here. Soon Erica will be able to go to a Secretarial school, our son is doing all right and he might even get a higher education, we have a lovely, comfortable home. We don't want more.'

I looked at her hands, while she was talking. They were red and swollen and the nails around the cuticles were black. She looked at my parents in turn and smiled:

'I can see you still have your old ideas. You will have to forget them if you want to make it here. You've left Bulgaria behind – you will have to leave all those old ideas behind too. Work isn't shameful – whatever it is.'

'My wife is not going to become a servant!'

'Maybe she won't.' Mrs. Solomon was looking intently at my father, 'I wish for her, that she doesn't become a servant. But for those who couldn't do otherwise, it isn't shameful, it isn't degrading. No work is degrading if you are earning your family's bread and butter.'

'But my health ... I haven't the health .... '

'You won't have to even think about it, I am telling you! Can't you trust me for a change? Now, Sarah, do you know anything about any of our family? Amelia and Dori for instance, do you know where they live?'

'As far as I know, they live in Jaffa. Most of the Bulgarians live there. Anyway, Amelia doesn't work because her husband, being an Ashkenazi and speaking Yiddish can get by without Hebrew. I think he works for the Jewish Agency. Her sister, on the other hand, they live on a farm, somewhere near Tiberias.'

'How can people become peasants when they have lived all their lives in the City?' I asked.

'Running a farm doesn't mean you are a peasant. Not here anyway. Besides, it is amazing what you can learn when you have no alternative.'

There was a heavy silence.

'Maybe' I said, just to break it.

'I must go back. Please excuse me.' she said to my parents, then turned to me: 'Why don't you come over to our place? Erica will be home this weekend; she will show you Haifa, I bet you are dying to get out of here.'

'Oh, I'd love to ... '

'She isn't going anywhere without us.' interrupted my father.

'Come on! She is a big girl now, you can't keep her tied to your wrist all the time!'

'I know how to bring up my own child.'

I thought that Mrs. Solomon would take offence at my father's rather brusque remarks, but she laughed instead:

'Oh, god, you will have to change here you know! Even to me you look old-fashioned! You will have to recognise the sort of new life you have come to and shake off the old taboos.' I felt in her voice that she felt sorry for my parents, but they didn't seem to realise it. 'Excuse me, I really must go in now. Please pop in again.'

She went in and I heard her say something in Hebrew.

'My stomach aches.' said my mother, 'I am thirsty.'

'Have a grapefruit. They say it's good for the stomach.'

'Let's go back, I want to lie down.'

'May I go and look at the sea for a while?' I asked.

'All right, but don't be long. Your mother might need you. Besides it will be time for lunch soon.'

'Yes father.' I said.

It was only ten o'clock. I watched them walk away, my mother leaning on my father. I looked at them for a while, wondering what problems there were in store for me and how I would be able, if at all, to deal with them.

Eventually I walked in the opposite direction, towards the sea. I tried to walk slowly, to avoid spraying sand, but the small particles found their way into my shoes and cut into my skin like razor blades. I stopped at the barbed wire and gazed at the scintillating blue expanse of the Mediterranean. I knew now that it would be there every day of my life, that I would be able to look at its shimmering surface, at the sun – setting into it, lighting a kaleidoscope of colour. I knew that I would never tire of gazing at it and its beauty would forever fascinate me. Just like during the voyage, which was when I had my first glimpse of the sea, poems and songs praising its beauty, its mystery, came to my mind; the Boat of Pushkin's poem, (or was it Lermontov's?) with its white sails appearing on the horizon ... 'lonely in the morning haze, where is it going, what is it seeking?'

Suddenly I became aware that someone was talking to me. I turned around and saw a young man standing behind me, smiling and saying something in Hebrew. I, not understanding a word, smiled back and shrugged helplessly. He then started to speak to me in English, but my English was very poor then and I could only understand a few odd words. I was hoping that he would give up, as there was no chance of a conversation; but he went on and on. I thought that it would be very rude to just walk away. It was getting quite frustrating when I saw the young Bulgarian coming towards us.

'Hi!' he said to me in Bulgarian, 'What's the matter, you look a little lost?'

'I don't know what he wants ... I can't understand him at all .... '

He turned to the young man in Hebrew. They spoke for a while, then the young man bowed to me very respectfully, turned around and walked away. The Bulgarian was laughing his head off.

'Please, tell me what was that all about?'

'He wants ... to ... marry you .... ' he managed to say whilst still laughing.

'What?'

'Yes, seriously ... he comes from Iraq ..., ' he was still choking with laughter, 'and girls there have dark skins. He likes your fair skin and wants to marry you.'

'You must be joking! He doesn't even know me, how can he want to marry me?'

'You have a lot to learn about people and their customs.'

'This is incredible. But what did you tell him in the end? Why did he give up so suddenly?'

'I told him that you were engaged.'

'Incredible. Thank you very much for helping me.'

'Not at all. Not at all. My invitation to show you Haifa still stands, but ..., ' he had noticed my father approaching and whispered, 'you don't seem to be able to shake your old man off!'

'See you.' I said so that my father could hear me.

The Bulgarian, whose name I never learned, bowed to my father. Instead of greeting him; my father gave him a cold look back.

'Come back quickly! Your mother is worried about you!'

I followed him toward the tent, still amused by the incident.

'You mustn't wander off like this again. We must try and spare your mother's nerves. She isn't well.'

I decided to keep the incident to myself.

The camp seemed to have a life of its own, the rhythm of which was established by the visits to the 'kitchen'. It was a life of which we never became a part.

After breakfast, men gathered outside tents, sitting on make-shift stools or benches, playing backgammon, or cards or chess; women sat around and chatted, some, holding babies in their arms. Young people gathered too, walked together or sat and talked; occasionally I would hear them laugh, or sing songs accompanied by the boy who played the guitar. I could hear them at night, when I was in bed; eventually I memorised the tunes.

My mother established a routine too, involving all of us in the fight against the sand. Every morning, after breakfast, my father would be given all the blankets and sheets to take outside the tent. I would join him and he would hand me, one by one, first the sheets, then the blankets to shake thoroughly and hand back to my mother inside the tent. She had in the meantime, turned the mattresses over – 'the only way to make sure there is no sand on them,' – and then, she would make the beds.

Things didn't always go as smoothly as I would have liked. A corner of a sheet or a blanket would sweep the ground as I was shaking it, and like in my childhood, my mother would see it even though she was inside the tent.

'Can't you ever concentrate on what you are doing! Must you always gape at the sky!'

This was most unjust, because I really tried to do well. One day I found an empty crate behind the 'kitchen', and pointing at it with a smile, wider than necessary, to compensate for language, to the man standing at the doorway, I then pointed at myself, meaning: 'May I have it?' He understood and nodded.

From then on, I stood on the crate whilst shaking the bedclothes.

My mother asked Mrs. Solomon to bring us a basin, which she did, and from then on we washed our feet before going to bed, making sure we didn't touch the ground after the wash. Yet, every night, there was still some sand in our beds.

With the money we had received on our arrival – one Israeli pound per person – we could purchase such essentials as toothpaste and soap from the kiosk inside the camp. Every other day, we went to the 'washeteria' to wash our clothes. In order to wash my dress, I had to wear the old thick blue scratchy one, which looked even more awful after a month in the bottom of the kit-bag.

It was warm enough for early morning or the evening, but in the middle of the day when the sun became burning hot, I felt sticky and uncomfortable.

The white dress dried fairly quickly in the sun, and although it looked awfully creased, at least it smelled clean.

My mother was luckier in that she had a skirt and blouse; the skirt could only be brushed, but still looked quite good, only her blouse was creased.

'Is this how we are going to live from now on?' she often lamented, 'We came to be free, and look at us, behind barbed wires, living like cave-men.'

'Please don't worry my darling. I will get you out of here as soon as possible ... please be patient ... you'll see.'

'See, what? We haven't even been examined yet. When is it going to be? When I am six feet under ground.'

'Oh, please my love! Be patient ... remember what the man said ... we are not the only ones.'

'This is no comfort to me,' she shook her head.

We had been in Israel for three weeks when we were called to the doctor's room. The doctor examined each one of us in turn. I noticed that he paid special attention to my skin; then we were X-rayed and told to come back in a week's time for our release papers. The doctor was Bulgarian so there was no language problem. My father wanted to mention my mother's constant stomach complaint, but she stopped him with her thunderous eyes. He implored, I saw it in his eyes, but she refused. All this was done while the doctor was bent over his papers.

The medical examination over, we went to visit Mrs Solomon, whom I was now told, I could call Aunt Sarah.

'That's good,' she said, 'in a week you will be free to go.'

'Go where.'

'The best thing is to go to Maabara.'

'What's that?' my father asked.

'It's a camp, like this one, but you are free there. You can come and go as you please, there is a 'kitchen' there as well, which means that your food is free, and you can work and save. Many people live in Maabara for a few years before they save enough to put down on a flat or something.'

'How awful! Live in a tent for months! I couldn't – it would kill me.'

'Some people have to; if they have children they want to send to school'

'We won't live there for any length of time,' my father said, 'just as soon as I get in touch with my brother ... '

'Your brother! He won't do anything for us; haven't you got it through your thick head yet? Wasn't his silence in response to your letters eloquent enough?'

'He will sort himself out.' Aunt Sarah said to my mother.

'You'll never know what he might find in town. At least he speaks languages, not like the likes of us – with just Bulgarian as a baggage one can't get very far. Anyway, now that you have had your medicals, why don't you let the girl come over for the week end? Erica will be at home; she will take her around and show her the town. Why keep her here?'

'Oh, please let me go?'

My father hesitated and I realised that he was waiting for my mother to react first. My mother didn't.

'Where will she sleep?'

'We have a spare bed of course.'

'Please dad, please?'

'Ask your mother.'

'She can do as she pleases.'

'All right,' said my father, 'but for one day only.'

'Oh, thank you dad! Thank you mum!' I went to kiss them. My mother brushed me aside, her face expressionless.

'Cut it out,' my father said.

'I am not working tomorrow,' Aunt Sarah turned to me, 'I'll write the address down for you. The bus will take you from outside the camp right to our door. You can ask the conductor in Russian or French – somebody will understand you in the bus, if not the conductor himself. You can't get lost in this country. Do you think you can manage?'

'Of course I can.'

'How can she?' said my mother, 'She can't concentrate to do the simplest domestic jobs, you want her to find her way, all alone, across the country.'

I fell silent at that remark. Aunt Sarah looked intently at me for a moment, then said:

'Come on, she can ask the way! I am sure you can give her credit to do that.'

I felt, in my mother's silence, her impotence to react without exposing herself to further criticism. I felt ashamed that my own parents had so little confidence in me, but most of all, I felt sorry for myself.

'Here!' Aunt Sarah's voice brought me down to earth. 'Take this – number 57, Herzl Street. You can't miss it. See you tomorrow.'

We went to the 'kitchen' for lunch.

'I better ask the supervisor to have a word with the gate-policeman, or perhaps you want to talk to him yourself dad?'

'I will.'

My mother and I went back to the tent. She wanted to lie down; my father joined us a few minutes later.

'It's all arranged. He will have a word with the policeman; you better leave in the early afternoon, taking into account that buses run every half hour.'

Chapter Two

First Steps in My New Country

My father gave me 50 piasters – that was the name of the sub-division of the pound. My mother made me take my awful, rough Bulgarian coat, and wearing my freshly washed but creased white dress, I made my way towards the main gate.

The policeman, in shirt sleeves, was sitting on a chair at the entrance to his little booth, reading a newspaper. He looked up as I came nearer and smiled:

'Bulgaria?'

I nodded. He spoke to me for a while, and although I didn't understand a word of what he said, I realised that he was talking about me. His winks and side-smiles, made that quite clear, but I didn't much like to think what the subject matter of his discourse was. He pointed to himself eventually, and said:

'Polonia.'

I understood that he was telling me that he was Polish.

'Yes, Warsaw.' I said.

'No, no Krakow!'

It was all Poland to me, but obviously, to him, it made a

great deal of difference. I wanted to leave as it was almost 2pm and I didn't want to miss the bus, but he took me by the hand and pulled me inside his tiny office.

He showed me two fingers, counting 'one', 'two' – I nodded, yes, I'll be back in two days. He pointed to himself, then repeated the 'two days' gesture, then he pointed down with his finger, which I took to mean 'here'. I also assumed that he would be in trouble if my absence from the camp were to be found out.

I kept nodding, until my neck ached, expressed my gratitude with wide smiles and finally he let me go.

Just in time, because, as I was crossing the road, the bus came into sight. It pulled up in a cloud of dust and I got on, brandishing my money and my note with Aunt Sarah's address. The driver – there was no conductor – shouted something at me, which I didn't understand, and so I just stood there, swaying to and fro and blushing with embarrassment. The driver looked up into his rear-view mirror and shouted something in Hebrew. I thought that he was telling me off and didn't know what to do, when suddenly I heard someone say something that I understood:

'Do you speak Russian?'

'YES!'

A woman sitting on the third bench along the bus, was waving to me.

'Come and sit down.' she said.

I did.

'Where are you going?' she enquired.

'To Haifa, here, I want to, pay my fare.'

'You must be a new immigrant from the camp?'

'Yes, I am.' The woman took my money, passed it on to the person sitting in front, who in turn passed it on, until it reached the driver. He pressed some buttons on a machine installed on his right, got some change from it, tore off a ticket and passed the whole lot back through the passengers, to me.

'I will tell you where to get off,' the woman said when I showed her my destination, 'Don't worry.'

I relaxed and looked out of the window. I was aware of my creased dress and tried to cover it by hugging my coat to me, such that very little of it showed, or so I hoped.

Soon we were in town and I saw a street of shops! One next to the other, their windows dressed beautifully with the most wonderful things! Shoes, handbags, jumpers, dresses ... oh, how attractive it all looked! I had never seen so many clothes, so beautifully displayed and most probably available to anyone who could afford them! Maybe this is what the streets looked like before the war in Bulgaria, but I hadn't seen them, or if I had, I didn't remember them and the revelation now was fantastic.

The woman pulled my arm:

'Come on, we are getting off.'

I followed her off the bus.

'Come this way.' she said, 'Your address is on my way. I was a new immigrant myself once, many years ago.' she said, 'during the British Mandate. It wasn't easy then.'

I wondered how much more difficult could things be, but didn't say anything.

'Here we are.' she stopped, 'This is it.'

'Thank you very much ..., ' and I nearly said 'Comrade', but checked myself in time. And said instead, 'Madame, I don't know what I would have done without your help.'

She laughed.

'You will get by, don't worry. Shalom.'

'Shalom and thanks again!'

Erica greeted me warmly, pulled me in, hugged me and looked at me:

'My mother said you have changed a lot, let me see. My God, you have!'

'So have you.'

We looked at each other for a short while. Erica was an Israeli. Her voice, her bearing, her short-sleeved, thin, nearly see-through blouse, her shorts, her bare feet in flat sandals with straps criss-crossing her legs to the knees, her short hair, her petulant eyes.

'Erica, you have changed so much! You look very nice.'

'Thank you. Listen, I have an idea,' she pulled me further into the flat, 'I have to wait for my horrible brother to come home from school and feed him, before you and I can go anywhere. Mum went out shopping. He will be home in half an hour and I'll deal with him. Why don't you, in the meantime, take a nice long bath, I bet you're dying for one!'

'Oh, yes, please!' I was so happy. 'I haven't had a bath since … we left Bulgaria.'

'Follow me.' I did.

'Wouldn't it be a little too late to go out at that time though?' I asked.

'Too late for what?'

'I don't know, just too late.'

'Not at all; I have it all planned. We will go for a walk, I'll show you the best bits of Haifa, then we will go to the cinema. I bet you want to see an American film?'

'That would be lovely, but can we stay out that … late?'

'Why not?'

'Yes,' I said, thinking about my parents, 'why not indeed.'

The floors in the flat were tiled in shiny mustard coloured ceramic tiles. The windows opened inwards, all the way to the walls where they were secured by catches, but the wooden blinds were shut and the sunlight cast horizontal lines of light and shade around the rooms.

Erica left me in the bathroom. I let the water run. The mixing taps had a strange shower attached to them, on a long lead, like a telephone. In Bulgaria the showers were always fixed to the wall. I looked at the glass shelf over the basin where there were various toiletries. They had unfamiliar shapes and colours, and had Hebrew and English writing on them. Erica pointed out the shampoo before she left me.

I had a long, luxurious bath, washed my hair over and over again, rinsed myself thoroughly with the telephone shower, trying to get rid of all the sand, then wrapped myself in the large soft towel. Erica peeped in:

'Have you finished? Good, here are some clothes for you, I think we are about the same size, don't you?'

She left the clothes on the stool and shut the door. I dried myself and put the items on, one by one, enjoying as I did so, the forgotten feeling of clean, sand free, freshly washed and ironed clothes. The thin cotton blouse, the cotton print skirt and finally the sandals. It all fitted perfectly. I felt wonderful, happy, refreshed and hungry.

I found Erica in the kitchen.

'Let's have a bite to eat before we leave.' She opened a large ice-box and took out some cheese, margarine, tomatoes and a bottle of orange juice.

'In this country, it's very important to drink a lot. Otherwise you get dehydrated,' she said filling my glass, 'I have finished with the brat – he is out playing, we can go out immediately. Do you want the hair dryer?'

I had never seen a home hair dryer. I said as much.

'Oh, let it dry naturally then, if it's the way you're used to. It saves a little time, but it dries your hair out – the hair dryer, I mean.

'Does it?'

Erica looked at me a while.

'You are a young woman already, you know?'

'What makes you say that?'

'Look at you – you have hips, and your legs, I wish I had legs like yours!'

'You are two years younger, besides I really have nothing for you to envy; you have lovely hair.'

She laughed.

'I like it! We can go on paying each other compliments forever! Gosh, do you remember when we were young?'

'Rashkov's coffee?'

'Yes, and the syringe!'

I had forgotten the syringe! We had found an old unused syringe somewhere and used it to wet Mr. Rashkov's clothes drying on the line

'How could we be so childish? And we were never once found out!'

We laughed again.

'Is it still as bad there?' she asked.

'Worse.'

'Ah, you can forget it now. I already have. Come on, let's go.'

'Erica, could we go to the Street with all the shops in it, please?'

'Yes, I remember how I was taken by them too, at the beginning. All right, let's go, but not for long; shops are shops, you'll soon get fed up with them!'

'No, I won't.'

She laughed.

'Have you had a boy friend?' she asked.

'No, not really. There was a boy I liked. I think he liked me too, but I couldn't see him. My parents ... are very difficult. They keep me in. They think that it is wrong to mix with boys.'

'If my parents did this to me, I would walk out, leave! and they know it. This is the twentieth century, not the middle ages! Besides, this is Israel.'

'I have a feeling my parents want me to get married.'

'Do they? But you are only, what, seventeen?'

'Yes, but my father says that I can do what I want only when I am married. Now I should obey him. And believe me, obeying him isn't easy.'

'That's daft. If you don't mind me saying so. If you are married you will have a home to look after, you can't enjoy yourself.'

It was getting dark and the shops' and street lights were lighting up one by one. I looked avidly at the shop windows and we dropped the conversation.

'Can anybody buy these things?' I asked.

'Yes, but you have to have coupons.'

'Rationing? Like in Bulgaria ?'

'Not in the same way. We have a booklet each, and you have to have so many coupons for woollens for instance, less for cottons etc., but there are more coupons than money, so that isn't a problem. Food is rationed too. Meat, vegetables, but there is enough.'

'How strange. In Bulgaria the rationing of food ended years ago, but you can't get what you want. As for clothes, well you have a choice of two in everything. That's your lot.'

'The rationing here is not for the same reasons. We are absorbing a large number of new immigrants and the country isn't producing that much yet. Our industry is only two years old and the coupons are supposed to make sure that the goods are evenly distributed. Come on, let's get out of here, I'll show you something else.'

'I am impressed that you are so well informed.'

'Thank you. Look, this is the Temple of the Bahai religion.'

The Temple stood in the middle of a magnificent landscaped garden, up on the Carmel mountain. Erica followed my glance and anticipated my question:

'Don't ask me who they are. I can't know everything!'

Our eyes met, as I remembered that she used to say that when studying for exams and burst out laughing, remembering the old days, in Sofia.

'Are you completely detached from that life now?' I asked.

'Yes, of course. How else.' she said simply.

We stopped by a kiosk and she spoke to the man, then turned to me:

'You haven't really been to Israel, if you haven't eaten a 'falafel'.'

'What's that?'

'Don't ask, eat!'

She handed me a pitta bread, filled with salad, crisps and some kind of deep fried balls. It was very tasty.

We walked up a steep street and arrived at a terrace where a sign said 'Panoramic View'. We were half way up the Carmel Mountain. I leant on the parapet, still panting from the climb. The view was indeed panoramic and breathtaking. Haifa was spread out beneath on the mountain slopes.

Just below us, were a few villas with beautiful gardens around them; further down, less built up areas, less green, more concrete, then – the harbour in the middle distance with its tall cranes and many boats along the quays. And finally – the ink blue expanse of the Mediterranean, where the sun, having already set, had left a trail of red which blended softly with the blue of dusk. I sighed, overwhelmed by all this beauty.

'Lovely, isn't it?' Erica's matter of fact voice brought me back to reality:

'come on,' she said, 'let's go.'

I looked at her face, untouched by the surrounding scenery, preoccupied with the fact that we would be late for the cinema. As we walked back towards town, down the street, I pondered over that look on her face. Suddenly, it struck me: she wasn't vulnerable! She had been uprooted so easily and now she belonged here ! If her parents tried to restrict her in any way, she would just walk out. She took things in a simple, straightforward way without too much feeling or thought and that, I found to be a strength I didn't possess.

'Hurry up! How would you like to see a film with Esther Williams?'

'I don't know her, but I am sure I'll like her.'

'She is fabulous.'

'The last American film I saw was ages ago, in Sofia. The life of Marie Curie, with a beautiful actress, oh it was wonderful!'

Erica had taken two jumpers when we went out, and now we had to put them on, as it was getting chilly. Erica kept pointing out various things on our way and teaching me the Hebrew words for them.

We saw a wonderful film. A dream of love, beauty and colour, with lots of swimming and no propaganda of any kind!

'Did you enjoy it?' Erica asked me as we were leaving the cinema.

'Oh, yes! very, very much. Thank you Erica!'

'Good. Let's go home now, I am tired and starving.'

'So am I. Won't your parents mind, really, that we should come home so late? It must be at least nine o'clock.'

'What if it is. They know we went to the cinema and provided we turn up within reasonable time of the end of the early evening show, they won't worry.

'Don't they ask you to be home at meal times?'

'Not if I am out they don't. How can I be home, if I am out?'

The whole family were waiting for us, to hear my first impressions of Haifa and also, hear more about Bulgaria and what had happened after they had left. They had already had their dinner, and Aunt Sarah gave us ours as we talked. She didn't seem to mind.

'Come on, you must go to bed now. You look exhausted.' Aunt Sarah said when I had finished my dinner.

'You are not used to the climate yet.' She had made my bed in the lounge. I revelled for a while in the feeling and smell of clean sheets; then I fell asleep.

'Stay another day or two, come on!' Erica insisted over breakfast. 'I am free with nothing to do. Besides, what do you want to go back to that bloody camp for?'

'I can't. I promised to go back. My parents will be very worried and cross.'

'Go on, stay. I'll tell them.' said Aunt Sarah.

'You know what they are like, auntie, they will worry.'

'They have nothing to worry about. After all you are in my home, not in the street and I will tell them as much!' she winked, 'I'll talk to your father, don't worry. Stay.'

Truly, I didn't need too much persuasion. I wanted to stay! And I did, for three days and three nights. Every day, Erica and I would tidy the flat, do the shopping, wash the floors, then spend the time as we wanted. We walked in the streets of Haifa, and talked and laughed. I learned quite a few words in Hebrew. I questioned her about life on the kibbutz.

'It's OK,' she said in her matter of fact, nonchalant way, 'we study Hebrew for four hours in the morning and two hours in the afternoon. We help a little in the orange groves. That's about it.'

'Who is 'we'?' I asked.

'Our group, the kids from outside. They have an 'ulpan' – that's a special course in Hebrew for new immigrants – for town children. We are too young to do real work, but we help where we can. We study Hebrew, that's all.'

'Where do you live?'

'There are the ... what do you call them ... quarters, dormitories. Four in a room.'

'My father would never let me go to a place like that. He gets all worked up if I want to go anywhere, as for being away from home at night – like here, his first question would be: 'where will she sleep?' It would seem that the worst things that might happen to me, or that I might do, will happen at night. He can't bear the thought of having me away from his supervision, especially at night.'

'If you wanted to, you could do those 'things' in the middle of the day, couldn't you?'

'I suppose I could, if I wanted to, but I don't even want to! What drives me so mad, is that he has never said anything to me, told me anything. He implies, gives orders that I am supposed to obey without questioning. Still, it will work itself out one way or another, I suppose.'

'It must do.'

Aunt Sarah would leave for work very early in the morning.

'You don't have to get up so early.' she said to me. 'Have a good sleep and come back later. I will tell your parents not to expect you before late afternoon.'

Erica and I went through the daily routine. We did the shopping and she let me ask for the items on the list because I had learned the words. We had lunch and then, I had to get into my old dress which I had washed and ironed. Erica walked with me to the bus stop. She waited until I was on the bus, and waved. I waved back, paid my fare and sat down. The bus was soon on its way and Erica disappeared from view.

I looked at the streets of Haifa, then – the fields and the sea. I wasn't looking forward to going back.

The bus stopped opposite the camp, and as I crossed the road, I looked in through the barbed wire. The dusk elongated the shadows; there was washing hung out on lines stretched from tent to tent; half naked children played in the sand; a woman sat, squatting outside her tent, breast feeding a child, at least two years old. The air was still and chilly. I took a deep breath and walked in.

'Aha!' the policeman came out of his booth.

I had completely forgotten him. He beckoned me in and I tried, with my newly acquired Hebrew words, to thank him and explain why I was late returning. Struggling for words, I didn't notice his smile, nor the changed expression on his face. He grabbed hold of me and started to kiss me. With one hand he held me close to his fleshy, repulsive body, and with the other, he fondled my breasts.

My surprise was so complete as to paralyse me, and I lost a few precious seconds before I could fight back. His hand was lifting my skirt now, his mouth was glued to mine filling me with disgust and rage. I struggled to free myself from him, but the more I leant back to get away from his mouth, the more he pressed his body against me over the desk. I felt his hand pulling at my pants, I panicked and tried to kick him away whilst with my hand I took hold of his hair and pulled. He let go of me as suddenly as he had attacked me. He doubled up in pain, and clutching his groin, I heard him swear in Russian.

His face was flushed and I thought that he was going to hit me. I didn't quite know what I had done to free myself, and I didn't waste any time finding out. I ran out of the booth, I ran desperately, as though my life depended on it – and at the time – I thought it did.

I ran until I reached the lavatories, got in, my eyes blinded by tears, my throat tight with anxiety. I sat on the seat, my whole body convulsed with sobs, until my fear, anxiety and rage gave way to tears of frustration and pain.

I don't know how long I sat there. I don't know how long before I was reassured that the policeman hadn't followed me and that now, I had to leave my refuge and face my parents. How lovely it would have been, to have run straight to our tent, to have fallen into my father's arms, to have told him about the policeman's attack and to have had the conviction that he would be on my side. To have had the confidence that he might even go and hit the man, to defend me.

I washed my face. My shoes were once more full of sand, my dress creased. I tried to straighten it the best I could. I walked slowly towards the tent. I knew full well what my father's reaction to such a story would be. I knew that I couldn't afford the risk of being cloistered even more than I was already, by confirming to him the existence of the very hazards he most probably, was trying to protect me from.

The cold air made me shiver and I wrapped my coat tightly around me. My eye-lids stung.

'Where the hell have you been? Sarah said you were going to be here in the afternoon. Your mother is sick with worry!'

'I am sorry mum, sorry dad, but I couldn't help it honestly, the bus broke down and we had to wait over an hour for the driver to replace a tyre.'

I don't know where the story came from, probably from some book I had read. I had not prepared it at all and the incredible thing was – they believed it!

'Come on, let's go for supper, I am starving.'

'As a matter of fact, I have a bit of an upset stomach. It may be wiser for me not to eat, what do you think mum?'

'If you have indigestion, perhaps not.'

I was grateful for the semi-darkness which hid my red-rimmed eyes.

'I'll go to bed, if you don't mind. I have 'been' six times today and feel rather tired.'

'All right, you go to bed, we won't be long. I eat so little anyhow.' said my mother.

'Don't worry and take your time. I'll most probably go to sleep immediately.'

'All right then, good night.'

I found the familiar, rather moist coolness of the bedclothes reassuring. I pulled them up to my chin and lay on my back, my arms straight along my body, stiff with cold, my mind disconcerted in a whirl of doubts. I had found out that there was, a real threat, out there in the open, something which I had been prevented from understanding so far, about which I knew nothing.

What sort of a threat was it? Where exactly did the 'wrong' lie? How did other girls find out about it? How did they avoid it? Or, did it happen to everybody, only it didn't matter that much to them? How much did it really matter to me? All I knew then was, that I was hurt. I knew I had not been raped, but my pride was sorely insulted and what little confidence I had – severely undermined. It had been a 'close shave', I escaped through some kind of instinctive reaction which I was not aware I possessed. My feelings were hurt by someone I didn't even know. Why had he done it? What did he want? Why me? I wasn't even good looking. Was I a 'loose' girl? Did men have a way of knowing these things without even talking to these girls? Maybe that's what it was all about – that was why my father kept such close watch over me! Because I was a loose girl and men knew that they could help themselves! How disgusting! Yet, I thought, if my father had been preventing me from any proximity with boys, or men, for this specific reason…why not tell me about it…explain it to me, warn me.

Questions and doubts harassed me for a long time; I might even have been feverish, then sleep came over me, and I had a long dreamless night's sleep.

Chapter Three

My First Job

One afternoon, about five weeks after our arrival, we were called to the office and told that we had 'passed' our medical examination and that we were free to go.

'Have you a place to go to?' the man asked.

'I have a brother in Tel Aviv .... '

'No, we have no place to go to.' my mother said firmly. 'My husband's brother is in no position to help us.' her eyes flared at my father.

'Do you want to go to a 'maabara'?'

'We have no alternative.'

'All right. We can fit you in Pardes Hannah, there are vacancies there.'

He filled in a sheet, in a pad, adjusting the carbon paper underneath, copying the necessary information – our names etc., – from the release papers he had just issued us with. He talked while he wrote:

'There is a lorry leaving tomorrow afternoon, quite a lot of people from your batch are going there. You can get on it.

Come here, to the office at five o'clock.'

I looked at his hand as it moved over the pad, from right to left. It looked so strange, so incongruous. Would I ever be able to do it? I wondered.

'What is a 'maabara'?' I asked when we left the office, forgetting Aunt Sarah's explanation.

'I am surprised at you,' my mother spoke angrily to my father, ignoring my question, 'you know your brother isn't going to help us! So you go and tell the man about him. What if we had lost our right to go to a 'maabara'? I am asking you, what would we have done then? Where would we have gone?'

'All I wanted to say was … '

'Never mind what you wanted to say, you should have known better! I have to be there all the time and watch over what mess you are going to get us into, next. I am fed up and I am ill. I want to rest.'

'What is a 'maabara'?' I asked again, not so much in order to get an answer, but to save my father from having to react to my mother's endless onslaught.

'A maabara is a camp, very much like this one, only one is free to come and go. That's all.' my father said.

The following day, after lunch, we packed the kit-bags and made our way over to the office. Two lorries, similar to the ones that had brought us here from the port, stood outside and people were slowly climbing in at the back. I noticed the letters GMC on the bonnet and wondered what they stood for, but I didn't think anybody had time to answer my questions. I stole a glance towards the policeman's booth at the gate, but saw no one. Perhaps he was inside. Perhaps there was a different man on duty. I hoped, one way or the other, that I would not see him, and that he would not see me. So I tried to stay hidden behind the lorry.

The journey from the quarantine camp to Pardes Hannah was a lot longer than the one from the port to the quarantine camp. Soon it was completely dark and I couldn't see anything of the scenery, also it was very cold, and so, we sat there, on our kit-bags, huddled together for warmth, swaying to the motion of the lorry.

The arrival was very much a repeat of the previous one, only here no one spoke Bulgarian but there wasn't much to be said anyway. The man in charge spoke Yiddish to my father who answered in German. We were taken, once more, to a tent for three, only this one was larger and erected on a concrete square base; it had little windows on its sides.

We made the beds and went to have our dinner. The 'kitchen' here was also larger, there were a lot more people and it was very noisy. I had a headache but didn't mention it since my mother looked pale and complained of stomach ache. We went to bed as soon as we had finished. It was very cold.

In the morning, after breakfast I went for a look around the camp. People left the 'kitchen' and hurried towards the buses waiting at the gate. The buses left one after the other, as they filled up. Within half an hour every adult seemed to have left the camp, leaving only old men and women, and children.

It was obvious that people had lived here for a long time. The tents were made to look more like homes; there were benches outside, children's bicycles, tables and chairs under canopies. Some, had fenced in areas where there were flowers and vegetables growing. I was most surprised to see those vegetables and flowers, growing out of what seemed to be just sand, hardened by the rain.

I found my parents standing outside our tent, gazing out over the camp.

I thought it marvellous that people were given this opportunity to live and eat free of charge, whilst at the same time working and saving. I was about to express this view, when I realised that a conversation was in progress and decided to keep my opinion to myself.

'I will have to go to town and see what I can find.' my father was saying.

'And leave me here, alone, in this ... horrible dump!'

'But how can we ever get anywhere if I don't make a start ... a move, to find a job?'

'And leave me here, all day, to rot in my misery! Other people may be able to do it – live here, for free, for years and amass money. I will die I tell you, I will die within a few months!'

'Please, please my love ... don't despair ... have I ever ... when I could ... left you without a roof over your head?'

'It is I who ought to go to the town,' said my mother after a short pause,'servants' jobs seem to be readily available.'

'Over my dead body! I have to be dead first for you to have to go out to work. After all, I can speak many languages, I have vast experience in the export business, I'll find a job!'

'You're talking nonsense. Your experience is worth nothing here. It's dated, can't you see, this is a Western country, with all the modern approaches, what do you know of the modern ways of conducting business? Nothing!'

'Have a little confidence in me .... '

'I am realistic,' my mother's voice, interrupting him, was full of contempt and impatience, 'I don't like to fool myself. Besides, can't you see, it's the Ashkenazis who get the good jobs. We – Sephardis – we will be lucky if we find a roof and, possibly a labouring job for you.'

It started to rain. We went into the tent. My father lit the paraffin oil lamp. We sat on our beds and no one spoke. The rain drops hit the tent with such force as to make it impossible for us to talk, even if we had wanted to.

My father left for town in the morning. My mother and I were still in the 'kitchen' having breakfast. There was no point in hurrying. There was nothing to do and it was still very early. Breakfast was served at seven, because of the people who had to go out to work. A few women at our table were speaking

French. I looked at them; obviously a mother and three daughters. They looked so alike! Two of the daughters sat on my side of the bench.

'Excuse me,' I turned to the girl sitting next to me, 'where are you from? I couldn't help overhearing you speak French?'

'From Egypt – Cairo, and yourselves?'

'We are from Bulgaria.'

'There are many immigrants from Bulgaria in the camp,' she said politely, 'many of them speak French, but you do have a language of your own, don't you?'

'Yes, Bulgarian.'

'Is there such a language? How interesting.'

I was taken aback. Did a country exist anywhere without a language of its own?

'What are you doing?' the girl asked. 'How long have you been here?'

'In the camp – since yesterday, in Israel – just over five weeks. I am not doing anything at the moment; we have to find a flat or something.'

'All Bulgarians live in Jaffa.' she said.

'Yes! We have heard that as well. What do you do?'

'My sisters and I work at the orange packing warehouse, down the road. Do you want to come? It's seasonal work and pays well. They are looking for more hands.'

'What do you do there?'

'We pack oranges. They pay you by the crate, if you are fast, you make good money.'

I turned to my mother who had been following the conversation but made sure to stay out of it.

'What do you say mum? I would very much like to! Besides, I have nothing to do all day.'

'I don't know.' she spoke Bulgarian to me, 'I feel sick. I must go and lie down.'

'I am sorry mum; maybe you shouldn't eat all those grapefruits after all.'

She shrugged.

'May I go?'

'I don't know. Your father won't like it.'

'Just for a few days mum, I'll earn some money then we can all go to town and see Aunt Amelia and the others. Wouldn't you like that?'

'Don't be ridiculous! with a few pennies earned at packing oranges, indeed!'

'Let me try.'

'Do as you see fit, but I warn you, your father won't like it.'

'Are you coming? We must go.' the girl pulled at my arm.

'Yes, I'm coming.'

'Good for you! Come on now, we are late.'

I kissed my mother's cheek. She remained motionless.

'My name is Angele, this is Ruth and ... I'll introduce you to the others later, come on now.'

We left the 'kitchen' in a hurry and took the road towards the town of Pardes Hannah. It was a narrow road at the end of which I could see the warehouse – a corrugated iron structure, about five hundred metres down the road. Tall lean palm trees swayed gently in the breeze. Beyond, on either side of the road, stretching as far as the eye could see, were orange groves. I could see their branches heavy with fruit, their leaves still wet, glistening in the hesitant morning sun. The air was scented with orange blossom and wet earth. Angele started to hum 'La vie en rose' and one by one, we all joined in.

'Come on, come on girls! You are late.' the young man had short curly hair, sparkling green eyes and an engaging smile. His French was broken and funny.

'Uri, we have a new girl with us, do you need another hand?' Angele asked

'Oh, yes I do!' he now switched to Hebrew and to my surprise I understood what he said. That is to say, I understood some of the words, the rest – I made up. He sent them to their jobs and then came over to me:

'OK young lady. Now, do you understand some Hebrew?' he spoke slowly.

'Yes, a little.'

'I am a 'sabra' you see; whatever languages I speak, I pick up here and there from new immigrants. Do you understand me?'

I nodded.

'But explaining – I must do in Hebrew, I'll speak slowly, OK!'

'OK.'

'Good. This is what you do. Sit down, here, next to me.'

He went on to explain, accompanying every word with a gesture, such that it was very easy for me to understand:

'Here is a crate full of oranges; here is another crate – empty. Here is a pile of paper. You take one, like this, you place it in front of you; with your other hand – to save time – you take an orange and place it on the paper; you roll one end of the paper over the orange, then the other – to wrap it, now you twist the ends of the paper, one-clockwise, the other-anticlockwise, to secure it, and here we are – a beautifully wrapped orange! You put it in the empty crate and take another unwrapped orange with one hand, and another piece of paper with the other, and so on. Want to try?'

'Yes.'

'Go ahead; let me see how you do it.'

He got up and stood by my side, his hands on his hips, looking down at me, while I wrapped an orange.

'Well done. Quick and well wrapped too. Go on – you're on your own.'

'Thank you.'

I felt his gaze on me and thought that there were more instructions coming up.

'Aren't you going to ask me how much I'll pay you?' he said.

I felt embarrassed and knew I was blushing. I had never been paid before.

'You won't get far in this country if you are shy about

money.' he said quietly, 'Anyway, it's 10 piastres per crate. Go on now.'

My hands were a little shaky as I picked my first orange and wrapped it, but slowly I relaxed and concentrated on my work.

I earned 80 piastres on that day. I had filled nearly 8 crates; the last one wasn't quite full, but Uri said that I had done very well for a beginner and, to encourage me, he paid me for 8 full crates. I observed my friends as they collected their money, satisfied looks on their faces, and I knew that the moment I would be there, in front of that desk, for my hand out, I would be blushing again. And I was.

It was raining now, and we ran all the way to the camp where we arrived soaked. I found my mother in the tent, lying down.

'Hullo! How are you mum?'

'How do you expect?'

'Stomach ache again? Shall I bring you your tray in here? Look, I earned 80 piastres today.' I gave her the money.

'We are getting richer every day!' she took the money and looked at it, like one looks at a stranger. It was indeed, unfamiliar money and I didn't know how much it was worth.

'I can't go to the 'kitchen'.' said my mother.

'Father hasn't come back I take it?'

'No.'

'I'll go and get you your tray, then I'll go for my dinner, I am starving.'

'You are lucky, you are healthy.'

'Shall I keep you company while you eat?'

'No, you go and have your dinner. I haven't much of an appetite anyway.'

I slept like a log that night. I woke up in the morning to find that my whole body ached. My legs were stiff from the long hours squatting on the floor; so was my neck and my back, but I wasn't going to tell my mother; I wanted to go to work.

'You're not going again, are you?' my mother asked at breakfast.

'Please mummy, let me go! I feel that I am doing something! Wouldn't you like to see Tel Aviv?'

'No.'

'Oh, please let me go.'

'Do as you please.'

I worked better on the second day and earned 1 pound and 20 piasters. I felt very tired but well pleased. We walked back in the twilight and I stopped at the camp's kiosk to buy something for my mother. I didn't know what I could afford to buy and decided on a bar of toilet soap. It was so luxuriously wrapped and we hadn't had anything luxurious since before the war. I wanted to do something which would bring a smile to my mother's lips. I hurried to our tent.

My father was sitting on the edge of the bed where my mother was lying and I made to tell them of my financial success and give my mother the soap.

My father spoke first:

'What do you think you are doing? I only have my back turned for a day, and you get completely out of hand! No daughter of mine is going to become a common labourer, not while I am alive anyway! When I am dead you can do as you please, but while I am here, you will go to school!'

'Dad … I haven't become a labourer … it's only … to help ….'

'Don't answer back! When I need your help, I'll tell you, in the meantime you will go to school where you belong.'

'But … there is no school here ….'

Defeated, I sat on my bed, my money still clenched in my fist. I looked at the bar of soap for a while and handed it over to my mother without saying a word. She, in turn, looked at it, then said:

'She hasn't earned a penny yet and she has spent it all! You'll never know how to manage money.'

There was nothing really that I could say. I just looked at her, incredulous that she didn't understand my action, that she didn't comprehend.

They discussed the dinner arrangements for a while; my father went and brought my mother's tray from the 'Special diet kitchen', then turned to me: 'come on, let's go, I am hungry.'

We were late, and most of the people had already had their dinner; the 'kitchen' was practically empty and unusually quiet. We took our trays and sat at an empty table.

'I want you to understand,' said my father, his mouth full, 'these are hard times. Hard on all of us, but this doesn't mean that we should let them ruin your education.'

His voice was mellow and conciliatory. I saw no logic in what he said, but took the opportunity to explain:

'All I wanted to do was to earn some money, to help out; for your trips to town perhaps, or for all of us maybe to go to town, to take mum out ... I didn't plan to take it up as a career.'

'We can do without your money.'

'Here it is, anyway. I have no use for it.'

'You keep it.'

'But can't you see dad, I want to take part in ... these as you call them, hard times, I want to contribute to … '

'Enough of this. Eat your dinner now!'

I gave up.

After a long pause, while I was swallowing with difficulty each mouthful, my father said:

'I saw Aunt Amelia and Uncle Dori and other friends in Jaffa.'

'How are they, Aunt Amelia, and the others I mean?'

'Well enough. They all live in what they call Arab houses. Rather gloomy, but better than tents. Apparently, when they all came at once from Bulgaria in '48', Jaffa was an empty town and they simply walked into the abandoned Arab houses. There isn't a hole now that's uninhabited.'

'Did you see your brother?'

'He is your uncle.'

'Sorry. Did you see my Uncle Isaac?'

'Yes. He is a very unhappy man. His wife is very ill.'

'What's wrong with her?'

'I don't know, something to do with her nerves.'

'Did you meet my cousins?'

'I didn't like Esther; the boy is on a kibbutz, his mother can't ... is not well enough to look after him.'

'Why didn't you like Esther?'

'She spoke ill of her father, and to me anyone who speaks ill of their parents, is evil.'

We returned to the tent without another word being said. It was cold and damp and undressing was an ordeal.

Three days later, my father went back to Jaffa with the money I had earned.

I was pondering over the people we knew and loved, Aunt Amelia and everybody else, living in houses which had housed other families. Families to which those houses belonged – why had they left? Where had they gone? We knew nothing, at that time of Palestinian refugees and what was to become a big international issue. But my little life experience told me that there was something very wrong here.

I was worried about my mother. She hardly ever left her bed. She complained constantly of stomach pains, often felt nauseous and sometimes was sick. Her nausea appeared to convulse her stomach, slowly at first, then gaining momentum, until it seemed to twist the innermost depths of her abdomen, and then the cramps would fade away.

I worried but I didn't know what to do, because she had become even more difficult to approach than she had been before.

'Shouldn't you see a doctor mum?' I asked her.

'How do you like that! And where am I going to find a doctor?'

'Why didn't you mention your condition to the doctor who

examined us at the quarantine camp?'

'I wasn't ill then. I was fine.'

I knew that this wasn't so, but didn't dare contradict her. There was another thing. Three times a day I would go for her food to the diet 'kitchen'; each time she said she wasn't hungry and sent me away to get my meal, and each time, upon my return, I found her tray empty. I puzzled over this, but once more, I didn't dare mention it or ask her about it.

My father returned on the third day after his departure, a wide smile on his face:

'Hi! We are saved! We are going out of here. We are leaving tomorrow.'

'You found us a flat? Really? Have you?' I was overjoyed.

'Where are you taking me?' my mother looked suspiciously up at him. He sat down heavily on the bed.

'Yesterday, I met Samuel. I just bumped into him in the street, in Jaffa.

We went to a café and talked; he told me about himself, and I told him about us. Anyway, he offered to take us in. I didn't ask, he offered. They live in a village, not far from Tel Aviv, in an Arab house.'

'I think this is marvellous!'

'Oh, shut up, will you!' my mother sat up in her bed and turned to my father:

'What sort of house?'

'A house is a house! I don't know. I didn't ask! The man offered to save us from the winter cold and rain, and you want me to ask him what sort of house they live in! Anyway,' he calmed down a little, 'it's an Arab house in an ex-Arab village. That's all I know.'

We sat in silence for a while.

'Rachel works in town.' my father said.

'Doing what?'

'She is … she looks after a child.'

'A domestic help.'

'Well, not really. Just a child minder. She might do the odd bit of house work, I don't know. She is working for a young 'sabra' couple. The husband is an Army officer.'

The rank of her employer didn't redeem Aunt Rachel in my mother's esteem. 'People seem to have become so greedy. They all seem to work in order to make more and more money. All those women of our class, who before the war couldn't do without a maid, all gone down to being domestic help themselves. How I despise that!'

Silence again.

'Now that you will be sheltered from cold and rain, I can concentrate on finding a job. It won't be long before we will be on our feet again.'

In the semi-darkness that had crept into the tent, I hadn't realised that my mother was shaking with inaudible sobs. Suddenly she broke into a long, loud whine:

'Why ... oh ... why did we have to come to this wretched place … oh … oh?' My father took her in his arms.

'Sh …. sh … sh … its just temporary … we will be OK soon. I promise. Please trust me.'

My mother freed herself from him and without looking up shook her head. Slowly at first, then faster and faster until I had to look away. It was so frightening.

Chapter Four

The Missing Donkey

The bus stopped as it entered the Tel Aviv central bus station. The driver pushed a button, which opened both doors with what sounded like a deep sigh. People pushed to get off and my father motioned to us to wait until everybody had left. He then carried our kit-bags down, one by one, not allowing us to help him. As he came down with the last one, we heard the bus doors shut behind us, with the same deep sigh.

We found ourselves standing on an 'island', with buses zooming all around us.

'This is dangerous, let's get out of here.' shouted my father.

'Where to ? Do you know which bus we want?'

'No, but I will ask.'

He turned to a man who was just passing by, but the man didn't even bother to look at him.

'Look' I had just noticed a building in the distance. 'There is a sign there, it says 'Information'. It looks like the ticket office.'

My father took two of the kit-bags and my mother and I struggled with the third. We ran from 'island' to 'island'. The buses almost ran us over, and people kept bumping into us. Finally we got there. We dropped the awful kit-bags and tried to catch our breath. My father went into the Information office.

'This is it.'

There was a plaque which read '56', beneath it there was some Hebrew writing, and in Latin letters: 'Yehud'.

'It doesn't say Kfar Ana.'

'Well, no. You see, the bus doesn't actually go to the village itself. We will have to get off at a T junction. Kfar Ana is about a kilometre from there.'

'How do you mean? 'A kilometre from there'?'

'Don't worry. I'll take care of everything .... '

'You never told me that! Where are you taking me? What Godforsaken place is that?'

'It is our only way out of the camp. The only place I could find. The rains are coming. Do you want to spend the winter in a tent?'

'What do you mean YOU could find? You didn't expect ME to do that, did you?'

'Of course not. But this is all there is and you will have to make the most of it!'

My mother began to cry.

'What have I said now?'

'You shout at me ... I only have to say a word, and you shout at me .... ' she sobbed.

'I am sorry darling ... I didn't mean to ... look here is the bus, we better get on.' There weren't too many people in the queue, so we got on without being pushed.

There were many more trees in the streets of Tel Aviv than I had expected. It was strange to see such rich foliage in November, having been used to the sight of denuded branches on the linden trees of Sofia. The houses here had a coat of plaster, some left in a natural colour, some painted over. It was quite different from the beautiful pink stone that Haifa's houses were built in.

Eventually the bus made its way towards the outskirts of town and through some very poor looking districts. There was litter outside the houses, plaster had peeled off the walls and shutters hung limply on one hinge, then, once more, out in the open countryside. Green fields and green trees. The bus stopped occasionally to take on some passengers; some also got off.

The driver announced the stops as he looked into his rear view mirror, waiting for his passengers to get off:

'Tel Litvinsky!'

'Is everything 'Tel' – something in this country?' I asked my father.

'Of course not, silly. 'Tel' means 'hill', it's just a coincidence, but let me tell you, Tel Litvinsky is a military camp, this is why all the soldiers are getting off here.'

Indeed, I had noticed a few young men and girls, all dressed in light khaki uniforms on the bus. I looked at the girls with envy. They seemed so smart and confident in their short skirts and neat shirts. They all wore a bag slung over their shoulder, and a smart cap fitted neatly over their hair, gathered at the nape.

'It's our stop soon.' my father shouted over the noise of the hard revving engine.

'Kfar Ana.' the driver announced, the doors sighed open and we got off, with our kit-bags.

Once the bus had disappeared into the distance, we found ourselves surrounded by deep country silence. Fields extended for as far as we could see, flat and green, shining in the sun.

'There!' my father pointed down the side road, 'That is Kfar Ana.' Following his glance, we could just see a few buildings in the distance. The road climbed slightly as it curved away from the main road. The field between us and the village was low, and the rain had filled it with water. It looked like a large lake, its surface shining in the sun. The village itself, seemed tucked in among trees.

'How the hell are we going to get there?' my mother asked.

My father patted a kit-bag:

'Sit yourselves down, I will go to the village and get transport.'

The sky was a beautiful deep blue, the sun shone brightly, lighting everything it touched. It wasn't warm, though. The drops of night rain seemed to respond to the sun, for after they had sparkled for a while, I could see them evaporate in a dense steam rising over the fields, carrying a strong smell of damp moss.

I turned to my mother, wishing to share my thoughts with her, but her face was closed, unapproachable. I felt awkward, I wanted to cheer her up, but didn't dare break her silence.

It seemed a long time before I saw something approaching from the direction of the village. I couldn't make out what it was; it wasn't a man or a car. Soon I realised that it was a cart, but there was still something incongruous about it. I pointed it out to my mother just as it became hidden behind a tree, then as it reappeared we both saw it clearly: it was a two wheeled horse cart, but instead of a horse, it was my father who was pulling the two shafts.

As he came to the slope where the side-road joined the main, he was forced to break into a run. My mother burst out laughing. My father tried to stop the cart by leaning backwards and digging his heels into the road. I found a stone in the ditch and placed it in front of one of the wheels.

'You ... replaced the donkey ..., ' my mother laughed uncontrollably, 'fancy that ... you ... instead of a donkey .... '

It wasn't funny. Not the way she said it. I looked at my father who looked away and having dropped the shafts, busied himself with loading the cart.

'Come on, let's go.' he took hold of the shafts again and turned the cart round. I pushed from the back and, eventually, so did my mother. The road leading to the village was boarded by eucalyptus trees. I had never seen eucalyptus trees before.

They were tall and willowy and their branches sprouted from the very bottom of their trunks.

As we reached the village I could see the houses more clearly. They were nice looking bungalows, with porches, rather small windows and green wooden shutters. The road then swerved to the left – into the village and led straight onto the village square, where we could see the village 'store', which, my father informed us, sold everything.

We took a narrow lane among the bushes. It was a lot more difficult to push the cart now, since we were walking in deep mud. An even narrower path led from the lane to scattered bungalows, half hidden by the luxurious green overgrowth.

Finally my father halted, dropped the shafts and wiped his forehead with the back of his hand.

'This is it.' he said.

'Oh, isn't it lovely!' I exclaimed, looking at the bungalow. We walked on to the porch and my father let us in.

Inside, it was dark, since the shutters were all closed. Once our eyes had become accustomed to the darkness, we could see that we were in a small hall. On the right, we could see the kitchen, and to the left there were two intercommunicating rooms. I recognised some pieces of furniture: the heavy walnut sideboard, dining table and chairs – shadows from my childhood in Moskovitch Mansions.

'Where are we going to sleep? I can only see two rooms, and there are four of them anyway!' my mother said.

'Elise doesn't come home during the week.' my father explained, 'She goes to school in Tel Aviv and she stays there, with a friend.'

'Still, there is only one bedroom!'

'The settee becomes a double bed, and there is a folding 'put-you-up' bed .... '

'But the rooms are intercommunicating – there is no door, can't you see?'

'It will have to do.'

My mother opened the shutters.

'What a mess!' she said, looking around.

She was right; there were clothes scattered everywhere, socks, dressing gowns, shoes, dresses, blouses and trousers, just left lying around. Nothing seemed to be where it belonged. The kitchen the sink was full of dirty dishes, the table was not cleared from last night's dinner, or this morning's breakfast; sand was crunching under the soles of our shoes as we walked around.

'Shall we tidy up then? I asked.

'Let's start by doing the washing up, I can't stand dirty dishes.'

My father cleared his throat; we looked at him.

'It isn't all that easy ... I mean, there isn't any water, not now. What I am saying is,' he hurriedly added, 'that there isn't any running water now. But the pump is operated twice a day, for two hours each time … '

'How exactly do you mean, and why didn't you tell me so before?'

'I mean exactly what I am saying … that a pump, a diesel operated pump – is worked twice a day to provide the village with running water … '

'This means, in plain language, that there is no running water! Real progress, I call it!'

My father left the room.

'Come on,' my mother turned to me, 'let's tidy up this mess.' We opened the wardrobe doors to find out what went where, but inside, the wardrobes looked just like the rooms – total chaos.

In my mother's wardrobe, the items had always been carefully placed one on top of the other, each item folded to exactly the same width; immaculate piles of underwear, handkerchiefs, towels, sheets.

'What has become of Rachel?' my mother said looking at the mess and shaking her head.

I noticed that there were paraffin-oil lamps hanging on the walls.

'Look!' I said before the implication of their presence dawned on me, 'lamps, paraffin-oil lamps!'

My mother followed my glance. There were two of them on each wall, their long glass tubes blackened by soot.

'Do you mean to say that there is no electricity either?' my mother shouted towards my father, who was on the porch, pacing and smoking nervously.

'No,' he answered from where he was, 'there is no electricity.'

My mother sat on a chair.

'How do they cook?'

My father came in, looking guilty.

'On paraffin-oil burners.'

We made the beds. We folded up each item of clothing and put it away; cleared the table and swept the floor.

'Auntie! Uncle! Hi!' Beatrice had arrived suddenly, and having parked her bicycle against the wall, came in and kissed us all warmly. I looked for her limp, left by her childhood polio, but there was nothing more than a very slight jump as she moved her weight from one leg to the other. She had grown up into a lovely, quite tall, fourteen-year old girl, her cheeks round and pink, her eyes and hair a beautiful shade of amber. She went over to the ice-box.

'They call me Ruth here.' she said, 'I am starving. Have you had anything to eat yet? My father should have got the shopping in by now. Oh, my God! Who has tidied up? I bet it's you auntie. This place is never this tidy, well, except perhaps on Saturdays.'

'Why did you change your name?' I asked

'They don't know Beatrice's here. Ruth is biblical.'

'I can't stand disorder.' my mother said.

'It really is my task. You see, we all have 'tasks', according to ability and availability, which automatically excludes both my sister – unavailability, and my father – complete and utter inability. Well, at least he does the shopping.' She was avidly chewing at the sandwich she had made for herself.

'Mind you, Elise is working very hard, I must grant her that. She is going through the whole rigmarole of matriculation exams, back two years! Fancy that, just to be able to go to university. A book worm, my sister is. But she is worth every penny my mother is investing in her. My school costs nothing, you see, but high school does, and a lot at that. How about you? What are you going to do?' she asked me.

'I will have to do the same as Elise, I suppose. I want to go to university, but I don't know Hebrew at all, well a few words that I have picked up here and there.'

'You go to the Army first, that's your best bet. There you will learn Hebrew for nothing and you would not have wasted time. You have to do the service anyway. After that, all you have to do is buckle down and pass the exams. Elise chose school instead; imagine – two years back, then by the time she will be able to go to university she will be over twenty! Hey, I am chatting away and it's nearly four o'clock – water time.'

She went over to the sink, took up all the dishes on a tray and carried them out, onto the porch.

'Ruth, what are you doing? I had … '

'The water doesn't come up to the tap, auntie. There isn't enough pressure, is that what you call it? I have forgotten Bulgarian.' She was crouching by a tap near the porch, which we hadn't noticed before.

'Wait, wait, we can't use the first water. Can you give me this bucket please.'

I brought the bucket over to her. Ruth turned the tap on and after a lot of gurgling and splashing, a feeble jet of yellow-rust coloured water poured out. Ruth didn't waste a drop – she had the bucket already in position and as it began to fill up, she turned to me again:

'Can you pass me the second one, please.'

When the first bucket was full, she handed it to me and quickly positioned the second one under the tap.

'Could you please empty it into the loo.'

I did and came back. She handed me the second, now full bucket, indicating that I should do the same with this one too. My mother just watched on.

'Now we need two buckets to wash the floors, or do the 'spondja' as we call it here.'

'What? Do the … what?'

'Spondja, I think it's an arab word, anyway, it means washing the floor. Watch me, we haven't got much time.'

She took a long broom handle, which, instead of a brush on its end, had a wide rubber blade attached. Ruth spread water generously over a portion of the floor then gathered it with the rubber blade and mopped up with a freshly rinsed rag. She had started at the far end of the bedroom, and was working systematically through into the second room, the hall and the kitchen. I changed the water in the bucket a few times for her.

'Good, that's done.' she straightened her back. 'It's the only way to get rid of the sand.'

My parents had gone to the village store to shop for dinner and also to allow the floor to dry.

'Now we can do the washing up.' Ruth went back and crouched by the tap. Indeed, the water was a lot clearer now, though by no means completely transparent. I took the dishes from her as she washed them, and took them inside to dry.

My parents returned from the shop. Ruth showed my mother how to use the paraffin-oil burners and she started cooking the dinner. The last of the water was stored for drinking and washing just before the tap coughed a few times, then went dry.

Then, Uncle Samuel arrived; he walked in slowly, looking at each and everyone of us, his arms outstretched.

'Good to have you with us! Good to have you here, with us folks!' He kissed us all in turn, then sat down heavily, his arms resting on the table. He looked like an old man. His face hadn't changed much, I didn't think, but it had become longer and his skin, somehow, seemed to be too large for it. His back was hunched, his hair-gray, and the fingers holding the cigarette were nicotine stained; I remembered the song he used to sing in that powerful voice of his, as he drank the slivovitz.

'I couldn't let you spend the winter in a tent; not the kind of winter we have here. You have no idea what it's like. Rain, rain, rain. Gets into your bones.' he coughed; a long dry cough.

'But where are you going to put us?'

'Don't worry! We'll manage. We're together, aren't we? That's what matters now. You got away from that snake-pit. You're well. We can manage,' his cough interrupted him again, he patted his chest and muttered, 'damn thing', then went on, 'anyway, as I said, we can go and talk to your sister Clara.' he motioned to my mother, 'There are no empty houses left in the village. But on the roof of their house, there are a few walls built, it won't take much to turn them into two rooms. All they need is doors, windows and a roof. We might even go there tonight if you want, but I'll have to find out who is on guard.'

'On guard?'

'Oh, yes. We have to have guards, patrols. Arabs, you see, infiltrators. They come through the borders and kill; throw hand grenades and the like.'

'Are we near the border then?'

'You are never far from the border in this country my girl. In our case, about five kilometres.'

'This is frightening.'

'Ah, you learn to live with it. Besides, we have guards.' he laughed, and his laughter turned into a cough again.

'Fine guards we are!' he said when he stopped coughing.

'All Bulgarian mummy's boys, never saw a gun in our lives.

Guards! Still, you hold a gun in your hand, it should make you feel secure. It doesn't make me feel better, I can tell you. I am scared stiff, but don't tell anybody.'

'Everybody knows, dad.' Ruth said with a smile.

'See, that's my young one. They have all become 'sabras' here. No respect. Speak their minds like nobody's business.'

'Are you studying Hebrew?' my mother asked.

'Me? Don't ask. It's a bastard of a language if you pardon my language! God be my witness, I tried. You have no idea. The masculines, and the feminines, and the neutrals, and the accordance of them all, depending on … something … no, not for me. Did you know that there are no written vowels? No written vowels! You have to guess at them. Honestly. No man, this is not for me. It will all have to happen without me from now on.'

He lit another cigarette.

'That will be Rachel now.' Indeed we heard footsteps outside. 'You should hear her babbling away in Hebrew, as though she has always known it. She is phenomenal.'

Aunt Rachel walked in, a wide smile on her face, her arms outstretched – her handbag dangling on her wrist, a cigarette in her hand. Without saying a word, she walked over to my mother, kissed her, then she kissed my father and then me. She dropped her handbag on the floor, sank into a chair and leant onto the table, her hands in front of her.

'Good to see you.' she said finally with a deep sigh. 'It's the walk – the walk from the crossroads that kills me. I don't mind the morning walk, I don't mind the whole day's work, I love the baby, but at night, it's the end of me.' she sighed again, still smiling. 'Eh, well, you are here at last.' Her hand went for the handbag on the floor, she extracted a cigarette without looking, lit the new one from the old, and went on: 'Tell me, how are you? What did they do to you there?'

My father thought that the question was addressed to him; I saw him preparing to answer, when my mother said:

'Better not ask ... there are no words to describe my ordeal.'

Aunt Rachel shifted her eyes from my mother to my father, her eye-brows raised:

'I would never have gotten out of there alive, had it not been for my wife.' he said.

'You are a heroine, you have always been.' Aunt Rachel's skeletally thin arm went up and down from the table top, where it rested, to her mouth; she drew avidly at the cigarette, inhaling deeply. Her long thin fingers were nicotine stained too and her face, parched by the sun broke into hundreds of lines when she smiled. She looked at me with tired eyes.

'My, my, my ... what a lovely girl!' she said looking back at my mother to whom I was, obviously, a credit.

'What are you going to do now?' she asked of me.

'She will study.' my father answered.

'Yes, that is sensible. She should go to Ulpan in Jaffa, it's the best.' Ruth had been busy all this time setting the table. Aunt Rachel now looked over at her and said, 'What do you think of my Ruth?'

'She is lovely.' my mother said.

'She has had two operations so far. Can you see the improvement? When she is eighteen, she will have a third operation and there are chances that after that one, there will be no trace left of the limp and she will be able to lead a normal life. Isn't it marvellous?'

'Yes, indeed.' my mother said, probably remembering how deformed little Beatrice had been.

'They have really performed a miracle. It's truly fantastic.'

'The miracle started with Rachel working with the child and exercising her against all odds, back in '42,' Uncle Samuel said, 'the doctors are all adamant about it.'

'Stop all this gossiping about me! Auntie has cooked us a wonderful supper and I am starving. Let's eat.'

My mother took over now and served the dinner.

'Did the operations cost a lot of money?' my mother asked.

'Well, not such a lot,' said Aunt Rachel. 'Your cooking is, as usual, delicious.'

'It was a lot of money,' Ruth said 'Why do you think my mother is working as hard as she is, if my operations and Elise's school hadn't cost so much.'

'Rubbish! I am working because we want your father to get a shop, and that costs money. So, I'll work a while. Say, how are things in Bulgaria? I do feel nostalgic sometimes.'

The settee at the far end of the room was opened up for my parents. Aunt Rachel and Uncle Samuel slept in their double bed, on the opposite side of the intercommunicating rooms. The table, which stood in the middle, was moved to one side and two folding beds were put up for Ruth and myself. Uncle Samuel blew the lamps out and we all undressed in the dark and went to bed in the dark.

'You go and have a word with Gabriel yourself,' Uncle Samuel said in the morning. 'There is no reason why he should object to your making yourself a home on his roof, but it better be you who talks to him.'

'You forget that Clara is my half sister, why should they object? On the contrary, I hope she will be pleased.'

'Don't forget, Clara has always been a funny girl.' my father said carefully.

'She isn't at home all day long. You won't see any more of her than you see of my Rachel.'

Chapter Five

An Unlikely Home

Uncle Samuel took us to the house during the day, when Uncle Gabriel and Aunt Clara were not at home, for us to see it in the daylight. It was situated on the opposite side of the village square, nearer the road.

It stood on one of the main lanes, and looked very much like all the other bungalows in the village. It had a porch and it's door and shutters were painted dull green.

We followed Uncle Samuel round the side of the house where we found the stairs leading up to the flat roof. The stairs were made of concrete and seemed to come out of the wall itself, they were narrow and there was no banister. It was a strange diagonal structure across the side wall of the house, and it took us up onto the roof. I had never been on a flat roof before; it hardly looked like a roof! It had a guard rail all round it, unlike the stairs and it was covered with tar. The rain had left little puddles on it's uneven surface.

'It's for insulation.' said uncle Samuel, having sensed my surprise at the strange look of the place.

'Is that it, then?' asked my mother, stepping inside the walls, which for all intents and purposes constituted the shell of our prospective home.

'Yes,' said uncle Samuel, 'you see there is nowhere else in the village. All you have to do is put a roof and doors and windows.'

I walked in through the opening. Indeed, the sky was above our heads, but there were walls which could make two rooms.

'They certainly believed in intercommunicating rooms, the Arabs.' I said.

'Yes, they did. Funny that, isn't it?'

The openings left for doors and windows were narrow and the whole of the structure covered only half of the area. The rest looked like a terrace.

I saw a hole in the corner for rain water drainage and walked over to the edge to look down. There was a short tin pipe sticking out and a bucket underneath it.

'What is this?' I asked, 'Why a bucket under the pipe?'

'Oh, that – the women collect this, I mean rain water. They wash their hair with it.'

'I am not surprised,' my mother said, 'the yellow muck that you get can hardly be called water.'

'How much do you think it will cost to do, Sam, roughly?' asked my father.

'It depends what you want to do. You can do it very cheaply if you only do the bare necessity, so to speak – just a roof and windows and doors. You can spend a lot more if you want to cover the floor, for instance – I mean tiles and all that; and paint it – decorate it I mean, and put a ceiling; see what I mean, it all depends of your budget.'

'Budget!' my mother said 'we don't know where tomorrow's bread is coming from.'

'I'll find the money, don't you worry.'

'I know, he is thinking of his brother again. Who, let me tell you, hasn't as much as tried to come and see us, not once.'

I saw the bitterness on my father's face. But he said nothing.

It started to rain and we ran down. The rain was so strong, that we had to take refuge on the porch. We just stood there, waiting for it to give us a chance to run home.

'So, this is what was waiting for us in Israel.' said my mother, looking away from us, into the distance.

'We will make it good.'

'Yes? What with?'

That evening, after dinner, my parents went to talk to Uncle Gabriel and Aunt Clara. I stayed home. Ruth showed me some of her books. One had to hold them upside down, because they started from the opposite side! Since I couldn't read the script anyway, I couldn't tell which was the beginning, and which was the end. We had a laugh; she was trying to teach me a few letters, when my parents returned.

'So?' asked Uncle Samuel.

Aunt Rachel had gone to bed and was sound asleep, despite all of us being practically in the same room. She was so tired.

'Of course, they were delighted to see us,' said my father, 'and don't have any objections to us living above them.'

'How could he honestly have any objections when the house is not his property.' my mother said. 'We only 'consulted' them out of courtesy, that's the way I see it. It is an arab house, and everybody in the village just moved into the abandoned houses, that's the way I see it.'

'Did you see Joseph?' I remembered the shy ginger boy, my cousin, whom I had seen in Shoumen, during our deportation, so many years ago.

'He is an Army officer. He only comes home every other week end.'

'Do they know anything about Sheri?'

'He is in the Army too. They see him every now and then.'

'Oh, jolly good! We might see him too!'

'We might.'

'So all you have to do now, is find a job, and then perhaps somebody would lend you the money. But there is no rush, you are welcome to stay with us for as long as it takes.'

'Thank you Sam, we will try and make it as short as possible. We are really grateful.' said my father, but I didn't detect much hope in his voice.

In the morning my father left for Tel Aviv, to see his brother, Uncle Isaac. Uncle Isaac had immigrated many years ago with my father's parents, when he was a young man. Both my grandparents were dead now, but there was an uncle, an aunt and two cousins I hadn't met. Esther – a few years older than me and now married with a small baby boy, and her younger brother, who's birth, apparently, had been the cause of my aunt's illness. My father returned in the afternoon, his head down, his brow furrowed. My mother took one look at him and said:

'He refused.'

'Yes. His wife is costing him a lot of money.'

'I told you didn't I? He is mean, I knew it.'

I don't think my father ever recovered from the blow of his brother's refusal to help him out. As for my mother, she never forgot it.

Uncle Samuel came in. He scrutinised my parents' faces and probably understood what my uncle's reply had been, because he said in a cheerful voice:

'There is a job. They are looking for local men to get rid of the disused orange grove outside the village. A maabara is going to be put up there. I have enlisted for the job, it's well paid. Do you want to come?'

'Sure I want to!' my father said.

'Come on then. We'll put your name down on the list at the store. We start next week.'

'Doing what?' my mother asked.

'Chopping down the old trees and burning them. You have

to learn to take whatever comes your way, in this country. Specially if you are new.'

'Yes, undoubtedly.'

'It won't take long before you will have a place of your own. And we like you being here!' Uncle Sam reiterated his reassurance ....

As the men left, I heard my mother mutter:

'It suits you to have a cook, and a daily, but nobody asks me how I feel about it.'

My mother had indeed taken on a difficult task and she would not be helped. Until he started to work, my father was only allowed to help with the water and I was sent to the village school, which was a primary school – 6 to 10 years olds, to just sit and listen.

When he received his first pay, my father said that it was time he took us to Tel Aviv, to meet his brother and my married cousin Esther.

My uncle was a small thin man, with an unpleasant half smile permanently on his face, and his eyes focused above or to the side of one, never looking you straight in the face. He looked uncannily like my father; same colour eyes, same, rather thick nose, but while my father looked you straight in the eyes, and was sincere, whether he was angry or happy, the feeling my uncle left me with, was that of a slippery and insincere man. I didn't like him. We stayed there for about half an hour, and when my mother suggested that we should leave, he made no objections, his wife simply kept quiet.

'Ugh!' said my mother when we were out in the street, 'What a horrible little man. And he does look like you!'

'I am sorry.'

'He could have asked us for lunch. It is lunch-time and we have travelled so far just to visit him.'

'Yes, you are right. We'll pay a short visit to Esther, and then we will go back to the village!

'That will take ages, and I am hungry.' my mother said.

'Perhaps Esther will offer us something to eat. I promised to go; she is expecting us.'

My cousin Esther and her family lived in what my father referred to as 'The North'.

'It's the more elegant part of town.' he explained.

Indeed, as we progressed, the streets became wider, the houses more elegant, the gardens – larger and better looked after. The street where she lived looked very much like Gladstone street, in Sofia – a garden square, trees, wide pavements. I sighed. Will we ever live like that again? Then the memory of the shared flat, being spied on and oppressed, surfaced, and I didn't really know which was the better thing to wish for.

We climbed up the two floors led by my father who had been here before. He rang the bell. A slender, tall young woman opened the door.

'Oh, Uncle! Auntie and my cousin! come in, come in!' We all kissed. 'How lovely to meet you all!' Esther continued. 'All these years I had so few relations no uncle or aunt, now you are all here – cousins, and aunts and uncles! Isn't it marvellous!'

Esther was a 'sabra'. She spoke with exuberance, uninhibited by the sound of her loud voice, her wide gestures and her laughter. She had sparkling blue eyes, her hair was cut short, with a fringe which brushed her eyes as she moved her head. She spoke in a rather affected way in Ladino, the only language we could communicate in. Ladino is old Spanish. The Jews who fled the Spanish inquisition took it away with them and passed it on from generation to generation.

'Uri, come and meet my family! I have a very cute little cousin here.'

Her husband appeared, the little baby boy in his arms. He put the baby down and shook hands with us.

'They have just been to visit my father,' Esther told him, 'and I bet he didn't even offer a cup of coffee and a biscuit. Isn't it true?' She asked my mother.

'Well, as a matter of fact ... we will be going home soon, so ... '

'Uncle has told me where you live and in what conditions. We will get something ready in no time, won't we sweetheart?' she asked Uri, and went on: 'and we will all have lunch together.' Her tone of voice left no room for objections.

'That will be very nice.' said Uri 'I'll leave the baby here; you, stay with your aunt and uncle, I'll see to things in the kitchen' and he left the room.

I had never in my life seen a man, any man, take over 'in the kitchen'.

'Tell me now, what are your plans? What are you going to do?

'Well, you see,' my father said, 'I have a job, but we need a sum of money to do some building in the village. We found a roof on which there are walls for two rooms, so all we have to, do is just ... well, spend a little money on it and get a proper home, at the moment ... '

'I bet you asked my father for a loan and he turned you down!'

We were all a little taken aback by Esther's bluntness, but wasn't that a 'sabra' characteristic? My father didn't say a word.

'You should have known better than ask him. He wouldn't do anything for anyone if there is money involved. Surely you remember him. You grew up together and I can assure you, he hasn't changed.'

'Esther, you mustn't talk like this about your own father!'

'And why not? If it's the truth? Let me tell you more ... well, perhaps not right now. Let's concentrate on you – unfortunately we can't help. We have no money. I would ask your nephew, the doctor, if I were you. '

She turned to me now: 'Isn't our cousin David a dish? My God, speaking of bed-side manners! He is absolutely gorgeous!'

I saw my mother look away; my father cleared his throat. Esther looked at him:

'He is doing very well, with that bed-side manner of his, he is loaded.'

'He is a good doctor,' my father said, a cold note in his voice.

'I didn't say he isn't. He could cure anybody, well, any woman, by just feeling her pulse, but he is in a position to help you, I am sure.'

I saw a twinkle in Esther's eye; I realised that she was greatly amused by my father's embarrassment.

'Lunch is ready!' Uri announced.

'What's wrong with your mother, Esther?' my mother asked as we went over to the table.

'She is just out of the loony-bin, and is due to go in again very soon. My father will see to it.'

'Esther! I don't tolerate anyone speaking in those terms about their parents!'

'And why not, uncle. I am telling the truth. Aren't I, Uri?'

'Leave that alone now sweetheart, let's eat.'

'I am all for the truth being said, not whispered or suppressed. My father is a miser and he has driven my mother mad. And that is the truth, or do you say, uncle, that parents, no matter what, are above criticism?'

My father stood up.

'I won't listen to this any longer. I want to leave.'

'Sit down, uncle, please.' Uri pulled him down to his seat. 'You don't know Esther. She likes to shock people, but she doesn't really mean it. Don't pay any attention to her.' He then turned to Esther and said something in Hebrew; she just smiled back at him.

'How about you?' she addressed me 'Are you looking forward to the Army?'

'She will study Hebrew and go to university.' my father said quietly.

'She has to do her army service first.'

'Did you go to the Army?'

'Of course, but I didn't do the whole service because I got

pregnant. Well, you are released as soon as you are married, really.'

'Did you have to learn how to shoot and all that?' I found it very difficult to express myself in Ladino, since I had never actually spoken it before, only heard it.

'Oh, yes you do. The drill is not as hard as the boys', but you are given a gun for which you are responsible. You even sleep with it!' she added special emphasis to the word 'sleep', 'and at night, it feels all cold in your bed. There are plenty of boys. You will have a good time there!'

'What did you say about girls not having to go if they are married?' my father asked.

'It's not quite like that. She has to go in. If she is married, she is given a 'job' – near home, but if she gets pregnant, she is released immediately. It's good for her to go, and have some fun.'

'She is not going!' my father said sharply.

'But why uncle? It's her patriotic duty. I suspect you want to keep your little girl at home, nice and clean? You are afraid of fornication?'

'Esther!' Uri scolded her.

I didn't even know the meaning of the word, but I could guess. I admired Esther's courage to speak in those terms to her own uncle.

My father blushed. That, I had never seen before. He actually blushed! He was going to say something, and I feared that he was going to lose his temper, the way he sometimes did, but my mother said, a pleasant smile on her face and firmness in her voice, in Bulgarian: 'Sit down!'

My father swallowed hard, but resisted my mother's pull and said in Bulgarian:

'She is plain vulgar.'

'And you are plain rude!' retorted my mother 'We are in her home!'

I saw Esther's amused expression throughout this exchange.

There was no doubt in my mind that she knew they spoke about her, and enjoyed it. Uri busied himself with the baby who was sitting on his knees.

'I have heard that the Ulpan in Jaffa is very good for new immigrants.' Esther said to me.

'Yes, so have I.'

'You better come and stay here with me, I will teach you Hebrew better than any Ulpan.'

'No way.' said my father.

'When you start going to the Ulpan, you might find it too much to go back to the village every day. You are welcome to come and stay here.'

'Thank you, Esther, that would be very nice ... '

'She will come home.'

'Well, uncle, what about that long walk from the main road to the village you told me about? The days are short now, isn't it a little risky for a young innocent girl to walk alone in the dark?'

'Perhaps you have a point there,' my father admitted after some hesitation.

'I am not being totally generous. I am also thinking that if she comes to stay, we will be able to go out. Baby-sitters are expensive and difficult to find.'

'When we became parents, we didn't go out. You must be prepared to give a lot up, when you become a parent.'

'But you are wrong, uncle. A parent mustn't give up everything, why I am still young, and want to live.'

'Then you should not have had a child.'

'But if I give everything up, won't I, one day, hold it against my child, and demand the same of him?'

This is not the way we see things.'

'But ... '

'Esther,' my mother interrupted this exchange, 'I appreciate your offer, we will see how it goes and it may very well be that we will hold you to your word. After all, her journeys will cost, even if the course is free. And we are not exactly rich as yet.'

'That's the way to look at it! I like my aunt!'

'We have been brought up in a different way.' persisted my father. 'We have been taught to respect our parents, not to judge them. And we expect the same from our children.'

No one answered, and I broke the silence.

'Thank you very much for offering Esther. I'll certainly come and see you anyway.'

'We must go now.' said my father, not looking at anyone in particular. They saw us to the door. Esther kissed my mother warmly, then my father and, as they walked out onto the landing, Esther took a step back, so that she was out of their sight, then gave me a wink, stepped forward again, kissed me on both cheeks and said:

'Shalom! See you soon.!'

It was already dark when we started our walk from the main road towards the village. I felt very tired, and as I tried to lift my legs off the ground, they refused to obey me.

'Shame on you,' my mother said to me when I mentioned my tiredness, 'you are too young to even know the word!'

It was pouring with rain and my father's umbrella sheltered just the tops of our heads, as we drew close together, but our bodies got soaked through and through. It seemed, at least to me, that by the time we arrived at the house we had been walking for hours. We took off our shoes, then our coats at the entrance and made for the paraffin oil heaters to dry ourselves and warm up. The smell exuded by the heaters was very strong, and I couldn't take it.

'I have a headache.' I said when my mother gave me an uncomprehending look. Only then did I see Elise. She was sitting at the table, writing; totally absorbed by what she was doing.

'Elise!' I was very pleased to see her 'Hi!'

She stood up to come and embrace me, all five foot-nine of

her! 'Good Lord, you have grown!'

'So have you.' we kissed each other, a little clumsily; we hadn't seen each other for so many years. 'How are you?' she asked.

'Fine, fine. But you – tell me about you, school and everything! Is it very difficult?'

'Nothing is really difficult if you want it badly enough.' Elise said thoughtfully.

'I am not the only one to have gone back, in order to go forward. Hebrew is a beautiful and complex language. What I really hate is the study of the Bible.'

'How do you mean? You study the Bible, at school?'

'Not only that, but the Talmud as well.'

'I don't even know what that is?'

'Why are you so flushed?' my mother asked me from across the room. 'Get away from that heater, no wonder you have a headache.'

'I am nowhere near the heater, mum.'

She came over to me and placed a dry, warm hand on my forehead.

'Good Lord, you are burning.'

'Oh, dear, what is it now?' asked Aunt Rachel.

'I do feel a little tired, perhaps I have a cold or something … '

'I know you. You don't just get colds, not with that kind of temperature. What am I going to do?' my mother lamented.

Aunt Rachel walked over to her bedside cabinet and came back, a thermometer in her hand. She handed it to my mother and turned to Elise:

'You better stay away, you can't afford to get it, whatever it is.' My mother stuck the thermometer into my arm pit.

'Always at the most inopportune times, she gets ill. One can almost take a bet on it.'

'No time is opportune for sickness.' remarked Uncle Samuel philosophically. 'I'll tell you stories, don't you worry.' he said to me.

'And you must sing to me too.'

'You do remember the old days then, when we didn't know whether we will be alive or dead from one day to the next.'

'Who can ever forget.' said Aunt Rachel.

'Lets see the thermometer now.' My mother's face fell as she read the thin line. She passed it on to Aunt Rachel, whose face did the same.

'How much?' I asked. No one answered. 'Please tell me!'

'Get undressed and go to bed,' said my mother, 'quickly! What am I going to do with her?' my mother turned to Aunt Rachel.

'There is nothing you can do. Not until tomorrow anyway. The doctor comes to the village then. You will have to take her there – to the village hall, where he holds the clinic.'

'How can I take her out in this weather, with that kind of temperature?'

'You will have to. He won't come. He visits I don't know how many villages in one day, he has no time for house calls.'

'You think that it is the same thing I had when dad was in prison, it isn't.' I said. 'I have no pain at all.'

'I didn't think it was that. I just don't know what to think.' She seemed worried.

'It's probably only a cold' I said and before I knew it, I was asleep. In the morning, my mother had to shake me, to wake me from my deep sleep. She wrapped me in a blanket and took me to the village hall. She had, apparently, gone to see the doctor earlier, while I was still asleep, and told him my symptoms. He looked me over; examined me with his stethoscope, which I was sure he had kept in the fridge overnight, touched my goose-pimpled body here and there, looked up and said:

'Jaundice!'

'Jaundice?'

'No cause for alarm. Keep her warm in bed. The diet must be kept very strict. Boiled semolina only and absolutely nothing else, and tea; lots of tea. One of these tablets every four hours – day and night. It will take some time but she will be all right.'

'What are those tablets?'

'Penicillin.'

My mother wrapped me up again and we went away; she was worried.

'Don't worry mum,' I said, 'I really don't feel too bad.'

But she didn't answer, she just walked, looking down.

I was feverish and half delirious. I woke up every now and then and didn't know what time of day or night it was; whether I had slept for a whole day or just for an hour or so. Occasionally, my mother woke me up to give me the penicillin or to feed me with the horrible mushy semolina. To make it more attractive and palatable, she put some cinnamon on it, and to this day, I can't stand the sight, or thought, of semolina or cinnamon!

My bed was put to one side, so as not to be in the way. I was aware of the rain, which I could hear beating on the window panes; the paraffin heaters were on all the time, but the rooms felt cold and damp. My father and Uncle Samuel went to work every day and my mother and I were left alone.

Sometimes, some woman or other would come to visit us, and in my semi-consciousness: I heard them whisper that it was bad luck 'for her to see herself now'. I wondered what they meant, but I was too ill to even ask. Two weeks or so passed and my temperature began to go down; I heard Ruth say; 'I hope for her sake that she doesn't stay like this!'

My curiosity was aroused, I asked my mother for a mirror but she pretended she hadn't heard me.

In the morning, I decided to use a 'ruse', so I begged my mother to go and ask the doctor whether I could eat anything other than semolina, because I was sick and tired of it. She refused to go at the beginning, I implored her and finally she gave in, and went.

As soon as the sound of her footsteps died out along the path, I ran to Aunt Rachel's dressing table. I couldn't make out the reflection in the large mirror, so I flung open the shutters to let more light in, and looked again. I didn't at first, recognise myself. The hair was my hair all right, a little messy and matted – but still my hair. Intrigued, I scrutinised the features. Yes, they were my features, but the colour of my face! and my eyes! I had never, in my wildest dreams imagined anything quite like it. It was green; well, not exactly green; but green, tinged with yellow. Had the nose been somewhat longer I would have looked like a witch from 'Macbeth'. I could go straight on stage, I thought, I didn't need any make-up! The skin was all horrible and dried up with dark circles around the eyes. And my eyes! the whites were yellow, not daffodil, clean yellow, but horrible, dirty yellow!

I rummaged quickly through a drawer and found a hand-mirror and, with the two mirrors, I could move my pupils out of the way and have a good look at the whites. They were glaucous and blood shot. The sight was quite horrendous so much so, that I burst out laughing. Fancy me, staying this way for the rest of my days! I would be able to get a job as a scare-crow. I was doubled up with laughter at this thought, and this is how my mother found me.

'What the hell are you doing? Get back into bed, you horrid child!'

'But mummy, I am so funny! How could you look at me all this time and keep a straight face?'

'It's bad luck to look at yourself when you have jaundice.'

'Come on, mummy, you don't really believe those old wives' tales, do you?'

'I don't know. It is safer not to look at yourself and anyway, I told you not to get up!'

I went back to bed.

'What did the doctor say about my food?' I asked, and she answered:

'Semolina.'

Chapter Six

It Doesn't Get Easier

It was raining day and night with only short-lived intervals, when the sun shone. The walls had all become damp. My father and Uncle Samuel worked every day at chopping down the old dead trees, then tractors or winches pushed and pulled them along the field where they made them into piles. The men poured paraffin over them to help them burn. The wet wood produced dark smoke which spread over the village; afterwards, the dry dead wood burned quickly despite the rain.

From my bed, I was a silent witness to my mother's hard tasks. She aired the bedclothes every day, she tidied up relentlessly, meticulously every item of clothing, books and papers left around; she hurried frantically, when the water supply came on, to finish within the two hours everything that needed doing; at the end she was tired, pale and irritable. I begged her to leave some of the tasks for the afternoon water supply, like washing the floors, or washing out clothes, but she was adamant that all the housework should be finished by lunchtime.

I often dozed off, even when my temperature fell, because

I was weak, I suppose; weak from all those weeks of fever and very little in the way of food.

One day, I woke up from just such a sleep and realised that there were voices in the room. I didn't stir, and as my mind became clearer, I recognised the voices, even though they were whispering. I recognised the nasal laughter, even though she tried to keep it down! It was Aunt Amelia! My first impulse was to jump up and kiss her, but the topic of their conversation stopped me and I remained motionless, my eyes shut and listened carefully.

' … it isn't something completely new with him is it? What can you do?' my mother was saying.

'It isn't new, you are right but somehow I could put up with it better when I was younger. In fact, as you well know, I retaliated with your disapproval, but at least I felt I did to him, what he was doing to me. Now, he has become so blunt about it, it's embarrassing and painful. He doesn't even try to clean the traces … on his trousers. And you know what, I do it. I brush and clean his trousers and I don't really care, not really. And this is what scares me. Why am I so apathetic? You know me! I should have been screaming at him, and making scenes. I have just finished an affair.'

'Amelia! sh … sh … sh … what are you talking about?'

'Oh, you tire me with your puritanism, what world are you living in, it's beyond me! What is important, really important, is that I have no interest, do you understand? I don't feel anything, I feel that something inside me is dead.'

I discerned sobs. Aunt Amelia was crying and I didn't have a clue as to what they were talking about. But it was very intimate and certainly not meant for my ears. I knew what 'an affair' meant.

'All I seem to care for, is my son. He is the only person in the world that keeps me going. I don't even love my own daughter, and that is terrible, but it's the truth.'

'Amelia, you don't know what you are saying! Of course you love her! But she is married and has a life of her own, you don't see her that much.'

'It's not like that, you don't understand. Yani is … I tremble for him, I await the sound of his steps outside the door like a young lover … '

'Amelia! Stop this nonsense. Yani is your child, and you care for him, that's all. Don't we all care for our children?'

'Not that way, I am telling you. I have a yearning … to have him at home all the time, to look at him. He is so gentle, so tender … and I … ' she broke into tears.

I felt so very sorry for her. I must have moved; I heard my mother whisper:

'Wait. She may be awake.' I imagined her tip-toeing to my bed, but didn't move and kept my eyes shut.

'Hullo!' my mother placed a hand on my shoulder, 'wake up, look who is here.'

I knew pretty well, that she didn't want to run the risk of my overhearing their conversation it was her way of cutting it short.

I looked up, pretending to wake up.

'Look, it's Aunt Amelia.'

'Oh, Auntie! So good to see you!' I sat up on my bed, and pretended not to see the red rimmed eyes. She wiped her face with a tiny handkerchief, and when she spoke to me, her voice was that same voice I remembered from my early childhood, strong, melodious and containing laughter:

'Good Lord! I hope she doesn't stay like this! What a face!' and she laughed. There was no trace of the tears, no trace of the distress that I had heard only a few moments earlier. The change was so drastic, that I began to doubt my own ears.

Aunt Amelia had changed too. Her fingernails were scarlet-red and so was her hair. Her beautiful large green eyes, were made up with a heavy black line all round them, mascara on her eye lashes, heavy patches of rouge on her cheeks and her lips as scarlet as her hair. She looked quite grotesque.

'You only have a daughter,' she said to my mother, 'you don't know the sweetness of having a son. Still, when this goes, and I hope it will, she is not too bad looking.'

'Do you think so?'

'Yes. She'll find a husband all right. But what will become of us, I am asking you, what will become of us who are getting old?'

'I am very ill,' my mother said. 'I am sick all the time and nobody gives a damn about it.'

That was unfair! We all told her to spare herself, not to work so hard, to rest, to see the doctor, but she wouldn't!

'Let's go and talk in the kitchen,' said Aunt Amelia, 'we are disturbing her here. She needs sleep.'

They left the room, and I was left musing over my mother's untrue statement; also, remembering how, when we were young, Yani and Mira and myself, Aunt Amelia would say: 'the children – in the kitchen!' It seemed that we have always been in the way. I lay back, turning over in my mind Aunt Amelia's earlier statements, trying to figure them out. The adults' world was more than ever, an unfathomable, impenetrable mystery.

The time between my father returning from work and the others coming home, was the only time my parents had on their own. Uncle Samuel always went to the village store where all the men, out of work, or after work, gathered for a chat, a game of backgammon or belote.

'I will go to Tiberias next Saturday,' I heard my father say to my mother as they sat in the kitchen.

'What makes you think that David will help you?'

'He is my nephew, isn't he? I have always loved this boy as though he were my own, and he loves me too. I am sure, if he can, he will help us.'

'I am not so sure. Be prepared for a disappointment. I think that people over here have become greedy and mercenary and selfish.'

I was still bedridden, although already convalescing. My father left early in the morning on Saturday and returned late that night, after everyone else had gone to bed. I wasn't asleep, neither was my mother; we didn't talk, not to disturb the others and also because we pretended to be asleep. I heard my father's footsteps outside and awaited to hear what he was going to say, hoping that he would speak loud enough for me to hear. Indeed, I heard his excited voice and from the few whispered words that I overheard, I understood that he had got the money necessary for us to turn Aunt Clara's roof into a home for us.

On the very next day, following advice from the foreman on the site, my father went to Yehud to find builders and to purchase materials. The construction began within a few days. I heard about the plans for the building. Words like corrugated asbestos, which I had never heard before were used to describe the roof that was being put over our two rooms. Doors and windows were being purchased and fitted. My mother went to see how things were progressing. I was still not allowed out.

'Come on, mum, tell me, how does it look?'

'Awful.' she said and refused to comment further.

In the night, I heard my parents talking when they thought everybody was asleep. I understood from their conversation, that the money had proved insufficient and only the very basic improvements had been done. I detected the reproach in my mother's whisper when she mentioned that we will have no ceiling, that the walls were not going to be decorated and that she will be left alone there to 'stare at the gray cement walls', that there had been no money to tile the floor, and that she would have to 'wash this horrible black stuff which suited her mood anyway', referring to the tarred floor, and finally that there was not going to be a door between the two rooms, and that I was going to be practically sleeping in the same room with them.

I felt cold and isolated. I was going to write to Mimi in the morning, I thought, but was I going to tell her all this? Could I explain what I felt?

We received a notice that our luggage had arrived. My father had to go to Haifa to clear it through customs. That coincided with the first day I was allowed out; my mother took me to the doctor for a final examination and I was given a clean bill of health. Before we went home, my mother agreed to take me round to see our future home.

'Now that our luggage has arrived, we can move in as soon as it's here, can't we mum?'

'Yes.'

'Mum,' I ventured to ask, 'why aren't you happy? Life is so difficult for you at Aunt Rachel's.'

'Do you think it will be easier here?'

'Not altogether, no; but at least there will only be the three of us.'

'With the water not just outside, but downstairs, the four gray walls and an even grayer roof for company, I can't say I am looking forward to it.'

How about us then? I thought to myself, my father and I, weren't we 'company'? I knew that I for one, have never been looked upon as much in the way of company.

The walls which had stood bare and exposed to the elements were soaked through and through. Now that the roof had been put on top, doors and windows kept the wind and rain out; the musty smell of dampness hit us as we walked in.

'We will have to get some heaters to dry out the walls before we move in, don't you think?'

My mother looked around without saying a word. Her face was dark and closed. In the morning after our luggage had arrived, we tidied up Aunt Rachel's house for the last time. My mother and I were going to spend the day there whilst 'the boys' were going to help my father open the crates unpack our furniture and carry it upstairs. After dinner, that night, we were going to sleep for the very first time in our new home, in our own beds.

The heaters had been burning for two days and one night; the air was heavy with the smell of paraffin and although the smell of dampness lingered, it was a lot better. At least I thought so. The lamps hanging on the walls gave a pale, weak light. Kitchen utensils were piled up on the table in the middle of the room which was going to be mine but only at night. The sight of familiar objects brought back memories; there was no way in which one could find an iota of comfort in them; my mother sat on my settee, open and ready for me to get in, and started to cry desperately. My father sat next to her, put an arm round her shoulders and tried to whisper comforting words.

'Tomorrow we will get organised, you'll see! and in no time we will make it comfortable, and who knows, if luck is on our side ... '

'Oh, shut up! Luck, if there is such a thing, has long since deserted us.'

'I'll help you mum, please don't cry.'

'If only you had a little more confidence in me,' my father said sadly. 'Do you think that I am happy, offering you this as a home? But we mustn't despair, we mustn't ... '

'I have no more strength, I have no more patience, I am sick, and I am tired, and fed up. Leave me alone all of you, go away!' She freed herself from my father and went into their room, through the blanket that had been hung across the opening, in lieu of a door.

My father followed her; there was nothing else for me to do but go to bed. Even though the sheets and pillows, pillow cases and duvets had spent a few months in the crates, they still had a soupçon of the smell of our flat in Sofia, of cleanliness and starch. After months of sleeping on camp beds, my own, felt like that of a princess. It was soft, hugging and warm. I wrapped myself in the light duvet. What a difference this made, alter the horrible, smelly, vaguely damp grey blankets!

A drop of cold water fell on my face and I woke up with a start. I sat bolt upright in my bed. It wasn't raining; I could see the sun shining outside. I recognised the room; my eyes fell on the blanket that separated the two rooms. Yes, I knew where I was. But where was the water coming from? I felt my cheek, it was positively wet. I looked up. The corrugated asbestos was covered in huge drops, all ready to fall at any moment. I looked at the walls and saw tiny, busy runs of water, springing from the pores of the cement and streaming down the wall. I looked at the floor – nothing, just a few small damp patches where the drops had fallen from the ceiling. I looked under my bed and saw a fairly large puddle. Another drop fell on my bed. I tried to brush it away before it penetrated the cloth, and it was then that my hand felt the dampness all over the duvet.

'Come on!' my mother shouted from behind the blanket, 'time to get up!'

'Yes, mum.' It was damp and cold in the room, and I dressed quickly, shivering.

'We have to let the sun in, and try to dry up all this mess.' My mother walked into the room and flung open both the shutters and the windows then the door to the terrace. The fresh morning air came into the rooms; it was by no means warm. I began to light the heater, but my mother stopped me: 'Get the chairs out on the terrace so that we can put the bedclothes on them to dry up!' her matter of fact, dry tone of voice surprised me.

I had expected her to complain about all this squalor we had woken up to. My father had left for work earlier, and we were alone. I did as I was told, then made some toast and tea for breakfast. My mother had put everything she could, out in the sun but I knew that it was a losing battle, for the weak sunshine didn't measure up to the dampness. In the middle of our silent breakfast it started to rain. We rushed out and grabbed the bedclothes as quickly as we could, before they got even wetter than they already were; we closed all the windows and doors, since the rain seemed to be coming in from all sides.

Among the many items unpacked the previous night, was our iron, which stood in the middle of the table. My mother put it on the heater. The blue flame licked the steel for a while, then my mother took it and applied it onto one of the duvets. A cloud of steam rose from beneath the iron.

'Lovely mum! You have found a way!'At that point, she lifted the iron and we saw it had left an ugly black mark – the paraffin oil exuded a sooty smoke which we hadn't taken into account. My mother grabbed the iron and threw it with all her strength – I didn't know she had that much – against the wall, then broke down, crying.

'Mum, please … don't despair, please.'

'Get out, leave me alone!'

I put my shoes on, took the breakfast dishes downstairs on a tray; it was just gone ten o'clock. I crouched in the rain. The tap sputtered its yellow water and I decided to let it run until it cleared a little. I didn't think we needed any water for washing the floors that day, so I just let it run and rather than wait there, I walked around behind the house. Our two crates were there, and, for the first time I notices a small chicken coop. There were a few chickens inside it and, just outside, a large white cockerel. It was busy pecking at the ground. I looked at the chickens an unusual sight for a city girl. I must have been staring at them very intently, for I was quite unaware of the fact that the cockerel had come up behind me and, to my complete surprise and horror, he jumped up and stuck his beak with a mighty blow into my thigh. The cockerel ran after me. He succeeded in catching up with me before I reached the stairs, and gave me another fierce blow.

My mother was sitting on a chair, looking at the floor,

motionless. She hadn't moved. I was rubbing my thigh, in pain.

'There is an aggressive cockerel downstairs,' I said, nearly in tears, at the same time aware how ridiculous it must have sounded, but I wasn't up to laughing, the pain was so acute.

My mother looked up at me with a vacant expression, then went back to staring at the floor.

'I am not going down again.' I insisted on having some attention from her. By now, my pride hurt more than anything else. 'It attacked me, and the water is running.'

My mother got up, and without saying a word, went downstairs. I took a towel to dry my hair and took my jumper off – it was soaked.

'Go and fill the bucket. The kettle too.' my mother said when she came back with the washing up, rain water dripping from her.

'There is no cockerel!'

I did as I was told. Pained at my mother's disbelief. I kept looking behind my back for the enemy, but he never showed up. He must have taken refuge from the rain in the coop, I thought.

Chapter Seven

Singing in the Rain

'Those crates are large enough to be used as rooms. I am sure that if this one were lying on its side, you could easily walk about in it; why, you could even have a table and chairs in it. 'You have not got a kitchen, have you?'

I was sitting on a chair out on the terrace and could hear Aunt Clara talking to my mother downstairs. It was Friday afternoon, and people came home from work earlier, than usual. It was sunny and warm. When it rained, the sky became dark, the wind seemed to want to destroy everything in its way and the water poured down, as if to drown the world. But when it stopped, the sky turned a beautiful deep blue, and the sun warmed up as though it wanted to make it up to us.

'Do you think so?' my mother was saying to Aunt Clara.

'Of course I think so, and what's more, the smaller one could very well be used as ... well, you can't have a toilet installed, that's too much expense, but it could do as a shower in the summer.'

There was a silence, then my mother said:

'Are those chickens yours?'

'Yes, why?'

'So unlike you, Clara. You … who had all the luxury you wanted … looking after chickens now … and being a house cleaner. Other people's houses.'

'They provide fresh eggs, and the occasional meal, that's reason enough. Forget the past. We are building a new life, the past is gone and dead.'

'I can't.'

'I forgot to warn you. The cockerel is rather nasty. I am full of bruises round my thighs from him, but we need him.'

'Why do you leave him outside?' my mother didn't even mention my encounter with the wretched cockerel, I was furious!

'We can't leave him inside. They fight; sometimes they kill each other.' Aunt Clara said. 'Why, did he attack you too?' there was a note of amusement in her voice which I resented deeply.

She didn't wait for my mother's answer.

'I must get on with my cooking. I hope my Joseph will be home for the week-end.'

'I would very much like to see him.'

'I'll let you know if he comes. He is wonderful, oh, such a boy! The apple of my eye!'

I saw my father turning round the corner. Greetings were exchanged downstairs, then my parents walked up together. I took my chair in, as with dusk it became colder and damper. I lit the lamps and the heaters.

'I am exhausted.' said my father as he fell onto a chair.

'So am I.' echoed my mother. I set the table for dinner.

'Clara says that we could use the crates. She thinks that the big one is large enough to serve as a kitchen,' my mother said over dinner. My father thought for a while.

'She might be right, but then, wouldn't it be difficult for you to have your kitchen downstairs?'

'You are hopeless! Can't you think of anything? It will have to come up here, on the terrace, of course!'

'But how? It's made of such heavy timber ... '

'I don't know how! You are the man, you should find a way.'

'Dad, don't you use cranes to lift the trees and pile them up? Perhaps, if the crane is large enough and if it can lift the crates, it might ... '

I stopped, discouraged, because both of them looked at me and I was expecting the usual 'mind your own business' but instead, my mother said: 'She is right.'

I filled with happiness and pride at the recognition of my contribution.

'I don't know.' said my father, 'I'll have to ask.'

'What a shame it will have to wait until next week! We could have had a kitchen tomorrow, if it were a working day. ' I said.

'Yes. It will have to wait until next week, and if ever, it will be done at the beginning of the week.'

'That's lovely!' I enthused.

'Why are you saying that?' my mother asked, a suspicious glint in her eye.

'Because I'll be out of a job by the end of next week.' My father looked at his empty plate as he spoke.

'Why? Have you quarrelled with somebody?'

'No. The job is finished. The trees are all cut and burnt, the tents will be erected the following week, but not by us. New immigrants from Iraq are coming to live here.'

We heard someone climbing up the stairs. There was a knock on the door.

'Who is it?' my father asked.

'It's me Joseph.'

'Which Joseph?' my father whispered to my mother not knowing what to do, but she got up and walked towards the door, a wide smile on her face.

'Come in Jo. Good to see you!' She kissed him on both

cheeks, then turned to my father, the same pleasant smile still illuminating her features:

'It's Clara's Joseph! Look what a lovely boy he has grown to be!' I recognised the features of my shy ginger cousin, whom I had met in Shoumen during the war. He shook hands with my father, then with me.

'Come and sit down Jo.' my mother invited him.

'Are you an officer?' my father pointed to the stripes on the sleeve of his khaki jacket.

'Oh, that's nothing.' he said, he paused a moment and turned to my mother:

'In fact I came to ask you all to come down. My mother is too tired to climb the stairs, and she has baked a cake. Would you like to come?'

'Yes, of course!' my mother accepted the invitation.

We all followed Joseph, who was lighting the way – with the powerful torch he held in one band; with the other, he was holding my mother's hand.

Aunt Clara's face shone with happiness and pride. The metamorphosis was patently visible, and she did nothing to hide it.

Later, I overheard my mother saying to my father in the darkness, behind the blanket. 'I really hate parents who show off their children like that. She really exaggerates! Why she was no better than a peacock showing off her plumage.'

We all sat around the table on which there were plates and, in the middle a large cake. Uncle Gabriel made the coffee.

'Tell us about the Army then?' my father asked.

'Nothing to tell really.' Joseph said. 'You've seen one Army, you've seen them all.'

'Come on, this is Israel, this is our Army!'

'He is not supposed to talk about the Army,' Aunt Clara said, 'it's all Military secrets.'

'Is it now?'

'Yes, you will see; when you have a child in the Army, you don't know exactly where they are, nor what they are doing. Well, you do, vaguely, but all you pray for is peace and that they should come home safe. You'll see what I mean next year. Although it's a lot easier for girls, isn't it Joseph?'

'Yes, it is.'

'We will wait and see about that. I don't want my daughter to go and serve in the Army. She is a girl!' I failed to understand my father's stubborn opposition to something which seemed to be the law of the land, and which nobody dreamt of trying to evade. I was then, naive enough not to see through his quarrelsome attitude whenever any mention was made of my doing my Army service. Secretly, I was looking forward to it!

Joseph brought his chair round, and sat next to me.

'Are you doing anything yet, or are you still 'acclimatizing' yourself to the new environment?'

'I am doing absolutely nothing. I am bored stiff, but soon I will begin to study Hebrew at an Ulpan.'

'Have you learnt some, in the meantime?'

'Just a few words here and there. I can ask my way, I don't think I can be easily fooled, that's about it, and to my mind it's very poor.'

'I am sorry I am not around. I would have helped you.'

'You have a foreign accent when you speak Bulgarian!'

'Do I?'

'Yes, and it's so strange. I have never heard anyone speak Bulgarian with a foreign accent.'

'You will do, soon, you'll see. What are you reading?'

'Nothing. All I have are my old books, which I have read and re-read.'

'I have some books in Bulgarian, do you want me to lend you some?'

'I'd be grateful.'

'Do you like philosophy?'

'I haven't read much. Descartes, and Nietzsche, but not to any great extent.'

'Come and have a look.' I followed him to the far end of the room, where the light was very faint. There was a book shelf, with rows and rows of books all hard covers, very attractively bound.

'Joseph!' Aunt Clara called, 'come and have your coffee and cake!'

'Where have you got to? Come back here!' my father's voice was rather aggressive. I was a little startled, but Joseph answered:

'We are looking at some books.' and he turned back to me; there was something deliberate in the way he had obviously decided not to obey either of the parents.

'This is Kant,' he went on, 'you might like him. Those are essays on Schopenhauer. That should keep your mind occupied for a while.'

'Come back here, and sit down!' my father ordered again. Joseph put the books down and we went back. We sat on our respective chairs, and ate our cake. I felt that there was a conspiracy between us, and I liked it.

'Do our boys make good soldiers? Do they obey orders etc?' my father asked.

'Sure.'

'I didn't think we would make good soldiers.'

'Who are 'we'?'

'The Jews. We have always been battered about, and no one ever fought back. We were always referred to as cowards.'

'We were never a nation.

'What were we then?'

'A minority. It's easy to batter a minority.'

'Come on, let's go home.' my mother interrupted, I am tired.

I was sorry my father wasn't given a chance to answer Joseph, because I was curious to know what his thoughts were. I must confess I had no opinion on the subject, but I liked

Joseph's. When we got upstairs, I realised that I had forgotten the books.

'As soon as my job is finished, I'll take you to see a doctor.' my father said in the morning.

Then, we heard someone climbing the stairs; quickly, heavily. A loud knock on the frail hardboard door and there he was, tall broad shouldered, smiling: Sheri.

My mother jumped to her feet and he hugged her, lifting her off the ground, and she seemed to disappear in his embrace. He hugged and kissed my father warmly on both cheeks and then grabbed me. I felt weightless as he lifted me into the air. He put me down carefully, and looking at me with an air of mock seriousness, said:

'My, oh, my, oh, my! I mustn't play these games any longer. What have we here? A budding young woman! A lovely girl! Hey, will you let your old uncle parade you through the streets of Tel Aviv and pretend you are my girl friend? They'll all be green with envy!'

'How good to see you folks!' he turned to my parents.

'Come and sit down, tell us what are you doing, where is Elsa, what is she doing?'

'I am a soldier!'

'What rank?' my father was obviously fascinated by rank.

'Rank? Who do you think I am, Joseph?' He is an intellectual, he can study all sorts of important things – strategy and that kind of thing. Me, I am a driver! Me and my GMC – we are a team, where I go, she goes.'

'What does GMC mean, Sheri?'

'Golda Meir and Company!' he answered and I didn't know whether to believe him or not.

'Seriously now.'

'Well, seriously, I belong to the Infantry, I am in a transport division. That means that for the better part of my life, I take things from one part of the country and deliver them wherever they are wanted. I have a pass for week ends, usually, sometimes during the week too, but that's never sure. That's my life and will be for another year. Then I shall become a civilian and God only knows what I will do then. How about you? Aunt Clara's neighbours in a small village of Israel, hey, who would have believed it?'

'Who would have believed that our Clara would become a daily help, Sheri, you tell me that. A girl who grew up with a French nanny' my mother said.

'In a new country, one has to adapt, to take things as they come, give up a bit, give in a bit – for a while, until one can stand on one's feet again.'

'Have you all Israelis gone to the same school? Through the same drill? I hear the same sermon from everybody! I am not prepared to do this. I will not clean other people's dirt! Never!'

'But you won't have to my darling, I have told you …

'Look! You have a lion for a husband. What are you worrying about?'

'Take a look around and you will see what I am worrying about. This is not fit for human habitation.'

'People have lived in worse conditions I can assure you, I have seen it, and with small children too. You must pull yourself together, after all immigration is not exactly … '

'Don 't you tell me to pull myself together!' my mother's high pitched voice took us all by surprise.

My father and I knew, that if she liked anybody at all it was Sheri, and I for one, didn't expect her to shout like that at him.

'I have suffered all alone, for years.' she went on,' and now, now I am at the end of my tether. Now I have no more strength to go on.'

'Please, auntie … of course you have, we all know that! We all know how well you coped; I know only too well that other people's ills are poor consolation. All I wanted to say was that, from now on, things can only get better.' I saw his dark blue eyes narrow, searching for the right words. I felt that he was fighting for my father, that he wanted, with each word he said, to re-instate my father who sat quite helplessly just looking at my mother, in the hope of seeing a spark of approval in her eyes. Sheri got up.

'I have promised to have lunch downstairs – I didn't know that you would be here. I came up as soon as Aunt Clara told me. I'll come back again after lunch …. All right?'

'Yes, Sheri, see you.'

The joy, the magic, the spark of good mood that Sheri's visit had initially brought was now broken; we sat and had our lunch in the usual silence that fell over us as soon as we were by ourselves. If my father or I tried to break it, we would be stopped short by my mother's glance, and her cold, closed face.

Sheri came back soon after lunch. I made coffee, he sat down, and put an arm around my mother's shoulders.

'Who would have thought that we should meet so far away from Shoumen, hey? My childhood fiancée my Thracian princess? I'd still marry you, if your husband would let me!'

This indeed had always been a joke between them – when my mother was a girl and Sheri a little boy, he had asked her to marry him, and from then on, he called her his fiancée.

She laughed. It was so rare for us to see her laugh, that both my father and I exchanged glances, and I am sure that he was as sad and as hurt as me, over the fact that neither of us ever managed to make her laugh.

'Listen folks.' Sheri said. 'I have a pass until midnight, how about taking you for a drive around Tel Aviv, what do you say?

'In that monster? No, thank you. I will be sick for weeks afterwards.'

'It's true that the ride isn't exactly smooth, but that's all I can offer for the time being, come on, be a sport.'

'No, I am sorry. I am not well.'

'Then perhaps I can take this … child here … to the pictures or something. I bet she hasn't seen much of Tel Aviv.'

I didn't say a word. My heart was pounding with excitement, because I knew they couldn't refuse Sheri.

'I don't like my daughter to be out after dark,' my father said, 'but, since, it's you … perhaps, but you will bring her home, back here!' he added.

If he read it, Sheri ignored the implied mistrust beautifully:

'Of course, how else?'

'And you mustn't go to a late show, she must be home by seven.'

'The show only starts at six uncle, but don't worry, I'll bring her back.' He put his cup down. 'I think we ought to make a move, because if we want to get into an early show, we should be in town by 5pm, and my beauty doesn't like speeding too much.'

'Don't you take risks! If you miss the show, you miss the show! Go slowly.'

'Sure uncle, sure. Well, nice to have seen you folks, I'll come as often as I can. come on, are you ready?'

I was! I just took my coat and we ran down the stairs in the rain. Sheri opened the passenger's door – it was quite a climb into the cabin. He came round the other side, and to my surprise, Joseph came out as though he had been watching out for us, climbed into the cabin and I found myself between the two of them on the wide seat.

'Everybody OK?' Sheri shouted over the noise of the engine as we were thrown from right to left as he tackled the uneven ground.

'Yes!' we both shouted back.

'I am not going to say too much Bambo,' Sheri turned to me as we reached the road, 'but I foresee problems for you there, with both your folks. One problem with your mother, and quite a different one with your father.'

'I am afraid you are right.'

'I saw that too, last night.' shouted Joseph.

'Are you going to be able to cope with them Bambo? That's what I am afraid of, I know your mother pretty well; she isn't easy. As for your father, I honestly thought he was more a man of the world.'

'He gives this impression to people. But when it's a question of me, he is quite different. I don't think I will be able to cope. I don't understand them, I don't know what they want.'

'Incidentally,' I turned to Joseph, 'you didn't let me have the books after all.'

'This was done on purpose. I wanted an excuse to come up later and ask you out'.

'We travelled in silence for a while, Joseph and I just watching the wipers fight the rain; Sheri was having quite a task, to see his way. Then the rain eased up a little, visibility became better and Sheri relaxed. He started to hum an old Bulgarian song, slowly Joseph and I joined in; then we sang another, and then yet another. We laughed; the cabin became warm and the windows steamed up a little.

Eventually, Sheri stopped the lorry; we were in Tel Aviv.

'Cousin,' this is how they addressed each other, 'where are we going to take this delectable cousin of ours?'

'As far as I can remember, nothing pleased me more, when I was a new immigrant, than to see American films. So, I suggest we take her to see an American film.'

'OK, But not a Western.'

'No, not a Western. Do you know what a Western is?' Joseph asked.

'Me? No.'

'Don't you think she should, cousin?'

'Yes, she should. OK, let's try.'

The rain had stopped. Sheri jumped down, onto the pavement, whilst Joseph and I had to get out through the passengers' door onto the road. Sheri had parked in the middle of a large puddle. Joseph slid down, held his arms up trying to save me from jumping right into it, but I was laughing so much at the sight of him, ankle deep in water, that I had no control over my movements. Then he began to laugh, I jumped down, splashing water and we walked over to the pavement, where Sheri stood dry and laughing at us.

'It takes some expertise to park like that!' Joseph said.

'Yes, I am well known for my ability to tackle this vehicle.'

Joseph went towards the cinema. I emptied my shoes whilst Sheri held me.

'No more seats.' Joseph announced when he came back.

'Let's try elsewhere. Come on.'

They grabbed me each by a hand and we sped towards the next cinema, down the road.

'Isn't that just right!' Sheri said 'Specially for us; 'Singing in the rain. Gene Kelly.'

'Who is he?'

'Don't you know him? Every girl in this country is in love with him!'

'I don't fall in love with people I don't know.'

'Come and meet him then, come on.'

'What does the title mean?' I asked.

'Oh, you have got to learn Hebrew!' Sheri translated the title. Joseph came back waving the tickets.

'We're on! So, you don't fall in love with people you don't know?'

'No.'

'Whom are you in love with then, that you do know?'

'Nobody, I am afraid.'

'Gooooooodeeeeeee! She's all ours cousin!'

When we walked out of the cinema, I felt like Alice walking right out of Wonderland. It was my second American film and I was no less fascinated than after the first one. The songs, the dance, the colour, the girls' clothes, the love and, above all – the lack of propaganda!

It was, very appropriately, raining again. Sheri took my hand, Joseph took the other and we ran towards the lorry. As we ran, we sang the song Gene Kelly had just sung. And we splashed no less water than he had!

'I have two more hours, folks, how about going for a cup of coffee at Rowal?'

'What is that?'

'A fashionable cafe.'

'I don't feel ... very fashionable though.' I was thinking of my wet hair and my ugly rough coat.

'Who cares what we look like, provided we feel good!'

'I have never felt greater!'

'You see! Come on.'

We sat at a little round table. There were many people there, well groomed and fashionably dressed. Women with impeccable hairdo's, and high-heeled shoes.

'I still feel a bit of a tramp.' I said.

'You look great. I wouldn't swap you for any of these hens.' Sheri said.

'I second that.' Joseph added. We sipped our coffees.

'I am very much afraid that my father will be standing at the window, waiting for me to come home.' I said. I felt Sheri's gaze at me, I knew he was concerned, but whatever thoughts he had, he kept to himself.

We went back to the lorry and Sheri brought the good mood back by breaking into a song. We sang all the way to the village, which was long enough to give me a sore throat.

'I must press on Jo.' Sheri said as he stopped by the path leading into the heart of the village. 'My pass expires in a few minutes and I better hurry, so please take Bambo home, which doesn't really take you too far out of your way!'

'You can count on me cousin.' Joseph jumped down.

'Sheri, thank you!' I kissed him. 'Thank you so very much! I have never enjoyed myself so much. You will come again soon, won't you?'

'Yes, I will.' he hesitated a moment, then added: 'listen to me, Bambo, you have rights, you just remember that. Don't just accept everything out of fear of authority: be yourself, don't be afraid to be yourself!'

He gave me a light kiss on the cheek and I joined Joseph. We waved to him as he drove off. His words puzzled me, I didn't understand what he meant when he asked me to be myself. Wasn't I already myself?

Once the lorry drove away, Joseph and I were left in total darkness and total silence. So much so, that we felt we had to whisper.

'I can't see a thing.' I said.

'Don't worry, I know the way backwards. Give me your hand, here is the path.'

From the firm road, we stepped onto the slushy mud.

'The mud is sticking to my shoes, and they are getting heavier and heavier with every step!'

'So are mine.'

'How quiet it is. Even the frogs in the pond are quiet.'

'Do you listen to them too?' Joseph asked.

'Yes, before I go to sleep at night. I never knew frogs had such powerful voices, did you?'

'No.'

My eyes grew accustomed to the darkness and I was surprised at how much I could actually see in the dark blue velvety night. I stopped and so did Joseph.

I became aware of his hand holding mine. He must have read my thoughts, because he let go of my hand.

'I can hear some crickets.' I said.

'Those are grass hoppers.'

'What are grass hoppers.'

'The ones are crickets, the others – grass hoppers.' We

laughed, then resumed our walk. We reached the house and Joseph came with me to the bottom of the stairs. 'Are you afraid to walk up? Do you want me to come with you?'

'No, no. I am not afraid. Thank you.'

It was darker behind the house, than it had been in the field and I could no longer see his face.

'Thank you very much' I whispered 'I really enjoyed myself today.'

'I should be the one to thank you.' he said.

I didn't know what to say, but I made no move to go. Neither did he. I felt something brush against my cheek, very gently. I turned my face quickly, to find out whether it was his lips, but found nothing. Perhaps he had just touched my cheek with his hand.

'Good night.'

'Good night.'

I walked quietly up the stairs and only when I reached the top, did I hear his steps as he went back towards the front of the house. My father's loud, angry voice startled me, after all that beautiful deep silence:

'Sheri was supposed to take you home!'

'He had to hurry to his camp. His pass expired and ... '

'Why wasn't I told that ... Joseph was going with you' my father went on from behind the blanket. 'Why didn't you tell me?'

'I didn't know, dad.'

'Go to bed!'

I had already gone.

Chapter Eight

My Father Tries to Earn a Living – I Begin Hebrew Classes

On the following day, Sunday, my father came home from work accompanied by a few of his colleagues who had volunteered to help with the lifting of the crates on to the terrace, thus promoting them to a kitchen and a shower. The yellow, grotesque looking crane crept up the path, driven by a man in blue overalls.

The larger crate was positioned immediately outside my door, it's opening facing mine, leaving about a foot-long gap between the two. It was placed on four stones, to avoid water collecting underneath and rotting its floor.

A corrugated tin square was secured between the top of my door and the top of the crate, which made it possible to go from the one to the other without the need of an umbrella.

My father's colleagues came over every day after work, and helped turn the crate into a kitchenette. A square opening was sawn in the middle of the outside wall and a glass pane fixed in it, which provided us with a picture window, with a view over the fields and the eucalyptus trees lining the road. The window could not be opened, but provided a good deal of light. Needless to say, none of the men was in any way professional. Nonetheless, they also made a shelf to accommodate the paraffin burners and the kitchen utensils.

A large, second or even third hand kitchen sink was installed. All the piping was done with ordinary, rubber garden hose and if ever the pump would supply enough water with enough pressure – we would have real running water in the kitchen as well as in the shower! – Well, the smaller crate, positioned in the far corner of the terrace, with its lid for a door and a hose poking through a hole in the ceiling.

In the kitchen, wind was blowing in through the gaps in the planks, but there was a remedy for that too: they covered it, on the outside, with sheets of tarred paper, which insulated it against the wind and rain, but at the same time, gave it the appearance, from the outside, of a gift parcel in mourning!

At the end of the week, our kitchen was finished, and my father – out of a job. He stayed in bed for two days; he ached all over. He wasn't really cut out for physical work. When he got up, he decided that it was time for me to start my Hebrew studies. For this purpose, it was necessary to go to Jaffa and as my mother refused to accompany us, my father and I went on our own.

I was, later, to become so familiar with the walk from the village to the main road, that I wouldn't even think about it. But in those first days, walking for half an hour along that road, with the cars zooming past, spraying mud all over us, was unpleasant and offensive. When later, I was on my own, cars would stop and offer me a lift. It was customary in Israel, but I was new enough, insecure enough and frightened enough, to be offended and refuse. Perhaps the attack by the policeman at the gate of the quarantine camp had something to do with it.

It took us an hour and a half to get to Jaffa. Jaffa wasn't

another town as I had thought, or if it were, it was an extension, so to speak, of Tel Aviv. One drove down Tel-Aviv-Jaffa road starting at the heart of Tel Aviv and two miles further on, one was in the heart of Jaffa. The Ulpan stood on Jerusalem Boulevard, which is the main artery of Jaffa. We went in to the office where I was admitted to a beginners' class, which was to start on the following Sunday.

My father became a night watchman that same week. He would leave home at about five o'clock in the afternoon, his sandwiches and a thermos flask in his hands, and come home on the first bus, around 6am. He ate gluttonously the breakfast my mother prepared for him and went to sleep, until we got him up at 4pm, gave him a meal and off he went.

My Hebrew courses were four times a week, and on the days I went to school I didn't see my father at all. He was already asleep when I got up in the morning, and by the time I came home, he had left for work.

My mother was left alone all day long. She had to cope on her own with the water, which still had to be carried upstairs for washing – floors, clothes, ourselves, drinking; the washing-up had to be taken downstairs, washed then taken up again; the shopping had to be done, the bedclothes dried and aired.

I knew the routine, I helped on the days I didn't have to go to school, but on the days when I wasn't there, I would return to find my mother sitting always in the same chair, in the same posture: her back hunched, her hands lying limply in her lap, her eyes either staring vacantly at them or at some vague spot on the floor.

It was at that time, that my father began to bring bread in from town; I did do the shopping in the village store before going to my classes but, on the days I wasn't there to do it, in an effort to take over some of my mother's burden he bought bread in town. He also began helping with the housework. He and I did the washing-up together on Saturdays, he took it upon himself to see that all the paraffin oil lamps, heaters and burners were full before he went to work, he even swept the floor when I wasn't there to do it. The evenings were spent in a deep, heavy silence. I tried to talk about my class, about the people, about the Hebrew language, but my attempts fell flat, and I would get no reply or reaction from her. She sat there, wrapped up in a world of her own, which she silently prevented me from entering.

I felt guilty for spending most of the day in a bright, clean, warm room, with people; that I had the privilege of travelling on the bus, the freedom of the walk to the main road, that I found my clothes washed and ironed whenever I needed them and that I did very little to deserve it. My father grew irritable, he lost weight and whenever we were all together, on Saturdays (the weekend did not exist at the time. There was one day off – Saturday), the atmosphere was heavy and tense. On the 18th day of his work as a night watchman, or on the 18th night rather, he came home in the middle of the night. I hadn't heard him climbing the stairs, but my mother, who was a very light sleeper, had. I heard the knock on the door, sat up, my heart pounding, and asked my mother:

'What is it mum? What's happening?'

The fear of infiltrators was by now embedded in my mind, and I was certain that we were about to be killed, but killers don't knock on doors!

'It's me, open up, don't be afraid!'

It was, undoubtedly, my father's voice.

'What happened? Are you ill?' I heard my mother ask; her voice was low and there was little compassion in it.

'I am fed up, I need sleep.' my father said meekly.

'You could have waited until morning.'

There was some movement behind the blanket that separated the rooms.

'I am tired,' I heard my father repeat, then all was quiet. He slept for 24 hours. When he finally woke up, the following evening and came to the kitchen where we were, my mother said:

'Now, what are we going to eat?'

'I am going to the American Embassy tomorrow. I am going to tell them about my work at their Military Mission in Sofia and what I have been through because of it, and ask for a job. That's the least they can do for me.'

'This is brilliant! Why didn't you think of it before!' I couldn't contain my enthusiasm.

'Wait. He hasn't got a job yet.'

'It's worth trying. I will go tomorrow.' and he went back to sleep.

Chapter Nine

Avi

My class consisted of about twelve people from at least six different countries, all of different ages and from different walks of life.

There were some Romanians with whom I could speak French, two Polish girls, with whom I could speak Russian, but Françoise, being the only French person and speaking no other language at all, took to me immediately. She came and sat next to me, and no matter how much I tried to get her to speak Hebrew during the breaks, she kept on babbling away in French. She had plans for her future and she had a compulsion to tell me about them. She was planning to get married. She wanted to have a home of her own and saw herself as a good wife to a successful man. But it wasn't until she told me in all seriousness that she was actually looking for the man in question, that I stopped listening.

My father went to the American Embassy, as he said he would, and told his story to the Personnel Officer who apparently, took a great interest in it. He called a secretary in and asked my father to repeat it all while she took it down in short-hand. He then shook my father's hand and promised to be in touch with him as soon as he had something to tell him.

The Post for Kfar Ana, was brought to the village twice a week from Yehud and left at the village store. People came in and rummaged among the envelopes for their mail; the envelopes were kept in an old greasy box. Since his visit to the American Embassy, my father became the most assiduous of rummagers, awaiting a reply, possibly an invitation.

A whole month elapsed and our funds were getting very low, so much so, that my father felt obliged to agree that I should stay in town at my cousin's during the week, to avoid the expense of travelling to and from the village.

My cousin Esther and her husband, made me very welcome indeed. She was a lively, fashionable and outspoken young woman whom I admired greatly. She never hesitated to say what was on her mind; she did it with feline grace, of which I thought I was totally devoid. She asked me to stay home with her and keep her company. I gave in a few times; on those occasions we put the baby in his push chair and went to sit in a fashionable café where we would sip coffees, eat cream cakes and watch the world go by. She would talk to me about our grand-parents, whom I had never met, and with whom she had spent most of her childhood; then she would talk about her father and how mean he was, how her mother had slowly grown more and more mentally unbalanced. But most of all, she used to flirt. She would smile at men sitting at the other tables, even if they were there with women. She smiled at men, passing by, who would slow down and come to our table, she would then look away and talk to me, not paying attention to them. She would smile at men driving by, who, many times, would pull up and stop, and if they saw a further invitation in her eyes, they would come to our table. She let this happen a few times. I knew that she was leading them on, that this was amusing her; I felt terribly embarrassed and looked away.

On one occasion when we were walking home, she said:

'Ah, in bed, you can do anything .... ' with a deep sigh.

'How do you mean?' I was curious and at the same time, almost afraid of the answer. But she didn't answer me, she just said with an enigmatic smile:

'You'll find out. You'll soon find out.'

My father received a letter from the Embassy, inviting him for a further interview. The day of the interview, I went straight home after school, impatient to find out what had happened.

'I start work on Monday!' he said, a happy, broad smile on his face. Letters of praise for his devotion to his work, his reliability, and his honesty, had arrived from his ex-bosses, in reply to the Embassy's enquiries. My father was pleased and proud.

'Yes,' said my mother, 'but the wages are very low.'

Ж

Françoise was waiting for me at the school door when I arrived there on Sunday morning.

'I have told my gang about you and they want to meet you!' she announced.

'Thank you very much. That would be very nice.'

'You will come then? Next Saturday? We get together every Saturday at Claude's and Eve's – that's the one married couple among us. We all go there because they have kids and can't go out. Besides, nobody else has a real home. Will you come then?'

'Yes, I'll try. If I won't be able to, I'll tell you so before the week is out.'

I was excited by the idea of meeting new people, but I just didn't see how I was going to be able to go out. Forever worried that I might let people down. I didn't promise, but I hoped that Esther might work something out.

'Of course you will go, you silly cow!' was Esther's reaction.

'But how? I have never stayed in town on a Saturday?'

'Leave it to me.' she winked 'I'll phone your father, and I'll ask – as a special favour from him! – for you to baby-sit for us on Saturday, or Friday for that matter. You can spend the Friday and Saturday here. He can't check up on you here.'

I felt sad.

'What's up now?'

'I don't know. I do know! I wish I didn't have to lie to them.'

'Ah, what do you care. They are asking for it.'

'But why, Esther, why?'

'Simply because they, and especially your father, I think, don't want to accept the fact that you are a grown up girl now, that you need a life of your own. They like to think of you as a child, and keep you home, with them, where they can exercise their supervision with ease. They can't keep an eye on you when you are not there! And, my dear, as far as I can see, they haven't taken any trouble teaching you anything, have they? What do you know about life? About people? I can see – nothing!'

'But how will I ever learn anything if I am not allowed to meet people? And why does he have to keep an eye on me? Why can't he trust me?'

'Obviously he can't.'

'What do you mean!' I was outraged, and ready to defend myself.

'It's him, silly! Not you. He can't bring himself to understand ever, that you are old enough to think for yourself, to be a person in your own right, which, may I tell you, you are.'

'Oh, Esther, you leave me no hope! I so want them to understand! Aren't parents supposed to … know … what's good for their children, or so it has been hammered into my head … I don't know any longer.'

'Rubbish! Parents only want what's good for them! In your father's case, it's his own peace of mind. Why you might be messing about with some boy, you might be even enjoying yourself out of his sight, and to him – this is danger, because messing about with boys, gets girls pregnant!' Esther said and added with a final touch of victory 'and this cannot happen when you are safe at home, under his supervision.'

'But I can't stay home all my life! They've got to understand that, sometime.'

'I am pleased you say that, because the way you have been behaving, I thought that you didn't have enough strength of character, and that they will gradually turn you into a nice little spinster.'

'I still want to explain, I want them to understand … '

'Sod them!' Esther said, putting an end to, the conversation. She telephoned my father in his new office, and asked his permission to keep me over the week-end because she and her husband wanted to go out. He agreed.

'You owe it to them.' my father told me when I arrived home from school on Thursday. 'You practically live there, you eat there, baby-sit for them is the least you can do for them. Esther says that you are very good with the baby.'

'Yes, I suppose I am. He is a lovely child.' I said, hating myself for not daring to tell the truth, for stifling my need to be truthful , to explain, to get him to accept me and my needs, what I felt and what I wanted to do, so, that I could accept myself! But I didn't dare.

My father had given Esther some money to buy me some clothes, and during one of our morning strolls down the fashionable Dizengoff street we purchased a skirt, a jumper and a pair of shoes. Those were the first new clothes I had had for years and although they were very simple, I felt elated and didn't try to disguise my joy. The gentle, soft yellow wool of the jumper caressed my skin and I ran my hand along the sleeve for the feel of its softness; the skirt fitted perfectly round the waist and flared away from the hips, to become quite wide at the hemline. I turned round enjoying the shape it took as I turned, and the slight caress of the wind on my thighs. My feet felt comfortable in the brown low-heeled shoes, with an elaborate buckle in the front. I was walking on clouds, I felt like a princess.

'You look lovely!' said Esther when I got there on Friday afternoon. 'What have you done with your hair?'

'Nothing, I just washed it. We gather rain water in the village. It's very good on the hair.'

'Doesn't she look delectable?' Esther turned to her husband, and I blushed. On Saturday afternoon, as I was getting ready to go, she handed me the keys to the flat:

'Enjoy yourself. You can come home whenever you like. We're not going to sit up and wait for you. Are we sweetheart? We have better things to do!' and she winked.

I arrived punctually at 6pm, and found Françoise waiting for me outside, as she had promised.

'Nearly everybody is here and they are dying to meet you! Come on. Unfortunately, Avi hasn't arrived yet, but he can turn up at any moment!'

She spoke excitedly as she led me towards the house. A large oak tree in the middle of the garden spread its branches over our heads, creating a moving green canopy with the breeze playing among the leaves, letting in here and there, a little light. The house was in the bottom of the garden.

'Here we are,' Françoise said, 'meet our host and hostess: Claude and Eve.'

We shook hands; exchanged polite phrases. I think that they were as embarrassed as I was at Françoise's inexplicable enthusiasm. Claude took my arm and led me through a narrow hall, into the lounge. He introduced me to at least seven or eight people. I shook hands with them, muttered my name, they muttered theirs reiterated by Claude, but in the end, I didn't know which name belonged to whom.

'Did you meet them all?' Françoise came over to me, 'What do you think? Wait until you meet Avi though, he really is something! We're never sure about him, he is in the Army.'

'So, you come from Bulgaria?' A boy with a red pimply face came over to us and practically pushed Françoise aside.

'Yes.'

'This is incredible.'

'Why?'

'Because you speak such good French.'

'I went to a French school.'

'I learned English at school, but you should hear me speak!'

I was rather bored by all this and decided not to answer, in the hope that he might say something more interesting.

'What are you going to do? I understand that you are a fairly new immigrant?'

I had thought it obvious what all new immigrants did; this question that everyone seemed to find of such paramount importance, especially when the answer was so obvious, was no less boring than his previous conversation.

'Where did you learn Hebrew?' I asked instead of replying to his question.

'On a kibbutz. All of us here,' – he swept the air with a wide gesture – 'Immigrated early on, illegally, you know? During the British Mandate … '

'I know.'

' … and we all went to Degania, that's a kibbutz on the shore of the Sea of Galilee, it's very … '

'Stop boring our lovely new recruit with your stories Dickie, you'll scare her off and she'll never come again!'

A tall, somewhat older man came up to us now. He was smiling at me; I had noticed him watching us from the far end of the room. He had two glasses of wine in his hands and handed me one:

'Here, have some wine and don't listen to him. He is a chronic Bolshevik, only not enough of one, to stay on the kibbutz. City life holds temptations that the kibbutz doesn't offer!'

Dickie was about to say something, but the man turned to me again:

'How long have you been in this country?'

'Just under five months.'

'Oh, so green … '

'How about you?'

'Long. Too long. I came here when I was ten. That's over fifteen years ago.'

'Were you on the kibbutz all this time?'

'No, not all the time. Only until '48. Then I joined the Hagana in the war of Independence and stayed on when it became the Israeli Defence Forces.'

'Are your family also here?'

'No. My family were all deported. None of them came back.'

This was the first time that I was confronted with anyone who was directly hit by the war in this way. I didn't know what to say.

'How terrible.' I said, feeling that it was a platitude, and I wished I had not said it.

'I have learned to live with it. One has to.'

'It's you now who is boring her with your stories.' Dickie put in.

I had forgotten about him; before any of us reacted to him, Françoise appeared from somewhere and whispered loudly enough for everyone to hear:

'He is here! He's just arrived! I told you that you will meet him, it's Avi!'

She was so excited, and I didn't understand what was all the fuss about. If the mere appearance of this person excited her so much, she must be in love with him, I thought.

'Really?' said the man who had been talking to me and whose name I didn't know. 'How interesting.' he seemed puzzled.

'Why are you saying this? Did you try to stop his pass?' Françoise asked suspiciously. I didn't understand what exactly was going on. There were implications and under-currents that flashed over my head; I kept quiet, intrigued.

A very good looking young man in a military uniform walked in. He strode to the middle of the room, a wide smile on his face:

'Hullo everybody!' he waved around. His behaviour suggested that he was the favourite, spoilt child of the family.

'What are you up to? Shall we have a game of cards?' Claude was already pulling up a chair, Dickie joined them, and they engaged in a casual game.

'Do you play cards?' the man asked me.

'I am afraid not. I don't find them very interesting.'

'Neither do I. Do you like music?'

'Yes, I do.'

'Would you come with me to a concert next week? It's a Menuhin recital.'

'Oh, I'd love to!' I knew that with Esther's assistance, I would be able to go out and could afford to make arrangements without hesitating.

'Thank you very much. Only I don't know Tel Aviv very well, but if you tell me where it is, I will find it.'

'The other way round. You will tell me where to pick you up, and I'll be there.'

I gave him Esther's address and he said that he was going to pick me up on Wednesday, at 6pm. I had no doubt in my mind, that he had a spare ticket; and that this, and this alone, had made him offer it to me.

The card game broke up now and Claude put a record on

the turntable, then came quickly up to me.

'Shall we …? '

He put his arm round me before I answered. We danced. He held me tight against his body; the sensation was very unpleasant as I felt him getting more and more excited and short of breath; I was also worried that his wife might get the wrong idea. I tried to push him away.

'Beware of Leon,' Claude whispered straight into my ear, 'he lives up to his name, but rather than a lion, he is more of a wolf really. What did he talk to you about?'

'This and that.' I was taken aback. Weren't these people friends? 'Did he tell you that he is a high ranking officer in the Army?'

'He didn't tell me that, no.'

'He isn't a young boy, as you can see for yourself, he is nearly 30, he doesn't do something for nothing, so be warned.'

And I had accepted to go to a concert with him! I got worried.

'He is taking me to a concert on Wednesday … '

'A concert? I haven't known him to go to these lengths!'

I didn't understand what Claude meant, but I felt an urge to clarify things with Leon – whose name I only now learned. The struggle to keep away from Claude's grip wasn't helping matters. The dance finished. I sighed with relief. Françoise came up to me:

'What do you think of our Avi then?'

'I don't know, I haven't met him.'

'Isn't he handsome? Like a film star?'

'He is very handsome. Are you in love with him?'

'No, of course not. But I wouldn't say no if he asked me! Neither would any other girl, that includes you, I am sure, but otherwise – he has nothing to offer.'

'That does not include me!' I was offended to be put in line with everybody.

'All right, all right, have it your way.'

'What do you mean 'he has nothing to offer'?'

'He is as poor as a church mouse.'

'What does it matter? If you love each other?'

'Of course it matters silly! A girl wants a home, security.'

'What use would a home be if you don't love …? '

Leon came and took me by the hand, interrupting our conversation.

'Come on, let's dance,' he said and took me in his arms. Françoise winked and walked away. Leon held me loose, which was nice – I could breathe, but he looked straight down at my face and made me terribly self conscious. I began to think of how I was going to tell him that I wasn't going to … I knew I was going to stumble there, but I also knew that I had to tell him, when he said:

'Is something worrying you?'

'To tell you the truth, yes.'

'Anything to do with me?'

I hesitated.

'Come on, tell me. What was Claude telling you?'

Well, I … '

'Come on, I know Claude.'

'He … warned me … he said that you don't do something … for nothing … and … .I mean … what I wanted to say was I won't mind one bit if we cancel the appointment for Wednesday because I don't sleep around and if this is what you want from me, it simply is not possible.' I said it in one breath.

It was the first time in my life that I felt I had stood up for myself and although the words had, at first, been difficult to utter, I felt better for having said them. Leon laughed.

'All I want is to take you to a concert. I want to enjoy the music myself and if it gives you pleasure – it pleases me too. I am not asking, and will not ask for anything in exchange. Your company is compensation enough; besides, I had the tickets anyway.'

'Oh, good. I am so pleased. That's settled then?'

'Absolutely.' I was suddenly aware of a presence and looked aside. Avi was standing right behind us, his wide smile revealing perfect teeth.

'May I dance with our new recruit?' he asked Leon, who stepped aside and as Avi put his arm around me, I felt Leon's long glance towards him.

Avi held me loosely as we danced. The music was somewhat faster than the pace Avi chose, and I had some difficulty in following him. We didn't talk. The silence became a little embarrassing, but I didn't know how to break it. He was looking at me, and I looked away, nonetheless flattered that he had chosen to dance with me. He kept staring at me; I sensed a smile rather than saw it, and somehow I knew that he knew that I was embarrassed and that he enjoyed my embarrassment. I was hoping that the record will come to an end but it seemed endless. Finally, he broke the silence:

'Did Leon tell you that he is my commanding officer?'

'No. Is he?'

'Yes; and he didn't want me to get a pass today.'

'Does that depend on him?'

'Mainly. But I managed.'

I wondered why it was that Leon should want to refuse him a pass, what had all this to do with me and why was he telling me as though he was revealing something important.

'Do you like the crowd?' Avi changed the subject.

'Yes, they are very nice.' I was relieved. 'But I haven't met everybody yet. Of the girls I only know Françoise and Eve.'

'You won't meet the girls very quickly. They are jealous of you. You see, Françoise has been talking about you for weeks; she made us very curious to meet you.'

'Really? I can't see why. Were you curious as well?'

'Yes, very much so.' He smiled and I saw the dimples on his cheeks; the dark blue eyes. He really was very handsome.

'You certainly didn't show it, if you were.' I said, daringly, blushing.

'I like to take my time over things; but I saw you all right.'

Dickie came up to us, took me away saying:

'It's an 'excuse me' dance.'

'OK.'

'You ought to be careful with Avi,' he said as soon as we had moved away, 'He has a way with girls. They all sleep with him.'

'How do you know?' I resented that all these so called friends, chose to speak to me, an outsider, against each other as soon as the opportunity presented itself.

'He tells us. He tells about the girls, especially the ones at the camp. He gets his fun, then shares it with us.'

'I think this is quite despicable.' I said, wondering if it were true. When the dance finished, Dickie took me by the hand and led me to where a few of the girls were sitting.

'This is my sister, Laura. This is our friend Aviva, and this is Tamar.'

I shook hands with each one of the girls. They were very sophisticated, they wore make-up, their hair was certainly 'done' by a hairdresser, and their clothes were those of young women. I felt like a child, standing there, in front of them.

'Leave Avi alone! He is mine!' Laura said in deep, angry voice. I was taken by surprise. So much aggression in her voice! She could keep her precious Avi if it were true that he shared his experiences with all the boys in the gang, but I wasn't going to tell her that. Why is it that in books, people always manage to come up with the right retort at the right time!

'Isn't it up to him.' I said, the words had just come out, I hadn't planned them but they had the necessary effect. Laura looked aside, drew at her cigarette, her hand trembling slightly. The others giggled. At that moment, I felt sorry for her. I was about to tell her that I had no interest in her Avi, when Dickie who was also laughing, said:

'That'll teach you! You possessive cow! And if that doesn't, then nothing and no one will!'

Somebody was pulling my sleeve. I looked back – it was Leon.

'Come and have something to eat.' he said.

'Yes, with pleasure.' I walked away with him towards the buffet. I wasn't hungry.

'Were they having a go at you?'

'People are so strange.'

'People are strange, as you call it; not only here, in this room, but everywhere.'

I was disconcerted.

'Why? Why are they like this?'

He took my hand and smiled, a warm, friendly smile. I felt that I could trust him, that I could relax with him.

'Your naivete is charming. You see beauty where there isn't any, and you are surprised and hurt when you find this out. I sincerely hope that you stay exactly as you are now unspoilt and charming.'

My feeling of uncertainty returned; I couldn't help feeling that he was being a little patronising 'unspoiled and charming' amounted to 'childlike'.

'I think I better go home. Will you excuse me.'

'I will take you home.'

'No, no, please. You don't have to interrupt your evening. It isn't far and I can manage.'

'There is nothing much to tempt me to stay on here. I'll take you home.'

I thanked my hosts for the lovely evening. They thanked me for coming and asked me to come back every Saturday, if I wished. I waved a general 'good night' and we left. It had all been so phony and disappointing.

Leon left me at the bottom of the stairs at Esther's. Everybody was asleep in the flat, and I crept into my bed as quietly as I could.

In the morning, Esther was very impatient to hear all about my evening and as usual, asked me not to go to school. But I swallowed my breakfast and ran off. At school Françoise told me hers, and everyone else's delight at my having 'joined' the gang. I was less than enthralled with the idea. When she asked me what I thought of her friends, I found it very difficult to tell her the truth so I just said: 'very nice' and left it at that. As usual, I was to stay at Esther's that Sunday night. I now spent up to four nights per week there; I telephoned my father on the days I didn't go home and in this way we maintained contact. In the afternoon, Esther questioned me again, in detail, about the party and the boys I had met. I told her now about my date with Leon, about the disconcerting behaviour of those people who were all supposed to be friends, and how I understood friendship to mean something completely different.

I had to talk about it to someone, I knew I couldn't tell my mother and although I regularly shared my thoughts and experiences with Mimi in my letters, it was a slow process and Esther was there and ready to listen. What is more, she was experienced.

'When I meet him,' Esther said about Leon, 'I'll tell you what he is all about. I have a flair about people. How about the others? This Avi guy sounds interesting.'

'I don't know about interesting, he is handsome. In any case, I don't stand a chance. All the girls are after him.'

'Yes, but do you like him?'

'Yes, I suppose I do, but what's the point …? '

'One never knows with men. They don't necessarily like the women who run after them. On the contrary.'

'Yes, but those girls! They are smart, attractive, experienced. Just take a look at me!'

'And he wasn't interested in you at all?'

'I don't think so, no. He just danced with me because he had probably danced with all the others already. I don't know.'

'I bet you would fall for him!'

'I told you, he is surrounded by girls and I don't know him.'

'Are you afraid to compete? Is that it, then?'

'I see no point in it. Besides, I am not so sure I want to win. He sleeps with the girls then he tells his mates about it – for fun. I think this is terrible. And also, you are right, I don't like to compete.'

'All men tell each other about their prowess; that's a known fact.'

'Well, if it is, I don't want to be the subject of it.'

'That's a form of cowardice, you know, and pride.'

'It may very well be.'

Leon came to pick me up as arranged. I introduced him to Esther and off we went. The recital was a unique experience. To see and hear a living legend play ! I had heard of him, not in Bulgaria, but in Israel. Leon was very pleasant and made me feel at ease. He took me back to Esther's after the concert.

'I hope you enjoyed yourself,' he said, rather ceremoniously, 'and I also hope that you will agree to come out with me again.'

'I enjoyed the evening very much.' I said, just as ceremoniously, 'My parents are very difficult as far as my going out is concerned. So, I wouldn't like to promise right now, if you don't mind.'

'But you will come to Claude's won't you?'

'Yes, I will.'

He wished me good night and left. I walked up the stairs, recalling my day out with Vlady and the warm feeling that I had experienced, the friendly, flowing conversation that we had had. I went to bed feeling rather sad and despondent.

'I don't like him.' said Esther in the morning. 'He is nice enough, but he should come back when you are a few years older and ready for marriage. Now you want to have fun, and he is no fun, am I right?'

'Yes, you are rather. But I won't marry someone who is not

fun and with whom I am not in love anyway.'

'Rubbish. A husband is a man on whom a girl can lean on, rely upon – a responsible, dull person.'

'Why should a husband be dull? I'll never marry a dull person!'

'Because marriage is dull! Nevertheless, it provides the security a girl needs.'

'Oh, you are talking like Françoise! I am not going to be married for 'reasons' – I will marry because I will be in love and want to share the rest of my days with that man.'

'Ah, what's the point.' She sighed, 'You'll learn. You're still young and full of illusions.'

'I may be!' I was angry now, 'and you can be sure of one thing – I'll stay that way!'

Chapter Ten

Conspiracies and Whispers

He was standing, leaning against the door-frame, a cigarette in one hand, the other in his trouser pocket. As I approached the school entrance recognition made my heart race. Obviously, he had been watching me getting off the bus, crossing the road, walking towards my school, squinting in the morning light. My first thought was: he has come to see Françoise. She talked so much about him, perhaps they were in love after all. As I got nearer and nearer, he continued to look at me without saying a word; so I felt obliged to speak first:

'Good morning Avi. Hasn't Françoise arrived yet?'

'I don't know. I didn't come to, see her.'

'Oh, I see … you were passing by?'

'I had to take some stuff from my base to a camp just behind these buildings and I thought I'd drop by and see whether you would like to come to the cinema with me tonight.'

I was so surprised, I didn't know what to say.

'I … I … would love to, but you see, I live far away and my parents are expecting me home this afternoon. I am sorry, but

I can't make it today.' I mumbled and was sure that he could sense my nervousness.

'That's all right,' he didn't stray from his casual way, 'next week then. I am not likely to get a pass this week end, this is why I am suggesting next week, can you make it?'

'Yes, Sunday will be all right. I usually stay at my cousins, in town, on Sunday nights.'

'Lovely. Shall we meet outside Mograbi then, at 6pm?'

'All right.'

'I'll try and get there in time but one never knows with us soldiers. If I am a little late, will you get the seats? I can never be sure, within quarter of an hour, of my timing. But I'll be there, don't worry.'

He dropped his cigarette on the ground, stepped on it, gave me a smile and a wink, and left. I stood there, where he had left me, as though struck by lightening, incredulous and confused.

Ж

Spring was nearing now, it didn't rain so often, the sun rose into a limpid blue sky and warmed the air gently. The large pond outside the village was still full and the frogs still sung their serenade every night. The walk from the main road to the village had become a habit by now, I even found it pleasant in the warm sun.

On my way home, that Thursday afternoon, my feet were not touching the ground, my mind was still whirring with the morning's event. At last someone had chosen me. At last someone had shown that he preferred my company to that of others. Avi had taken the trouble to come and find me.

As the village came into view, I realised that it was time for me to 'sober up' if I didn't want to be found out. Since I had last been home, so many things had happened to me! Things about which I was going to have to lie to my parents; not so much lie, as withhold the truth, which in the final analysis amounted to the same thing.

I found my mother sitting in the kitchen, in her usual position – hands limp on her lap, eyes fixed on the floor and her back hunched. I had only been away for a few days, but the village, our home and its squalor, my mother's incomprehensible behaviour, her apathy and occasional aggression, it had all faded away from my mind.

'Hi, mum.' I kissed her cheek – she didn't move.

'Am I in time to help you with the four o'clock water?'

'Everything has been done. You don't want me to do housework in the afternoon as well, do you?'

'Not you, mum, me. Why do you work so hard when you know I can do something when I come back? I could have washed the floors.'

'Yes, of course, I will wait for you to come home whenever you please and perhaps do something.'

'This is not fair, it's not when I … '

'Leave me alone!'

I went into my room to change. With the hours of sunshine lengthening every day now, the warmth had begun to dry out the walls. There were dry areas and the darker, wet patches were edged by a white line of fungus. The smell of condensation was even stronger than before and hit me as I walked in.

My father arrived home soon and we sat in the kitchen.

'Go and close the windows and doors and light the heaters and the lamps.' my mother told me and as I got up immediately to do as I was told and get away for a while, she added: 'Don't put the wicks up too high! the glass gets black with the smoke and difficult to wash.'

Alone in the rooms I thought about Avi as I was closing windows and lighting lamps and paraffin oil heaters. The glass chimneys in the lamps were shining with cleanliness and I was careful, as I touched them, not to leave finger marks. The heaters exuded a strong smell as I lit them; that, mixed with the smell of dampness, was quite unbearable.

We had dinner in our usual silence. My father enquired about my studies and also whether I was going to be top.

'This isn't school dad, there are no marks here. We are all grown ups trying to learn a language. If we don't work well, it will be to our own detriment.'

'As long as you are aware of that, I am happy. Do you agree mum?' he said.

My mother shrugged, not saying a word. She looked down at her plate, her face closed.

'Let's go and visit someone.' my father suggested. 'How about Sam and Rachel, shall we?'

'No.'

'Why not? It's only seven o'clock, what can we do? Besides it will do you good to get out, and see some people.'

'I don't want to see anybody.'

'Come on, you don't really mean it. Let's go out.'

'You call this 'out'? Walking in the dark, the mud as deep as my ankles, and all the bloody dogs barking? No.'

'We have a torch and it's only a short walk. We will see people, and it will improve your mood a little … and mine!'

'Yours – perhaps, but not mine. You forget this place as soon as you are out of the door, but me, I am left alone here to rot!'

'This is not fair … I don't forget, not at all, but I have to earn our living don't I?'

My mother didn't answer, just shrugged. I felt that my father was trying to control his temper and wished he would. I wished he wouldn't start shouting because then it would be horrible.

He left the kitchen and we heard him walking down the stairs.

'Mummy, please, don't upset yourself!' I took her hand from where it was lying, limp on her lap. It was dry and hot.

'It's easy for you to speak.' She withdrew her hand from mine.

I so wanted to comfort her, to say the right words, to do the right thing, but I didn't know how. There was no escaping the reality of the awful squalor we were living in.

My father came back. Thank God, he had only been 'behind the wall' – this is where we went in lieu of a toilet – a half demolished clay wall, which might once have been part of an 'out building'.

'Let's play a game of rummy.' There was no trace of irritation in my father's voice as he spoke.

'I don't want to play rummy.'

I cleared the table, and we went to bed.

Ж

Joseph came out when I was washing up. I stood up, my legs numb from squatting.

'Hi.'

'Hullo, how are you?'

'So-so. I was looking forward to a lie in. I am exhausted,' he stretched.

'You don't get a chance to lie-in at your camp do you?'

'No! You should take advantage of it while you can. You just don't know how sweet it is! Are you doing anything today?'

I looked up to make sure my father wasn't at the window and said:

'No. I seldom do anything on Saturdays.'

'Would you like to ... '

At that moment my father appeared at the top of the stairs.

'Are you nearly finished? I'll help you with the tray.' My father came down, ignored Joseph's presence, took the tray and turned round, motioning that I should follow him.

'Good morning uncle.' said Joseph.

'Good morning.' my father answered, then turned to me: 'Come on, your mother needs you upstairs.'

'Wouldn't you like to get those books I promised you?' Joseph said.

'Yes, I would. I'll be up in a moment dad. Just getting something to read from Joseph.'

'Don't be long.'

I followed Joseph inside. Aunt Clara was dusting.

'Hullo auntie.' I greeted her.

She looked at me briefly. Her greeting was just about audible: 'Good morning.'

We went over to the book case; Joseph extracted the volumes.

'You haven't had your breakfast yet! I got up early to cook it for you, specially!' Aunt Clara said.

'Back in a second mum.'

We went out on the porch.

'I hope you'll find these interesting.' Joseph said, whispering. He then looked carefully towards the door and added, 'My mother is as petrified of you as your father is of me! Aren't they funny?'

'She shouldn't worry on my account.'

'Hm, I wouldn't know about that.' Joseph said with a smile.

'In any case, I can't say I really understand them.'

'My mother is afraid that I shall marry. She fears for my career, what she really is afraid of is that I won't be around to be smothered any longer when I am married.'

'Do you really think so?'

'I know so! And your father, he is petrified that you might

have some personal experience which he can neither prevent, nor be a part of. He is jealous as hell.'

'Oh, no, he is trying to protect me from being hurt!'

'Protect your virginity? Protect you from a man ever touching you? Protect you from life! But you have to live your life!' Joseph noticed that I was blushing, I suppose because he stopped suddenly and added softly, 'I have shocked you haven't I? I am sorry … I … '

'Jo!' Aunt Clara's loud voice came from inside.

'Coming!'

'Thanks for the books.' I ran upstairs.

When all the housework was finished and lunch was over, I took one of the books and sat on the bench we now had outside, on the terrace, to read. It was pleasantly warm. The title of the book was: 'Thus Spake Zarathustra' and I immersed myself in it for a while. But the thought of Avi imposed itself upon me and I ended up in a dreamy, semi-absent state, my eyes on the page, pretending I was still absorbed by the text.

After school on Sunday, I went to Esther's and told her of Avi's visit to the school last Thursday and that I was going out with him that evening. She listened to my story, then said:

'Rubbish. He didn't happen to be there, he made it his business to be there, to see you!'

'What makes you think so?'

'Because that's how it is. I know. Now, he is becoming a lot more interesting.'

'Please help me do something with my hair! and perhaps put some make up on, or pluck my eye brows!'

'You need nothing. You look just fine as you are.'

'I don't believe you! You are trying to prevent me from making the best of myself, like my parents!'

'You fool! How can you say such things! You know you can trust me. You look just fine. Can't you see, he didn't go for any of the made-up, sophisticated – as you call them – girls! He went for you, the way you are.'

At 6pm, it started to rain. I was clutching the tickets in my hand, standing outside the cinema and my heart, with each beat told me: 'He is not coming … he is not coming … ' People went in, and I was now the only person standing outside, in the rain, looking to my left and to my right, trying to, keep a straight face, in case he turned up. Every young man in uniform – and there were many passing by – I mistook for him; my eyes were blurred from staring. I moved nearer the wall for protection from the rain, my hair was wet and I knew my face betrayed my worry and my eyes were red because I was fighting tears.

He turned the corner at a quarter past, a wide smile, on his face.

'Hi, You got the tickets ? Let's get in, we'll miss the beginning!'

He took the tickets from my hand, led me towards the entrance, showed them to the usherette and in we went. Only when more than half the film was over, did I begin to recover from the experience of waiting. I don't remember the film. It must have been a Western. All I remember is his presence in the darkness and my total disconcertedness.

When the film was finished and we found ourselves out in the street, Avi took my arm.

'Let's go for a walk by the sea. You are not in a hurry are you?'

'No. I am not.'

The rain had stopped now and a chilly wind was blowing from the sea. Avi led me towards the railings of the barrier. He leant, his back on the rusty metal. I felt his face near mine, and when a passing car's lights shone, I looked at his beautiful, regular features with fascination. I could hear the sea, angry and turbulent just a few metres below.

'I have been in this country too long.' he said.

'Have you? How long is that?' I was pleased that we could finally talk.

'Eight years. I came illegally with the others.'

'Yes, and you all were on the kibbutz together.'

'Yes, then as the Army service came along, they all left one by one. Not one returned to the kibbutz after their service. I won't either. That sort of thing is OK when you are young. I am going to England as soon as I am demobbed.'

'Are you? But why?'

'I have a sister there. I want to get married, I have been alone too long.'

'How do you mean? How old are you? You speak like someone with a lifetime behind them.'

'I am 22 and I have been on my own since I was nine.'

'Nine? But … how come?'

'My parents were deported then; I have been alone ever since. Not one of them returned.'

My heart ached for him. There was no emotion in his voice as he said it, but I felt the tragedy, I wanted to hug him, to somehow make it up to him.

'I am so sorry.' was all I said, although I felt a lot more.

'I know too much about people,' Avi went on, in an even unemotional voice, 'I know too much about this world's nastiness.'

'But, how did you survive? How did you manage?'

'It's a long story. I'll tell you some other time.'

'Why are you going to England?'

'Because I want to get married and I don't like the girls here. They are all too vain and too loose, too easy.'

I didn't know what to say to that.

'Are Bulgarian girls easy?' he asked, a light note in his voice which I took to be his way of amusing himself by embarrassing me.

'I don't know. I can't answer for all of them. Do you think English girls aren't easy?'

'My sister says that I would find a nice girl there; they are rich too.'

'You want to marry money, like Françoise?' I felt a strong pang of disappointment.

'No, no, I don't want to marry money, as you call it, what I want is a good girl. Do you understand what I mean?'

'Yes, I think so.'

'Do you want to get married?'

'I don't know. I haven't thought about it really. I wanted to go to university; it seems that I'll have to do my National Service first.'

'You mustn't go to the Army!'

'Why? Why not? You are talking like my father now.'

His hand reached out and took my hand. It was the first time that we came into any physical contact.

'If Bulgarian girls don't sleep around, you mustn't go!' His voice was as intent as his grip. Surprise made me take a step toward him. We still didn't touch. He let go of my hand.

'You went out with Leon last week.' Avi said suddenly.

'Yes, he took me to a concert.'

'It's true then.'

'What is true? Did he tell you?'

'No, I guessed. He left the camp on Wednesday, but wouldn't say where he was going. He hinted that he was going to get married soon, that he had found a lovely girl, a 'nice' girl, intelligent, at that.'

'What are you talking about?'

'I just wondered whether he had you in mind when he said all that.'

'This is diabolical!' I was furious and my voice went a few octaves up, 'I don't know what Leon thinks, neither what his intentions may be, but one thing is certain – they have nothing to do with me!'

I saw his white teeth flash in the semi-darkness.

'Do you think you are the nice girl he was talking about then?'

Avi teased.

'I may or may not be 'nice', it's got nothing to do with him.'

'I am pleased to hear it, very pleased.' he took me in his arms and let my body rest on his. He held me for a little while, then kissed my cheek lightly, his lips lingering a moment on my neck. I felt my whole body tingling; the cold salty air on my face was pleasant against my burning cheeks. I put my arms around his neck, and for a brief moment experienced that same wave of warmth spreading through me, that I had felt when Vlady had kissed me.

Avi moved away. I took my arms from his neck, a little embarrassed that he had been the first to move away, secretly longing for a passionate kiss.

'Let me take you home. It's getting late.'

'Yes.'

'Do you want to go to the cinema again tomorrow?'

'I have to go back to the village tomorrow. Home I mean.'

'I know where you live. Françoise told me. It's not far from Tel Litvinski – my camp.' he said 'I could pop in.'

'I am afraid my father won't approve of that one bit. He doesn't allow me to go out with boys. He is … very strict.'

'I think that this is a good thing. I will respect your father's wish and not come over but shall we go out on Wednesday then?'

'Yes.'

'Shall I come and pick you up here?'

We had arrived at Esther's.

'Yes, it's flat no 5, on the second floor.'

'See you Wednesday then, around six.'

Ж

'You are in love! I can see it all over your face!' said Esther as I walked brightly into the kitchen next morning. 'Did you have a good time?'

'Wonderful. He is so … wonderful.'

'Tell me, tell me what happened?'

'How do you mean 'what happened?', nothing happened, we … '

'Tell me from the beginning! Was he there already?'

'Oh no, he was a little late, the Army you know how it is.'

'I know. Did you sit at the back?'

'What do you mean?'

'Did you kiss all the time?' Esther's voice contained impatience. I was outraged:

'Of course not!'

'Oh, sorry. And then?'

'We went to the seafront and chatted for a while. He has been on his own since he was nine, can you imagine? His parents and family were all deported.'

'I've heard that story before.'

'Of course you haven't had the second World War here, have you? You don't … '

'We had a War as well. The War of 1948, but that's unimportant now, what else happened?'

'Nothing, I am seeing him next week.'

'Sounds promising.'

'He is going to England.'

'Why?'

'He has a sister there. He wants to get married to an English girl.'

'And he didn't touch you, not even a little?'

'He kissed me. A little.'

'How do you mean? 'A man either kisses or doesn't.'

'He gave me a light … brotherly kiss on the cheek.

I must have felt that Avi was not coming across too well, because I added:

'He also agrees with my father that a girl should not go out with boys.'

'Charming! And what is he?'

'Well, he ... '

'Who paid for the tickets?' Esther asked, her eyes sharp and alert, full of suspicion, piercing through me.

'I did. But I had to, because he was late and ... '

'Did he reimburse you?'

'Nnno .... '

'Not even for his seat? He didn't even offer?'

'Well, we forgot. In any case it doesn't matter.'

'Oh, but it does. A soldier without a family is usually broke, I know that to be a fact. But an honest man, a well meaning man, either says so and doesn't suggest the cinema, or if he does, he says that he can only pay for himself. You see, it isn't the fact that you paid, it's the whole approach which is wrong. I don't like it at all.'

'He will come to pick me up here, you will meet him.'

'It is good that he is going to England.'

'Oh, you spoil-sport! You know-all!'

'It doesn't really matter. You have time to fall in love ten times before you find the right one, don't you?'

I wasn't so sure.

Between that Sunday night and the following Wednesday when I was meeting Avi again, nothing really mattered; nothing really happened around me; nothing penetrated my mind because there was no room in it for anything or anyone, but Avi.

I was a little surprised and very relieved that my mother, who usually saw through me so easily, didn't see the change. Even I could see it. My eyes seemed larger, somehow and there was a light in them that wasn't there before; my cheeks seemed flushed and my skin glowing. Once my mother remarked on the fact that I was being 'slow' and 'daydreaming more than usual', as she put it, but then, she thought that this was just typical of me. I didn't mind. It didn't hurt me as it used to, because now I had met someone who cared. Avi hadn't taken advantage of me and that meant, to me, that he would never do anything to hurt me.

Finally Wednesday arrived. I went over to Esther's after school. We had lunch and chatted. I took a shower and got dressed. The baby was a little restless, so I sat and played with him on the floor while Esther did some ironing. Time seemed to have stopped.

'You are being ridiculous.' Esther caught me looking at the clock every minute. The guy is going away, he told you so himself so you don't get yourself involved. OK, so you like him. Go out with him, enjoy yourself, but don't lose control in the process.'

'Who is losing control? I am impatient, isn't it natural?'

'I would be pleased to find out that he is at least as impatient as you are, but I don't know, do I? Neither do you. And his being late, points to the opposite, I would say.'

'He can't do as he pleases. He is a soldier.'

'You seem to forget that I have been in that establishment. I know. If you are at Tel Litvinsky – you are a 'jobnik' – he is out at four o'clock.'

'Perhaps he has some special assignment?'

'The specials are not based at Tel Litvinski.'

Avi arrived three quarters of an hour late. I was by then, sick with worry, but the moment he arrived all my anguish vanished. I introduced him to Esther. He then knelt down and played with the baby. Esther pulled out her tongue at me, over him. I flushed with anger and we left.

'Shall we pay Claude and Eve a visit?' Avi suggested when we got downstairs.

'That would be nice.'

He put his arm round my shoulders and I felt elated, happy, warm and secure.

'What have you been doing?' Avi asked.

'Nothing much.' I said, my ears popping. 'The ulpan is taking up a lot of time. I work hard because I want to be fluent quickly.'

'You are ambitions, aren't you?'

'Oh, I don't know. I just like to understand what's going on around me, to make myself understood.'

'You are doing that very well, in French.'

We were walking down the boulevard Ben Zion; it was already dark and the evening was mild.

'I couldn't live in a country whose language I couldn't speak.'

'What's all this about going to university, you were telling me about?'

'I would like to study architecture, or interior design, but I can't see it happening, not at the moment.'

'Tell me about your parents. You said your father was strict.'

'Yes, He is. He would kill me if he saw us now. I don't know why.'

'I know. Because he knows what boys are like. He is right.'

'He doesn't want me to go to the Army either.'

'Right again.'

'But I want to go! Why should he think that just because I would be away from his constant vigilance, I would ... sleep around! This is rubbish! I want to experience life, to meet people, to be the responsible for myself .... '

I was beside myself with indignation, but with Avi, at least, I could speak my mind. He pulled at my sleeve.

'Let's sit on a bench. I don't feel like visiting any longer. Do you mind?'

His voice was soft and quiet. We sat down.

'So,' he said slowly ,'you don't sleep around.'

I looked at him. What did it matter to him? His face was serious and I thought I had detected a note of urgency in his voice, as though it did matter. I had never felt that anything concerning me mattered very much to anyone, not for my own sake. My parents didn't care, they worried, and that was different. Avi seemed to care. I wondered why.

'All right,' he said, 'I can see you are shy, you don't have to answer me. I am sorry I embarrassed you.'

'Tell me about your family.'

'Are you sure you want to know?'

'Yes, please.'

Avi leant back and looked straight ahead as he spoke:

'We were seven, at home. My parents and five brothers and sisters; I was the youngest. I can still remember the feeling I had when my father took me on his knee. He was a very big man. We were hiding from the Gestapo. We had two flats and spent a few days in each, so that they wouldn't track us down. Early one morning, the door bell rang. Somebody must have denounced us. My father got us all up and let them in. I looked up at him and he made a gesture, his eyes pointing towards the door. I thought he was telling me to get out. I was in my pyjamas and it was winter. The men were looking the flat over and I knew that my father had hidden a lot of jewellery in the upholstery of the settee. We all knew. He had told us, in case he was arrested in the street. He knew better than try to escape through the window. We had heard that others, who had tried, were shot dead. The Gestapo had men outside, just for that purpose.'

Tears ran down my cheeks as I listened to Avi's story, looking at his profile as he sat motionless, looking straight ahead. His voice placid as though this hadn't happened to him but to somebody else. I wiped my cheeks as he looked at me. Now I could see his face. It had a cold, distant expression, his features tight, his eyes wild.

'I walked backwards towards the door,' he went on, 'looking all the time at my father who kept on encouraging me with his eyes. I reached the door. From there I could see just half of him. I blew him a kiss and he smiled at me, only with his eyes. He didn't want the men to realise our little game. I slipped out onto the landing. I remember the Gestapo downstairs and wondered, what to do. Then I saw the cupboard with the electric meters. Luckily, it wasn't locked. I went inside, pulled the door shut, and stood there, holding my breath. I heard them leave the flat. I heard my sisters' and brothers' voices, my mother's sobs, my father's voice, and then a slight knock on the door and I knew that it was my father, that he was just passing on the landing now, that between him and me, there were just these doors and that this, this little tap, was his final 'good bye'.I waited until there was no more noise, got out and quickly unstuck the seal they had put on the door. It was still wet. I got in took all the jewellery from the settee – the Gestapo hadn't found it – stuffed it all in my pockets, I had changed into some warm clothes, put my winter coat on, and left. I put the seal back across the door and went back into the cupboard.'

Avi paused a while. I was still crying and shivering. He went on without looking at me:

'I stood there until dark. I was all numb. Then I walked, and went to the opposite side of the city. I had no money you see, I couldn't get on any public transport.'

'What happened then? How did you live?'

'I found a room.'

'But who lets a room to a child?'

'They do, when you pay them with jewellery. That kept my landlady quiet. So long as she knew she would get more jewellery from me, she wasn't going to give me away.'

'How did you manage?'

'There were some rich Jews who had organised a kind of a clandestine kitchen for destitutes like me. I went there.'

'And what happened then?'

'I started to work for the Resistance. I could go anywhere in the town, because I didn't look Jewish. They were making false papers somewhere – they didn't tell me where, for safety. What you don't know – you can't tell. I delivered those false papers to Jewish families in hiding. The papers enabled them to leave the country. Many prominent men here now, owe their lives to me. I even helped blow up a bridge once, and another time, I was in a bus, and I had false papers for delivery on me. The bus was raided – they were looking for Jews. I slipped the papers into the hood of the coat of a girl in front of me, put my hands in my pockets and whistled a Hitler Jungend song. Nobody touched me. I have learned to live with all this,' he went on, 'a rich family wanted to adopt me then, but I preferred to be on my own. They still are my adoptive family, but I find them boring. They are very rich.'

'You were only nine … '

Avi took me in his arms.

'This is why I want to, get married and have a family of my own. I have been alone too long.'

'Yes, I understand now. I really do. I hope that in England … '

'I don't necessarily have to go to England … if Bulgarian girls are good girls … and you are a Bulgarian girl … I may not have to go anywhere.'

'I will do anything to make you happy! If I only knew how, if I only could make it all up to you!'

He kissed me. He kissed my frozen lips. Then my cheeks, still damp with tears, then my neck, slowly, without passion.

'I must be going back now.' his breath burned my neck and I shuddered, but he stood up suddenly, his face smiling and relaxed. I got up too.

Perhaps, I thought, it was possible to live with those things. Perhaps he is strong, a lot stronger than me.

'I'll take you home now.' We walked up the Ben Zion boulevard, his arm in mine.

'Will you be at Claude's on Saturday?' Avi asked.

'I don't know. Will you?'

'Yes.'

'So will I then.'

'All right. See you on Saturday then. We might not stay there, we might wander off, on our own.' He gave me a wink and left. I wished I knew what the wink meant!

I had a bad night's sleep. I dreamt of bells ringing, of my father's arrest, way back, in Sofia, only instead of the green Bulgarian Militia uniforms, the men wore black and were shouting in German. I woke and slowly returned to reality. Avi. I wanted to hug him and with my love, heal all his wounds, with my love, erase all his suffering.

The smell of coffee came from the kitchen and I heard Esther's voice talking to the baby. I got up and went straight to the kitchen, still in my pyjamas.

'Good afternoon.' Esther said.

'Hi. What's the time?'

'Nearly nine.'

'Oh, god, I must hurry!'

'You are late anyway, stay here today! Come on, keep me company.'

I sat down. I felt tired. Esther put the baby in his cot and came back.

'How was it, tell me?'

I shook my head, not knowing where to start. Avi's story came back to me in all its gloomy details and I felt I was going to cry again, when Esther shook me out of my introspection with a shout:

'WHAT IS THAT?'

'What?' I jumped up. 'What is WHAT?'

'THAT !' She was pointing at my neck.

I ran to the bathroom; indeed there was a large brownish bruise, I must have been bitten, by some insect. It looked quite awful. I returned to the kitchen:

'This is quite awful, Esther, do you know what it is? A spider or what?' I remember her look, to this day. Her lower jaw dropped, then she started to laugh. Her laughter grew and she shook with it, unable to utter a word. I stood in front of her, barefoot in my pyjamas, disconcerted, already ashamed, although I didn't know why. Eventually she took a deep breath and said:

'Do you really mean you don't know what this is? Am I to believe you, or are you making a fool of me?'

'If anybody is a fool, it's obviously me. I haven't a clue! What seems to be so funny?'

'This!' said Esther, serious for the first time, 'is a love-bite; it only happens when people make love. He must have sucked your skin pretty hard to make it so bruised.'

I was numb.

'You made love.' Esther said.

'He kissed me.'

She looked mistrustful.

'We sat on a bench, on Ben Zion Avenue and talked, then he kissed me.'

She thought, a while, then said: 'In this case, he has done it deliberately. In love play, in passionate love play, it can happen; it is connected with sex.'

'We sat on a bench.' I repeated fearfully. 'There was no passion. He kissed me very gently … or so I thought …. '

'I suggest you stay here today. I'll ring your father and tell him I want you to baby-sit for us.'

'I want to go home.'

'If your father sees this – I am not responsible for the consequences. You know what he's like.'

'I want to go home.'

'Do as you please. It's your business. I'll give you a scarf. Wrap it round your neck.'

Chapter Eleven

Humiliation

I don't remember the journey home. All I knew was that I felt ill. I was going to say that I had a sore throat and go to bed. If I did this as soon as I got home, I would avoid my father. Once in bed, he couldn't see my neck. I felt guilty anyway, with all the lies I had been telling my parents lately, or with all the truths that I hadn't told them and I wished I had! My hand went to the place on my neck where the mark was; I scratched it under the scarf, hoping it might disappear, but Esther had told me that it took at least four days, if not longer.

I walked up the stairs, my heart pounding with fear. Fear that my mother would read through me, and would, like Esther, think that I had done things I hadn't done. I found her in my room, in her usual position, in the semi-darkness.

'How are you mum?'

'How do you think?'

'I am not feeling too good, may I go to bed?'

'If you have to. But fill the lamps first. I am fed up.'

'Yes, mum.'

I took the lamps down from the wall one by one, took them out to fill, my hands trembling with fear that time was running short and that, if I don't hurry, my father will arrive home from work. I did my best not to drip any paraffin on the outside of the lamps – to avoid the smell, took the lamps back, hung them on the walls trying not to leave any finger marks on the thin shiny glass as that would irritate my mother; I lit them, trying not to betray my hurry.

'May I go to bed now.'

She shrugged:

'Do as you please.'

I heard my father's steps outside, just as I bent to undo my shoes. 'Hullo' he came in.

'Hullo dad.' He walked over to my mother and kissed her cheek. I was struggling with my shoe laces when I 'felt' him straighten up and look at me. I went on undoing or trying to undo the now entangled laces; a long moment passed during which I felt that I had been discovered, hoping I was wrong.

Then, came the roar:

'WHAT IS THIS?

I stood up; I saw his eyes flashing at me, his jaw tighten up, his hands – in fists. My hand went to the scarf; it must have moved away as I was bending down.

'WHAT IS THIS?' he took a pace towards me; I took a pace back, away from him. 'WHO DID THIS?'

I wanted to tell him; I wanted to tell him about Avi, his suffering in the war, his awful loneliness and how 'this' really didn't mean too much … but my father's eyes petrified me. They seemed quite mad. I couldn't talk to those eyes. I was paralysed with fear.

'TELL ME THE NAME OF YOUR LOVER!' He took another pace towards me and I receded again. He picked up the wooden pole, the one that was wedged to keep the door open. He took it in both his hands, like one holds a golf club and came towards me. 'YOU DONT EVEN KNOW THE NAMES OF YOUR LOVERS, YOU DIRTY WHORE!' It wasn't his voice. It wasn't a human voice. It came from somewhere a lot deeper in his body, than his throat, I didn't know where from. I stepped back as his hands now lifted the pole and, as I felt the wall behind me, I realised that there was no way out, the pole was above my head now and was going to smash down at any moment. I shut my eyes and, not looking at my father's eyes any longer, felt my heart slow down, felt a great peace inside me.

'It's better that way,' I thought, my body leant against the wall. I was ready.

It was then that my mother screamed. A high-pitched shrill, long whine. With my eyes still shut, I became aware that my father's attention was drawn away. I opened my eyes. My father was looking at her now; he then looked at his hands, clutching the pole. Without looking at me, he threw it on the floor, his jaw trembling. He swore loudly, bit his lower lip and left, slamming the door behind him.

My mother was sitting, her hands between her knees, her face down, swaying from right to left. I ran to her, knelt down and put my arms around her knees.

'Mum ... mum ... I am sorry, I am so sorry .... '

But her swaying became stronger and stronger until I had to move away. I looked up at her and realised that she wasn't aware of my presence, she was wrapped up in that world of her own, a world of darkness and despair to which I had no access. I listened now to what she was saying, amazed, uncomprehending:

'I can't take any more of this ... this has been my life ... I can't take it any longer ... his jealousy ... his madness ... my life ... my young years ... wasted ... a life ... gone ... a youth ... gone ... to a madman .... '

No. She wasn't speaking to me. I moved away and sat on a

chair. I now realised that I was shaking. I went to the kitchen. My legs were shaking and my knees gave. I staggered out, drank some water, sat down and looked out of the window, trying to calm down and understand what had happened.

I couldn't. I took a glass of water to my mother.

'Leave me alone:' she brushed my hand aside and the water got spilled on the floor. I sat down again.

'I want to go to bed.' she said. I helped her up from her chair and led her, through the curtain, to their bedroom. I had an arm round her shoulders; she felt very small and docile. I helped her undress, watching all the while for a sign, a look which would tell me how she felt about me. But her eyes avoided mine, her face was inscrutable.

'I must disgust her' I thought.

Once in bed, she shut her eyes, and I pulled the covers over her. Her hand pushed me away . I went to my room and to bed. I curled up and cried. I had brought nothing but worry and aggravation to my parents and I loved them so much, I wanted them to love me.! Yet, I only seemed to give them cause to hate me for being such a source of worry. I cried for a long time, my head tucked under my duvet. I didn't hear my father return home.

I woke up and found my eyes stuck together. Eventually I forced them open. The mirror showed me a pale face with red-rimmed, puffed, half-shut eyes.

I found my mother in the kitchen.

'Good morning mum.'

'You're up, then.'

'Mum, please, let me talk to you, let me explain.' She didn't answer. She didn't encourage me, not did she discourage me, so I took a deep breath and told her everything.

'If I don't turn up on Saturday, he might come here and … I hate to think what might happen then. Dad will kill him.' I awaited my mother's reaction, I hoped for her understanding of the situation and her absolving me of all my father's unjust and humiliating accusations. But my mother didn't react.

Then I thought of something:

'Mum, if I went to Eve's now, this morning, and ask her to tell Avi not to come to the village, a lot more trouble might be avoided. Please let me go.'

'You can go, as far as I am concerned. But your father forbade you to leave home if he finds out – I don't want to be involved.'

'Oh, thanks mum! I will go there and back as quickly as I can!'

Ж

'What's the matter with you?' Eve asked, as she let me in and I followed her to the bathroom where the children were splashing water while she was trying to give them a bath. 'You look ill, what's the matter?' She was bent down struggling with the soap, the flannel and the children. I stood behind her and, tears once more running down my cheeks and burning my eye-lids, I told her the story as briefly as I could.

'This is horrible!' she straightened her back. 'He shouldn't have done it. the rascal!'

'Oh, Eve, please don't tell him any of this, I beg of you! Please, just say that I asked him not to look for me.'

'Of course I will tell him, if that's what you want. The rascal! Don't worry love, I will tell him to leave you alone, if that's what you want.'

'Yes, thank you. Tell him to just forget about me. I must go now. Please forgive me for barging in on you like this.'

'Don't mention it, lovey' she was now taking the twins out

of the water one by one and drying them with a large towel. I didn't like the term 'lovey' it made me feel uneasy. 'You can rely on me, don't worry.'

I got home around two o'clock in the afternoon, well before my father was due home from work.

On Saturday morning, I woke up with a heavy heart. My father hadn't once addressed me since the incident; during the day we didn't talk about it with my mother, who seemed to have forgotten all about it; we went about the daily routine of cleaning, airing, washing and cooking without much communication between us. But I was still kept on edge by the fact of the ban on my leaving home. Saturday was going to be a long day, with my father home all day.

Over breakfast, I had the feeling that my father's anger and hatred of me had subsided somewhat. I was in the kitchen, drying the dishes I had just washed up downstairs when I heard voices on the terrace. They were mainly male voices and I thought for a moment that Sheri had arrived. I was pleased, because his presence would ease the tense atmosphere, but then I realised that the voices were talking French. I listened. It was Avi's voice!

I could swear it was him! What cheek, to come after I had asked him not to! I heard my father's voice; they were actually talking and my father laughed! I had to sit down, my heart was racing so much, it seemed to come up to my throat. Eventually I heard my father say: 'Ah, well it's a long time ago now. I had forgotten about it ... ' or something to that effect.

Forgotten about it! How could he say that to a perfect stranger, when I had been subjected to such humiliation!

I was summoned. My father's voice was soft and calm. One wouldn't believe it belonged to the same man who nearly killed me a few days ago! I stepped out of the kitchen onto the terrace.

'Come on, come on,' said my father in his best French, 'look who is here, your friend Avi.' I no longer considered Avi to be my friend. 'He has had the decency,' my father said distinctly, 'to come and apologise to me.'

I stood in the middle of the terrace. Avi looked at me, his dimples deep, his eyes flashing blue lights at me. My father was smiling too; there was another soldier sitting on a chair. 'Who would apologise to me?' I thought, but said nothing.

'Do you know why Avi brought his friend?' my father went on, smiling 'for protection, protection from me!'

'Good morning.' My upbringing overtook my revulsion which I stifled the best I could.

'Eve told me,' Avi said to me, 'and I couldn't leave things as they were .... '

'She shouldn't have. I asked her not to tell you!'

'You don't know Eve. If you did you wouldn't have confided in her.'

'It's a bit late now.'

'You are being very' impolite.' my father said. 'He is a guest in our home'

'I have come to invite your parents, to come over this afternoon and meet all of us, so your father will know where you are and with whom.'

My mother hadn't said a word so far. I looked at her awaiting a negative reaction, but Avi went on, 'And they have accepted, isn't it marvellous!'

I was about to say that it wasn't marvellous at all, that I didn't want anything more to do with all these deceptive people, when my father said:

'Why didn't you tell us. They are nice people, all Europeans, with good education and upbringing, all you had to do was – tell us.'

Tears came to my eyes, I wanted to burst out and shout that I have been trying to tell him for years! but I couldn't bring myself to say anything, I just stood there, fighting my tears.

'Avi will come for us in his friend's car this afternoon,' my father said, and turned to Avi, 'Do you play belote?'

'Yes, of course I do.'

'We can have a game.'

'That will be my pleasure sir.'

My father patted Avi on the shoulder, I looked on, bewildered.

When Avi and his friend had left, my father said: 'Such a nice boy, and serious too.'

At three o'clock an old black Buick stopped outside the house. Avi jumped out of the passenger seat and ran upstairs. We were ready. Avi helped my mother down the stairs. My father and I followed. Claude held the door open for my mother and father. As I was getting in, with my parents, our eyes met, and he gave me a wink. I thought I would shout something rude to him, but self control prevailed, and I said nothing. Avi went back to the passenger seat and off we went.

It all seemed unreal; I felt nothing for Avi now; I was overcome by my father's attitude. What had been a major disaster a few days ago was, by some magic, turned into a casual, easy-going friendship; but I felt left out. I caught my mother's eyes go towards Avi with that way she had of looking at people, mistrustful, appraising. As for Avi, he was radiant, he talked and laughed addressing my father most of the time and sometimes very respectfully – my mother, but never actually speaking to me.

Eve greeted us as we arrived at the house. The twins had miraculously disappeared; the lounge was spotlessly clean. We were ushered in. It was too early for the others, Avi explained. Tea and cakes were served with undue ceremony. And all the time, I had this feeling of being on the stage, or in a dream, that I will wake up and find out it hadn't happened. It couldn't happen!

'We must go now,' my father stood up. I followed suit. 'I want to visit my brother, since we are in town.'

Avi came between me and my mother and addressed me directly for the first time:

'Shall we escort your parents to the bus stop; I can tell them which bus to take.'

I was about to say that I was leaving with my parents, when my father said:

'Yes. This is a very good idea.' He then turned to me: 'Avi has promised to bring you home early. He will see to it that you are all right.'

'Don't worry sir, I will. You can rely on me.' Avi said.

My father patted him on the shoulder and again, I said nothing, too surprised to find the words for what I wanted to say; how I felt.

The bus took my parents away. Avi waved. As soon as it had turned the corner, he put his arm round my shoulders.

'We made it!' he said triumphantly – 'We have won him over, he isn't going to be in the way any longer, isn't that clever?' I freed myself from his arm, I wanted to tell him that there was nothing to be gained by all his manipulations, because we were not going to see each other again, but he spoke before me, 'I must apologise! I put you in terrible trouble, it's unforgivable, yes, I know, Eve told me and I am to blame, you must be very angry with me, please forgive me!' I looked at him. He smiled at me, 'Please. Please say you forgive me!' And I did! His smile, his charm pierced through all the pain, the anger, the frustration, my father's humiliating treatment , and I smiled back. 'Good!' he said, 'lovely! You are great! And of course, you know what we are going to do, don't you?'

'No.' I thought he meant that we would go to the cinema and not join the crowd at Claude's, 'we will go to the cinema?'

'No.'

'A concert?'

'No.'

'The theatre? I am not sure my Hebrew … '

'No, no something that concerns us – you and I – alone!'

'I don't know … I give up?'

'Come on, what do young people do when they love each other?'

'I …, ' he took me by surprise, he had never told me that he loved me, 'I … don't know, they get married I suppose.'

'Exactly! That's what we are going to do.'

'Are you mad?'

'You don't love me then?' his voice was heavy with disappointment.

'I didn't say that. It's just that … '

'You are surprised, perhaps. I am a little too brusque, because I didn't think I would find a girl … like you here.'

I didn't know what to say.

'Am I to understand that you feel nothing for me?'

'No, it isn't that.'

'Well then?' He took me in his arms, in the middle of the street, and kissed me. I felt the warmth of his body. The nearness of him brought back the emotions of a week ago; I kissed him back, I hugged him; I wanted him; I loved him!

'If you only knew how much you matter,' I whispered in his ear, 'I have been so lonely … so very lonely!'

'You couldn't have been lonelier than me, I have no one.'

'You have friends.'

'They don't fill the space; they are for fun, superficial fun. You have your parents.'

'They don't fill the space either,' I retorted, 'and they are not ever fun!'

We resumed our walk.

'I don't think we should tell your parents yet.'

'OK.'

Avi held my hand. We looked at each other, his smile meant to me: 'don't worry, I am here'. And to me, nothing else in the whole world mattered any longer.

We arrived home at about 7pm.

'Here she is, Mr. Ashkenazy, as I promised. How are you, Mrs. Ashkenazy?'

My mother answered with a Mona Lisa smile:

'Thank you.'

'May I take her to the cinema next week Mr. Ashkenazy?' Avi asked.

'Sure my boy, sure, but can you be certain of getting a pass?'

'I have my contacts.' said Avi with a chuckle.

'OK.' my father agreed.

'I will meet you outside your school on Wednesday.' Avi said to me.

'Good night and thank you.' He left. I felt that the room was suddenly colder and somehow emptier.

'What a well mannered boy. And smart too. He will go far,' my father said and my heart filled with pride.

Chapter Twelve

Being in Love

My world changed its colour and its shape. There was nothing sharp or angular or ugly or painful. Everything was harmonious; everything was music and verse. I didn't think of 'L'Isolement' any longer; the only verse Lamartine whispered to me was: 'Un seul être vous manque – et tout est dépeuplé' when I wasn't with Avi ; when I was with him nothing mattered. I wanted to be transformed into the gentle spring breeze – to caress his golden hair; I wanted to become a sun-ray and warm him up – inside; I wanted to invent more words, new words to express the nature of my love. I didn't see the damp patches on the walls; the semi-darkness seemed romantic now and bringing up the heavy bucketfuls of water made me feel like Rachel at the Well.

With my father's permission we met in town at 6pm. There was little we could do but go home immediately because I was not allowed out after 7pm, but the journey on the bus and the walk home were heavenly experiences.

I asked my mother if we couldn't invite Avi for dinner, since we always got home when dinner was just about to be served, but she refused: 'That would be tantamount to treating him as a fiancé. No! It can't be done.'

'But mum, he has a long way to walk back from here to his camp. He misses dinner there and many times has to go without. I think it's silly not to ask him, and let him go hungry, especially because he goes out of his way to do as father asks him.'

'Don't you talk back to me! I am ill enough without you adding any more to my suffering! Besides, if he doesn't like it – he shouldn't do it!'

'Don't you care for him at all? For my sake?'

'Why should I? What is he to you? Or to me? Leave me alone!'

In my pink, mother-of-pearl world, I was blind to the gray patches. They were there, but I didn't see them; not Avi's manipulative behaviour, nor my father's. And even if I had, I was incapable of seeing the omen they carried. My mother was more than just 'moody', she had lost weight. What appeared to be tiredness on her face, were deep dark circles around her eyes which deepened and darkened with every passing week; her stomach, forever revolting against food with long, painful contractions; her glance, stubbornly fixed on the floor, her eyes vague. Her arms, tucked between her knees, her back hunched; and the swaying.

It was all there for us to see, and we did not. I believed her constant rejection of anything I said, of my very presence to be disapproval of me, personal against me – and although I tried over and over again to gain her approval, I hung on to my love, I looked to it as a refuge, as a salvation.

My father took her sulky silence for a reproach; reproaching him for her past and for lost youth, the conditions she lived in through his ineptness to provide her with better ones, and he tried to please her, he jumped to do whatever she wanted before she even formulated her wish, he bought her clothes, he held her hand and whispered tender words when she was sad, and she was always sad.

Ж

I told Esther about Avi and our decision to get married. I had to tell someone! She thought for a moment, then said:

'I wouldn't be in such a hurry if I were you.'

'But why?'

'I don't know. The way it all happened, but more importantly, I don't think he is trustworthy. I don't like that air of mischief that he so likes to give himself. It isn't just mischief, there is something deceitful about him. I am not sure.'

'Oh, Esther, please! We love each other so much! He may have been a bit of a bastard with other girls, but they flung themselves at him, can you blame him? He couldn't respect them.'

'Is this what he says?'

'No, we haven't discussed the subject but this is how I understand it. It will turn out fine, you'll see.'

'What are you going to live on? Love? And where? With your parents? This is no future for you.'

'Money doesn't matter to me. I don't mind where we live, how we live. If we love each other we will make out.'

'Do your parents know about it?'

'No.'

'You better tell them, before you are pregnant.'

'Esther! What are you talking about! Avi hasn't as much as … he hasn't touched me!'

'If he really hasn't – either he doesn't love you as much as you think he does, or he isn't much of a man.'

'I am not going to listen to your rubbish! You have a set of values which don't agree with mine at all! You have no understanding for respect and real love!'

'Oh, you can be quite eloquent where defending your boy is concerned; I wish you did the same when your own life and future are at stake.'

I went downstairs to wait for Avi; I didn't want him to come up.

'Hi!' he kissed my cheek.

'How are you?' I threw my arms round his neck and kissed him passionately.

He held my arms and slowly pushed me away:

'Hey, what's the matter?'

'Nothing. I missed you.' We started walking, 'Shall we tell my parents?'

'Yes, I have been thinking about that. I am due to be demobbed soon; it's better that we get married while I am still in the Army – we will get a lot of food, you know we get extra rations and all that.' I didn't know. 'Let's go home, I'll talk to your old man.'

'How will you do it? It's so … difficult. He would like the old fashion 'asking for the hand' business. I feel sick, honestly.'

'Leave it to me. I know how to manipulate, both of them.'

We found my parents in my room and if any conversation was in progress when we arrived, it stopped as soon as we walked in.

'You are late.' said my father.

Avi took over:

'Yes. We talked and now I would like to talk to you – to both of you.'

I stood in the darkest corner of the room, and noticed, the glances exchanged between my parents. My father's eyes were asking her a question, and the answer in her eyes was 'no'.

'Speak up, son.' said my father.

'You see sir, I have been alone for many years, I have fought for my life, I have wrestled with life. We love each other, and I can assure you, although I haven't any wealth to offer, I am capable of looking after a wife.'

'What are you saying, son?'

'I am asking you ,sir, and you Mrs. Ashkenazy … ' Avi walked over to me and took my hand, 'for us to get married.'

My father's face lit up with a broad smile. My mother's remained dark and closed.

'What do you want me to say children.' said my father slowly, 'You haven't taken us totally by surprise. If you have decided, I can't stop you. So, even if I say no, you would still get married … so, I … '

'But how?' my mother interrupted, 'what are they going to live on?'

'I have nothing to give you children. If I had – it would all be yours, but we are new immigrants and we have nothing. All I can offer is a roof – this roof, until you sort yourselves out.'

'Oh, I have a rich family abroad, they will help us!'

'We mustn't hurry … there is plenty of time … ' my mother kept muttering, her head down.

'I'll tell you what, you get yourselves engaged, this will simplify matters,' my father said and I wondered what would be simplified. 'Let's have supper now, I am hungry.'

'There is no hurry … she is only a child yet …. ' my mother repeated.

'Congratulations, children, I hope you will be happy for many years to come.' My father kissed us both and said to my mother, 'Come on mother, kiss them and bless them!' I felt my mother's cold lips on my cheek. 'Let's have supper now, I am hungry.'

Avi followed me to the kitchen. As soon as we were outside the door, we hugged and Avi said:

'We won! Your mother is difficult; more so than I thought, but I will get round her, don't you worry!'

Chapter Thirteen

Unable to See the Obvious

Avi began coming home every day. My mother was a little surprised at first but my father was pleased to find him there when he returned from work. I was, needless to say, delighted. Avi had a beneficial affect on the atmosphere. He praised my mother's cooking so profusely, that it sounded, sometimes, just a little insincere, but my mother seemed to come to life, her face lit up in a smile, something that my father and I didn't see very often.'

'It would be wasteful for us to meet in town, 'Avi said to my father. 'The journey is so expensive. If we feel like going to the cinema, we can always go to Yehud, don't you think?'

My father agreed and I heard him say to my mother in Bulgarian:

'Isn't he reasonable! And how thoughtful about money.'

Sometimes, I expressed the wish to meet Avi in town, which would have allowed us more time to be alone together.

'As usual, you have your head in the clouds,' said my mother, 'Avi is so much more responsible. With only your father's earnings, we haven't a penny to spare.'

One day, Avi didn't come home. I had my eyes glued to the road, but no matter how hard I looked, he wasn't there. When my father arrived, I realised that Avi was not coming. Some Army duties, no doubt, had held him back, I thought.

'Wipe the frown from your face, you are pathetic.' my mother said to me in a cold distant voice. 'I am pleased he is not here, I want to talk to you,' and, before I could ask what about, she went on, 'I don't think this boy is suitable for you to marry.'

And I had thought she liked him!

'Why? Why are you saying this mum?'

'I don't know. I can't put my finger on it, yet. What do we know about him? About his family? Nothing! In the meantime, he is compromising you.'

'Oh, mother! What are you saying! He loves me, isn't this enough? And I love him! Who cares about his family? They are all dead anyway, and what is this 'compromising' bit! To whom is he compromising me?'

'I'll tell you whom, if he disappears, what will happen to you? To us? The whole village thinks you are engaged! And if somebody makes enquiries about you, and he is told that you have already … had … that … you have been through one man's … hands …. '

'Mum! What a thing to say! This is awful. If he disappears, as you say, and I don't marry him, well, one thing is certain, I am not going to marry anybody who enquires with other people about me!'

'I don't know. I don't have a good feeling and that's that.'

'The boy is honest.' my father said.

'How do you know he is?' my mother asked.

'Oh, but he is!'

I read only one meaning in the word.

'You mustn't hurry to marry him. Besides, I need you.' said

my mother, and I didn't understand what she meant.

'Avi is not here for a reason tonight.' said my father and we both looked at him.

'Yes. Something strange happened today.' he went on, 'Somebody came to see me. A man by the name of Leon, I forgot his surname. Do you know him?'

'Yes, I met him, at Claude's. But, why did he come to see you?'

'He introduced himself like a real gentleman. He told me he had met you at Claude's, as you say, and he asked to marry you.'

'What!'

'Don't shout, I have a headache!' My mother wasn't particularly interested in this strange incident.

'He told me,' my father continued, 'that he had been away from Base, on a military operation and that upon his return, Claude had told him of the latest development with Avi and you. Claude gave him the information as to where I work and he came to see me. His intentions are most honourable. He is a high ranking officer, he has his own flat, a car, you will want for nothing. He asked me to tell you to think it over; he doesn't want you to jump into anything before careful consideration; he can wait. If you want my opinion, he is a much better choice. Also, he doesn't mind that you haven't got a penny.'

'But dad, I don't love him!'

'Avi isn't here tonight, because he didn't grant him a pass. He wanted us to talk things over. Think about it – a flat in Ramat Gan, fully equipped with everything a housewife wants, a car, a good position.'

I hated Leon for having kept Avi in! How could he reduce me to this! I was besides myself with indignation.

'Are you seeing Leon again?' I asked my father as quietly and as calmly as I could.

'He will telephone me tomorrow.'

'Well, tell him that I find all this very distasteful. He has no right to discuss my life, my future behind my back! I will never marry a flat or a car or a position, as you call it! I will marry someone who loves me, who appreciates me, and whom I love and appreciate, and that is not Leon!'

I left the kitchen surprised that neither of them, tried to stop me. I went to sleep on my settee. I felt strange, knowing that Avi had slept there. I put Leon out of my mind and thought about Avi. Now I felt that I wanted our love to be full, to expand beyond the boundaries where we had kept it, I didn't want it to be a burning, consuming, stale love. I didn't want my virginity any longer. I wanted it out of the way, I now felt it was a barrier, restricting our love. I had wrapped myself in the warmth of the bed, and tried to imagine Avi – next to me. If losing my virginity before I was married, was such a stigma, so shameful, I was going to deal with it if I had to, in the future. It was my life and my virginity and the decision was mine! Avi didn't come home for three days. I had no means of getting in touch with him. Had he changed his mind about me? Had Leon told him lies? Had he thought better of it and decided to go to England after all?

My mind was tortured all the time; the days at school passed in painful expectation as did the afternoons waiting for the familiar figure to appear on the road or the path.

'If he wanted to give you a sign, he would have done so.' my mother said.

It hurt me to think that my mother accepted so easily that I could be rejected and hurt in such a way. At the same time, I didn't accept what she took to be a fact.

'I will go to the camp. He might be ill.'

'If he were, he would have sent word. He found someone to accompany him when he came for the first time, remember?'

Avi came home on Friday afternoon, his usual wide smile on his face; he walked in as though nothing had happened. I ran to meet him, tears choking me.

'Avi ... Avi what happened to you? I worried so much!'

'I didn't get a pass.' he said in a most matter of fact voice, as though it followed without saying. 'What's the matter with you? What did you think?'

'All sorts of things. That you might be ill, among others.'

'Come off it. I am fine and hungry. Hullo mum,' he said to my mother,'You don't mind me calling you 'mum' do you? I haven't uttered the word for ... many years.'

'I don't mind.' said my mother.

'It would seem,' said my father, smiling, 'that we have a son now.'

I looked at Avi lovingly. I was so happy that he was back, that nothing had changed and that, through me, he had found a family and, I hoped, happiness. Later, back on my camp bed, at the foot of my parents' bed, I heard them whisper in the darkness, probably thinking that I was asleep.

'It would seem that it was a bet ... between them ... ' my father was saying.

'You mean ... Avi and ... ' my mother's whisper was a lot quieter.

'Leon had bet Avi that if he didn't turn up for a few days, she would change her mind and agree to marry him.'

'She is in love with this boy, what can we do?'

'I want them married before anything ... '

My mother interrupted and I didn't hear what was it that my father feared. My heart was racing, sleep escaped my troubled mind. Why did they always have secrets? Why did they always have something to hide, something they couldn't tell me? Was I a plaything being used by Leon? A bet between them? No, I couldn't believe this of Avi. Even if my father allowed these games to take place, I was certain Avi wouldn't. He would never be deceitful. If I doubted his integrity, I knew that I couldn't possibly look him in the eyes, let alone marry him. How awful of Leon, to use such tactics! And I had thought quite well of him. Thank goodness I had Avi.

Within a month Avi was introduced to everybody. People who mattered, or so my mother thought. We took him to meet people and people came to visit us; because they cared, I thought, or out of curiosity, my mother thought, to see this phenomenon – a very handsome 'European' who was going to marry our plain girl. Aunt Rachel expressed her envy to my mother by saying that she wished 'something like this happened to her Elise', Aunt Amelia said that I was a very lucky girl, Aunt Clara also seemed delighted. As for me, I was a little embarrassed and quite confused not understanding really why what concerned me was such a matter of general interest.

Avi met everyone patiently; he spoke French to whoever in the family spoke French, and Hebrew to the ones who spoke Hebrew. He answered their embarrassingly prying questions as to what his occupation was going to be when he would be out of the Army, and what were our plans for the future. I thought that it had nothing to do with them; Avi answered calmly.

I wrote to Avi's adoptive family, under his dictation. I tried my best calligraphy and scanned the letter for spelling mistakes. I didn't want the family to think that because I came from a country generally considered rather backward, I was uneducated.

Ж

With the heat of the summer, our floor melted more and more under our feet and chairs and other heavy objects became stuck to the soft tar. We found that it was easiest to move them at the height of the heat as the night chill set the tar and then nothing could be moved.

As soon as the new immigrants' camp outside the village was in operation, representatives of the village applied to the authorities for us to be connected to the main water supply. As a result of this development, we now had running water all day and all night except for the peak hours, when it didn't have enough pressure to climb upstairs, but the discomfort this caused was negligible, in comparison with the situation before.

The black rubber irrigation hose, stuck in through the top of the smaller crate, could now be used as a shower; the water came down in a strong heavy flow through the inch and a half hose and ran freely down, through the timber and on to the terrace from where it had to be swept towards the drainage hole. With time, we learned that in the mid-day heat it was impossible to take a shower – the water was boiling hot, but up until midday, and after 5pm, it was a very refreshing experience.

Avi's adoptive family replied to my letter, informing us that the Uncle was coming to Israel the following month, and was looking forward to meeting me. Avi had withstood bravely all the members of my family, now it was my turn to meet someone of his! I was a little nervous but determined to make the right impression on him.

It was May now, and we wanted to be married as soon as possible, since Avi was living with us, there was no reason why the engagement should be prolonged. We went to the Central Religious Authority, the Rabbinate in Tel Aviv to register; the first available date was in August, and we put our names down. In a few months we were going to be married!

When we came home, we found my mother curled up on her bed, crying.

'Mummy, mummy, what happened? Why are you crying? Did you hurt yourself?'

She didn't answer me, she just went on sobbing. Avi and I looked at each other, not knowing what to do.

'Mum,' said Avi, 'has anything happened? Tell us.'

'No, nothing has happened! Leave me alone. What can happen that's worse than what has already happened!'

'Mummy,' I said, trying to cheer her up, 'We have got a date for the wedding, mum, I want you to be well, and beautiful.'

'I don't care' she shouted back 'I don't care! Leave me alone.' We tip toed out.

I was crying of course. My happiness didn't matter to my mother.

'Do you think she meant what she said, not caring about us being married?' asked Avi, looking at the curtain that separated us from my parents' bedroom.

'I don't know. I don't know and I don't understand.'

'Stop crying! not you too! Do you think she is ill or something?'

'I don't know. She is often in a bad mood, and cries a lot, but you see, as soon as there is somebody else other than my father and I around, she brightens up, she is totally different. It's us she can't stand. With others, she is pleasant, and smiles and this is what I don't understand.'

'Perhaps she ought to see a doctor.'

'Can a doctor help?'

'I don't know.'

My father walked in.

'Where is your mother?' he asked.

'She is in bed. She is not well dad. She is crying.'

'Why? What have you done to her?'

'Nothing! I can assure you … '

My father was already with her. Avi and I went to the kitchen to get dinner ready.

Eventually, my parents came in. My mother leaning on my father, pale, her eyes blood shot. We ate in silence.

'I am taking your mother to see a doctor tomorrow,' my father said when we had finished the meal.

'I don't want any doctors.'

'You will come with me tomorrow. I am taking time off work, you are not well, and you have to see a doctor. I can't leave you without medical care any longer.'

'There is no cure for sick nerves, and my nerves are shattered.'

'Let's hear what the doctor will have to say, perhaps there is.'

'You must go mum, we want you well. A doctor will be able to help.'

'Will you leave me alone! All of you!' my mother shouted with such a high pitched shriek that she gave us all a start.

Avi looked at her and I noticed the cold, unsympathetic glance.

'Mum, please.' I pleaded with her.

'It may not be serious, it may be that all you need is a little help and think how nice it would be if you were healthy and well again.'

'Have I ever been healthy? Never! What's changed now? When your father was in camps, Nazi labour camps, communist labour camps, and I was left alone, who cared then? And now – this … ' she looked around, 'No, I will never be well.

She got up. My father followed her. He returned after a while.

'She has fallen asleep. I must take her to see a doctor tomorrow.'

'Yes.'

'Come on, children, to bed. I am tired.'

'Can't we sit outside a little? It's so hot dad.'

'No, go to bed now.' He had to make sure we were in two different rooms before he went to sleep. We blew the lights out and went to our respective beds.

My parents returned from town late in the afternoon. Avi and I were sitting on the terrace. Dinner was ready and the table laid.

'What did the doctor say?' I asked as they came up

'She has to see a specialist in Jerusalem,' my father answered.

'What kind of a specialist?'

'A psychiatrist.'

'What he is trying to tell you,' my mother interrupted, bitter mockery in her voice, 'is that I am going mad; if I am not mad already.'

'No, darling, please don't say such things! All the doctor said was that your nerves are a little tired, strained perhaps and a specialist is better qualified to prescribe the best course of action.'

'This sounds reasonable.' said Avi.

My mother's heavy glance turned to him, but she said nothing.

'When will you go to see the specialist?'

'On Thursday.'

Ж

Avi and I sat on the bench, awaiting my parents return from Jerusalem. The evening was unusually hot and dark. There were no stars and not a movement in the air which was oppressively heavy. We hadn't lit any lights to avoid the mosquitoes.

We heard steps coming up the stairs and the beam of a torch swept the air.

'Who is it?' Avi asked.

'It's me, Uncle Gabriel.' He emerged on the terrace, trying to catch his breath, 'Your father telephoned my office this afternoon, from Jerusalem. He said that they will be staying there tonight.'

'But why? did he say why?'

'No, all he said was, to tell you not to wait for them.'

'Thank you very much, Uncle.' He waved his torch and left

without another word.

'Let's eat. I am hungry.' Avi said.

We went over to the kitchen. It struck me that this was the first time that we were going to be all alone, the whole night. I thought of my decision and perhaps now was the time to tell him. We were eating in silence, I wondered what his thoughts were.

'We will be all alone tonight.' I said.

'Yes. We won't have to go to bed because he is tired!'

'Yes.'

We finished our meal, tidied up and went to my room.

'Avi,' I said with difficulty, 'there is something that I have thought of, some time ago, but I haven't told you. There hasn't been the opportunity. I can now. It's about us … ' we were sitting on the settee, Avi – at some distance from me. He didn't say anything and I went on, 'I am talking about the barrier there is between us …. '

'How do you mean?'

'Well, when we are … together … we can go that far and no further … what I want to tell you is that … it doesn't really matter to me … I mean, as far as I am concerned, we don't have to wait until we are married … do you understand me?'

'I think I do, but what will your father say?'

'It doesn't concern him. It concerns us. Everybody seems to think that a girl's virginity is very important, well as far as I am concerned, even if we don't get married, if something happens … well, I love you, and if we have to part, somebody else will just have to accept the fact,' I swallowed with difficulty and went on, 'that I have loved before, I mean.'

'Are you sure?'

'Yes, I have thought a lot about it.'

'All right then, let's.' Avi said. 'If that's what you want. We better sleep in your parents' bed.'

'Oh, Avi … no … '

'It's larger, more comfortable.'

'No, please!'

'Come on, I know better.'

We went in through the curtain. Avi blew out the light in my room, now there was just the very faint glow from only one lamp hung on the wall. I looked at Avi not knowing what to do. He unbuttoned his shirt and took it off; slid the zip of his trousers down, then pulled off one trouser leg and then the other.

'Go on, get undressed.' he said to me. I did.

He took off his underpants and I closed my eyes. 'It's Avi.' a voice said inside me, and I opened my eyes. I looked at him, with bewilderment. I had never quite imagined what a naked man looked like. He came to me and gently pushed me onto the bed. I was desperately aware of my nakedness. Avi's hand suddenly came between my thighs, I felt my body convulse, my muscles tighten, and the voice in my mind repeated: 'It's OK, it's Avi'.

I felt his hand pressing, pushing my legs apart. I felt a sudden urge to stop him, to cover myself and to say to him, no, not like this! but I didn't know what I meant, what I wanted, so I did nothing. I searched his face for a glance, a contact, but he was looking down, intent on trying to part my legs. I touched his arm but he didn't look up. He pressed his body against me now and I felt his penis pressing, thrusting then suddenly a sharp pain somewhere deep inside me.

I drew back instinctively.

'Don't do that!' Avi said impatiently, 'otherwise it will never get in.'

There were tears in my throat. I held the sheet and shut my eyes. He pressed again, I looked at him. His face was twitching slightly; it had gone red; I wanted to hug him but his hands rested on my shoulders and pinned me down; he was getting impatient, I knew it. He took my legs in his hands now, thrust himself against me, while pulling me towards him. I wanted our eyes to meet, I wanted to see his love for me and I wanted to communicate mine; he was biting his lip as he did when he was concentrating.

Tears ran down from my eyes and onto the bed now, Avi was pulling hard, his fingers stuck in the flesh of my legs, then I felt that he had finally found the place, he pushed himself forward; a sharp deep pain cut through my whole body. I twisted the sheet in my hands and didn't utter a sound. Avi went on pushing in and out, the pain decreased eventually; then he relaxed suddenly with a little start and fell on me. I put my hands on his shoulders, but he got up.

'There isn't much blood.' he said. I had forgotten about the blood. 'Did it hurt much?'

I shook my head, unable to talk, still fighting my tears.

'It's always difficult the first time. I am exhausted. Do you want a drink of water?'

'Yes, please.'

'Here,' he came back from the kitchen, 'I found some chocolate, have some.'

'Thank you.'

'Not too much blood,' repeated Avi. 'It is the first time,isn't it?'

'Yes.' Tears were still running down, but as I stopped myself from sobbing Avi couldn't see them.

'Go and wash yourself.'

'How do you mean?'

'You don't want to get pregnant, do you?'

I didn't know exactly how I was supposed to wash, or what, for I didn't know that sperm had been released inside me. I went to the shower and had a wash.

'I am exhausted,' said Avi when I came back, 'let's go to sleep.' He did. I lay for a long time. The barrier was now removed, I wasn't a virgin any longer, I had 'slept' with Avi, I had had the forbidden, mysterious experience people spoke of with secrecy and excitement, and I felt as miserable as hell. Why all the mystery? Why all the fuss? If this was all there was to it, all adults must be terrible hypocrites! To have found out the truth about it, and perpetrate a myth, something that didn't really exist. Did all adults live a lie?

It took me a long time before I could go to sleep.

My parents returned from Jerusalem just before noon on the following day. My mother seemed to hang onto my father's arm, as I looked at them from the terrace. It seemed to me that if he weren't there, she would collapse on the ground, and just stay there.

My mother came up the stairs first and I hugged her.

'Mummy! I am so glad you are back! I missed you so.' I was being truthful, had they been there, 'it' would not have happened, and I would not have had this frightening hollow feeling deep inside me.

'How was it mum? What did the doctor say?' She swept by me, pushing me aside with a strength I would not have thought she possessed and went straight into the bedroom.

My father and I followed her. 'Dad, tell me, please. What's wrong with mum?'

'I am thirsty.' my mother whispered.

I went to the kitchen to bring her some water. We were told that if we wrapped the bottles with a damp cloth overnight, the water would keep cool for most of the day. My mother took a sip and handed me the glass:

'Ugh!' You didn't wrap the bottle last night!'

'Yes, I did, mum but it's very hot today. Please tell me what the doctor … '

'I am tired; leave me alone.'

'Come to the kitchen,' my father said, 'your mother needs rest. Is there anything to eat?' he asked. I served him lunch and sat down waiting for him to speak.

'The doctor gave her some tablets. They are tranquillizers. It's a course. When she will take them, she will be drowsy and will sleep most of the day. She needs looking after. I can't stay home, I have to go to work.'

'I'll look after her!' I was pleased that I could be of help. 'My course is nearly finished anyway. What will these tablets do? Did the doctor say?'

'Calm her down. Calm her nerves.'

'But will that change her mood?'

'Has anyone ever been able to change your mother's mood?' I felt my father's irritation as he spoke. There was nothing I could say to this and I couldn't help being surprised at this statement made to me; it sounded very much like a 'confidence', and I didn't remember ever being taken into my father's confidence. Was his attitude towards me changing? Was he going to treat me more like an equal now?

He sat there, his head down, looking defeated. I felt sorry for him. I regretted that I had, in a sense, betrayed him last night in disobeying his wish. I wondered now, looking at him, what is it one did to make people happier? What could one do, except love them and try to please them?

'What would you like me to do now dad?' I asked.

'I wish I knew. I don't want you to interrupt your studies .... '

'Dad, these are not studies; I have my books, I can study by myself, at home. It's a question of priorities and mum needs me most now. Right?'

'Well, yes, but ... '

'I so want her to be well for my wedding, don't you?'

'Yes, of course, your wedding.' He seemed to have forgotten all about it. 'I am so sorry ... this is not how I wanted things for you my child .... '

'Don't worry dad ... I am happy. I really am.'

'Yes. I like Avi too.'

My mother appeared at the door; we looked at her, surprised.

'Mum! come and sit down. Would you like something to eat?'

'I feel sick. But perhaps I should eat something … ' She sat down; she looked at me first, then at my father, her eyes cold, distant.

'You were discussing me.' she said.

'Dad was telling me about your treatment. I will stay home and look after you. I can study a little on my own, besides Avi can help me.'

'Avi! He is illiterate, don't you know? Are you so blind?'

I put the toast and the cup of tea in front of her. Her words hurt me.

'It was the war … he couldn't go to school … you know the circumstances he was in … he has been to school on the kibbutz, here.'

'I can't tell about his Hebrew, but from the French he speaks, I can tell, and so would you if you cared to see – he is illiterate. You must come to your senses, he is the wrong boy to marry. He is a child, it all seems a game to him, and he has no profession, no position. We gave so much in order to give you a proper education. Do you know how much your French school cost?'

'Yes, mum and I am not ungrateful. I appreciate it very much, but Avi – he was left all alone, he couldn't help it! Besides, what does it matter … if there is love … if we love and care for each other.'

'You like the fine things in life … you like music, you like the theatre. Has your precious Avi been to the theatre once? Once in his life?'

'Please don't get excited my love,' my father pleaded with her, 'this is exactly what the doctor said you should avoid. The children love each other, they will sort themselves out.'

'Do you want some more toast, mum?'

'I am not hungry … but perhaps I should …. '

I made more toast. My father put three little bottles, containing different coloured tablets and capsules on the table.

'Here, look,' he said to me, 'the instructions are distinctly written on each and every one of them. You mustn't forget one, not one! Because they work in conjunction with each other, and the whole treatment would be a waste of time if not administered properly.'

'Yes dad.'

'Can I trust you with it? and go to work with a clear head?'

'Of course you can.'

'Sure you can,' said my mother, 'with her head in the clouds, she will muddle it all in the first day. But what does it matter. You can leave this place and forget all about me as soon as the door is shut behind your back.'

My father sighed.

'I promise I won't mum, I will be very careful.'

'I am tired.' She said.

'Take these now.' My father handed her a capsule and a tablet. She swallowed them, docile and rebellious at the same time, her slender body leaning on my father. He led her towards the bedroom. I sat down and read the labels – I could read the Hebrew writing. 'Keep in a cool place and away from children.' I looked out through the window. The fields had turned yellow under the burning sun; I could see the air shimmer in the distance and I became aware of the unbearable heat in the kitchen.

I decided to freshen up. I went in to take a change of clothes from the wardrobe; both my parents were asleep, and I slipped out noiselessly. I ran downstairs to open the tap which was connected to the shower hose in the smaller crate upstairs, then ran up again, undressed quickly in the kitchen, wrapped the large towel round my body like a sarong and went to the shower. The lid-door was heavy and hung unevenly on its hinges, such that I had to lift it up, unstick it from the tar and then pull it open. I struggled for a while, succeeded, got in and pulled the door to.

I hung the towel on the nail provided and let the water – quite hot by this time of day, but still refreshing – run over my head and body, my eyes shut. Eventually I opened my eyes in order to get the soap from its holder in the corner and to my horror, I saw a snake. An enormous green snake, coiled round itself, it's head sticking up from the middle, like in pictures I had seen – looking at me. I froze with fright. I felt the blood drain from my head; I also realised that I had to do something. Shouting won't help, I thought and looking at it all the while, with my hands behind me, I succeeded in lifting the door and slowly I let myself out. I ran towards the kitchen just as Sheri, climbing the last step, emerged on the terrace.

'A snake! In the shower. There is a snake, I saw it … '

Sheri was with me in two strides:

'Did it bite you?'

'I don't think so.'

'What colour was it?' he was already going towards the shower.

'Don't go there! The snake is in there!'

Sheri came back and handed me my towel.

'Here, wrap yourself up and go and drink some water. I'll have to find this snake.'

Only now I realised that I had been stark naked all this time. I took the towel and with shaking hands tried to wrap it round myself, when Avi walked in.

'What is going on? What is this?' he asked, angry.

'Snake … in the shower … this is Sheri … he is my cousin … he is … '

'What the hell are you doing, naked in front of all these people?'

'I was taking a shower … Avi, please, there was snake inside … '

'Go and get dressed!'

'What's going on?' my father opened the door and looked on the scene, his eyes swollen with sleep.

'This is preposterous!' Avi was saying as I left, 'naked in front of everybody ... what kind of a behaviour is this!'

I was shaking like a leaf.

'What's all the noise about?' asked my mother from her bed.

'There was a snake ... in the shower .... '

'Oh, my god! what have we come to! Living in the wilderness, with snakes ...! '

'I got it.' Sheri came in, followed by Joseph. 'I think it was only a grass snake but I wouldn't have rested until I found it. It could come back, you see. We killed it Jo and I.'

'Thank you Sheri.'

'Here, you are still shaking. This girl has had quite a shock. I'll get you some water.'

Eventually I calmed down. Avi continued to sulk all evening.

He made it quite plain to me, that he didn't like Sheri; he couldn't stand Joseph and he was not going to make any efforts to like them for my sake. Sheri didn't need any more hints, he was sensitive enough to realise Avi's mood; he spaced his visits and made them as brief as possible, even though my mother – who had missed the whole thing – pleaded with him to come more often and 'brighten up her day'. Once I returned Joseph's books, we barely saw each other again.

Chapter Fourteen

New Life

I had gotten into the habit of waking up very early in order to get Avi up. I was sleeping in the camp bed, at the bottom of my parents' bed.

With the day breaking so early, around 5am, the bright light filtered in though the wooden shutters and woke me up. I used to lie for a while, listening to the morning sounds, quite different from the night ones. There was the cheerful singing of birds against the chatter of the crickets, the occasional car zooming by on the road and the voices of people, leaving early for work and talking as they crossed the field.

The early morning air was clear and warm, in those few moments I tried to recall our recent relationship and look for the warmth, security, communication and closeness I craved; but I always failed. I rejected the thought that I failed just because these things hadn't been there, and blamed it instead on my inability to sense it all, preoccupied as I was with my own pain, and the fact that it was my very first physical closeness with a man.

I was about to put a stop to my day-dreaming and get up, when loud screams made me jump. My father was the first to react. He sat up.

'What is that?'

I was wrapping myself in my dressing gown, 'I don't know,' I said and went for the door. My mother, under the influence of her drugs, stirred but didn't wake up. There was no movement behind the curtain.

It was an unusual sound – a man screaming. I walked out onto the terrace. The sun was shining straight into my eyes and I squinted as I looked around to find where the screams were coming from. The sound was inhuman, mad.

Eventually I saw the milkman, running around in a little clearing a few houses away from us. He was making wild gestures with his arms as he did so, and screaming all the time. People were gathered around him, men still buttoning their trousers, walking slowly towards him, not quite knowing what to do. Finally, a few of them got hold of the milkman and stopped his mad running, but he still went on shouting. My mother came onto the terrace now, her face puffed with drugged sleep, swaying slightly. She looked on a while then said:

'He has obviously gone amuck. I am not surprised, what with this heat and the kind of work he has to do. He used to be a prominent merchant in Sofia.'

Avi emerged, rubbing his eyes, uncomprehending. The milkman had obviously calmed down a little because we could hear some of the words he was uttering:

' … they are all dead … dead … they have killed the … '

Avi took things in his hands then:

'You and your mother, go right in. I'll go and find out what's happened.'

'Go on.' my father urged us and we obeyed. They both went towards the scene of whatever accident, or murder had occurred.

It was frightening to sit inside and listen to the man's

screams, but we sat and none of us said a word. Eventually silence was restored and with it, all other sounds seemed to have stopped.

'What do you think has happened?' I asked my mother, whispering, as though if I had spoken aloud, I would have brought the screams back.

'I don't know. I am going back to bed.' she said. 'It would seem that somebody must have been murdered.'

'Here in the village, but why?'

'You forget the infiltrators.'

'The Arabs, yes of course. But we have guards, haven't we?'

'Our men can't measure up against those trained assassins.'

'How do you feel mum? Shall I make you a cup of tea?'

'Yes, please.'

As I crossed the terrace to go to the kitchen I saw Victor, the man who used to operate the water pump, now the ice-man, riding a bicycle towards the main road. My father and Avi were coming up the stairs.

'What happened?' I asked.

'You will be better off not knowing.' my father said.

'She must know! In this country of ours, everyone must be aware of the dangers that lie around every corner, if we want to stay alive, we must know the enemy.' I was so proud of my Avi! He turned to me in a matter of fact voice, 'A family have been killed during the night. It's obviously the work of Arab infiltrators. It's pretty horrific in there, they have cut them up as they often do, but we found the older boy and the baby alive under one of the beds in their room. Unfortunately, the third child was killed together with his parents.'

I was stunned; my brain didn't take Avi's words in.

'Come on, I must go, I am late,' Avi went on, 'Victor and the others have gone to Yehud for the police, for all the good they will do now. Where is my shirt?'

We had arrived upstairs and I got Avi a clean shirt. He ran

off, still buttoning it.

'You mean to say that men have … gone into the house … in the middle of the night … and … '

'Better not talk about it dear, it would upset your mother, and she is very delicate now.'

'And that boy … he had the courage to save his little brother while he could hear his parents being … oh, dad!'

'Yes, I know it's awful. But don't mention it to your mother.'

'Yes,dad.'

My father took a last gulp of his coffee and left. I was washing up the cups, immersed in my thoughts about this morning's events; my mother's voice, coming from behind me, startled me:

'It could very well have been us.' she said flatly.

'Mum! Why did you get up? I was going to …. '

'It could have been us, and perhaps it should have been!' aggression was mounting in her voice.

'But we are upstairs, it was easier for them to get into … '

I began to improvise, but she interrupted me:

'I heard every word your father said! What do you think that I can be kept away, drugged, so you can be rid of me?'

'Oh, mum, what an idea. The doctor said that you need rest, and sleep … all we want is that you should get better … all we are doing is following his instructions. If I knew how to help you in any other way, I would, believe me I would!' She had sat down and didn't answer me. 'Shall I make you some tea and toast perhaps and a soft boiled egg?' She shrugged. 'Shall I?' I was afraid to take initiative, in case she brushed me aside.

'I don't know. I suppose I better eat something, what with all the poisons I am swallowing ….'

When she finished her breakfast, I gave her the morning tablets and capsule and she went back to bed. I busied myself round the kitchen, washed the terrace, tiptoed into the rooms to make the beds and dust. I washed the floors there too, a difficult task on the uneven tarred surfaces, having to go round the chairs and table which were stuck well into it.

I saw the bread van come into the village and went to the store for some shopping, having made sure that my mother was asleep and wouldn't wake up to find herself alone. I hurried back; people in the shop were discussing the murders and I heard a few more gory details before I ran out.

There were comings and goings around the house of the murders all day. Police arrived with dogs and tried to trace the infiltrators' route, people simply hung around; each time I had to go out onto the terrace I tried not to look in that direction. We learned later that the traces led to the border, which, quite frighteningly, lay along the rolling hills at the end of the fields; the two surviving children were eventually adopted by a kibbutz, because they had no relatives who could afford to look after them.

At one o'clock I had to give my mother another dose of tablets. I took them out of their little bottles, together with a glass of water and went into the bedroom. My mother was asleep, her face pale, her eyes deep in their sockets. She seemed so small and vulnerable under the sheet, and I felt guilty for being instrumental to this induced sleep, which so far, at least as far as I could tell, had failed to produce any results. I touched her gently. She opened her eyes and looked at me, but her glance was not clear, not coherent. I wished I could be certain that what I was doing to her was the right thing to do! But who was I to question the specialist's word?

'Your tablets mum.'

She leant on one elbow, took the tablets from my hand, put them in her mouth, then took the glass of water and swallowed them all at once without saying a word.

I tiptoed out since she was already asleep again. I didn't feel hungry, and thought that I could take a shower now, and freshen up a little. Having checked that there was no snake, I took my shower, then went to see that my mother was all right. She was asleep, her eyelids pressed together, her lips also tightly closed and I thought that she didn't seem relaxed at all.

My father turned up in the middle of the afternoon. Of course, it was Sunday today, and he didn't work on Sundays. He was carrying a large black box, a little like a portable sewing machine. I wondered what he had been up to.

'What is this dad?'

'How is your mother?' he asked, panting.

'As well as expected, I think, she is asleep. What is this?'

'Did you give her the tablets regularly?'

'Of course I did.'

'It's a radio, look!.' He took the lid off the black box, pulled an aerial out of one corner at the top, then turned the 'on' knob. 'It works on batteries!'

'Isn't this marvellous! Where did you get it? We will be able to listen to music, and the news! We won't be isolated from the whole world any longer!'

I cleaned the radio, polished its body and glass face, then switched it on and listened with amazement to some music. My father had gone to see that my mother was 'all right'; he came back and asked me for some coffee.

Avi arrived just then; it was the very first time that he arrived home without my spotting him and running to meet him. He was carrying a large green metal box. He put it on the table and said:

'This is going to be our ice box, until we can afford to buy a real one. I will build a platform in the middle for water bottles, butter and milk next to the ice itself, and the melted water will drip underneath, how's that?'

'Oh, my darling you are a genius!' I kissed him, 'To have real cold water, and milk, and butter! But look here, we also have a radio!'

'Yes, I saw it. They are quite nice, they're Zenith radios, I have seen them before.'

'Dad brought it. We won't be so isolated any more, we will be able to, hear some music, and all sorts of things.'

Avi peeped out, looked at my father who was sipping his coffee on the terrace, turned back to me and asked:

'How is Mum?'

It warmed my heart to hear him call her mum.

'Asleep,' I said 'I hope we are doing the right thing, she seems so ... I don't know ... so small and weak and dependent, sometimes I can't bear the sight of her on the bed ... '

'Stop fiddling with those bloody knobs!' both Avi and I were taken by surprise. My mother was standing at the door, we hadn't heard her at all. I wondered how long she had been there. 'It gives me a headache! What is it anyway?' She seemed excited, agitated. Avi left it to me to do the talking.

'It's a radio mum.' I said carefully 'Dad brought it for you ... you will be able to listen to some music, you so love music ... '

'I don't want any music! Switch it off! I have a headache and I am going to be sick.'

My father came in, worried by the raised voice.

'What is it my love?' he put an arm around my mother's shoulders, 'did she annoy you?'

My mother shrugged him off.

'You all annoy me! I don't want your stupid radio! I can't understand it anyway, so don't tell me you were thinking of me when you bought it, and how much have you paid for it? I bet the money could have been spent more usefully!'

We were quiet for a while.

'I'll get you your dinner mum, it is soon time for your tablets and you better eat something before ... '

'That's what you want! All of you! To get me out of the way! But don't you worry, the day isn't far now when I will remove myself!'

'Mum, please ... you know it's not like this! All I am trying to do ... '

'Why do you talk like that to me ... ' my father had tears in his voice. I am only trying to do my best ... '

'Shush,' Avi tried to shut us up, 'The news!'

'To hell with the news!' my mother turned the knob and switched the radio off.

I made her an omelette, toast and tea and she ate in silence.

Uncle Samuel appeared at the door, we hadn't heard him climb the stairs.

'Come on boys, we are all going to Yehud, the police are going to teach us to defend ourselves.'

'I can't go,' my father said, 'my wife is not well.'

'Women! Wet blankets! She'll have to learn one or two things yet! Come on!'

My father looked at my mother awaiting her reaction. She remained inscrutable, sullen.

'What do you say, my darling, shall I go?' She shrugged. 'I can't go.'

'Come on,' Uncle Samuel insisted, 'the whole village is waiting!'

'You go dad, I'll look after mum.'

He kissed her and left.

'Here mum, your tablets.' She took them without a word, got up and said to Avi:

'Don't play with the wretched radio, I can hear it in there, and I can't bear it!'

Avi and I had our meal, I cleared up, washed up and joined Avi outside, in the warm night. We sat on the bench and waited for my father to come home.

The police had definitely traced the infiltrators to the border. They gave Sten guns to the village and taught the men how to organise nightly patrols. The house of the murders remained empty. With time, people stopped talking about it and the frightening deaths sunk into oblivion.

Chapter Fifteen

An Important Visitor

Every Sunday, I went to Yehud to purchase our ration of meat. It was about a half an hour's walk there and another half hour back. It was fine when it wasn't raining. I went on Sundays, because my father was at home and there was no need to leave my mother alone. She was still almost all the time under sedation but insisted that she couldn't bear to be left alone. I didn't know how to cook, but in her waking hours my mother gave me instructions, and even though my cooking wasn't up to her standards, we ate it.

One afternoon Avi came home, all smiles:

'Look, a letter from my uncle, he's a kind of an adopted uncle. He and his wife and others ran the clandestine kitchen during the war. They wanted to take me in … but … never mind that now, his letter arrived this morning, at the camp, he is coming this week and we are going to see him on Friday. How's that?'

'Oh, Avi … this is lovely! I must say I am a little nervous ….'

'Don't be silly. He is stinking rich and will help us, he might even buy us a flat. He owns land and flats.'

'I wish I could do something for you children,' said my father, 'but I have nothing.'

'Don't you worry dad,' said Avi, 'he is rich, he can afford it, and besides, he is childless!'

'You know,' I said, 'it doesn't really matter whether he helps us or not, we will manage. The main thing is we have each other, isn't it?'

'If Avi's uncle wants to help you he should, after all, if he is a Zionist, which Avi says he is – he will be helping a young couple who will live and work in this country, while he, the Zionist, is living in his European luxury.' said my mother.

None of us found anything to say to that.

On the Friday, Avi and I were going to meet in town, by the sea-side, near the uncle's hotel. I busied myself with the house-work; I had to finish it all earlier than usual, get ready and leave as soon as my father came home. My mother responded less well to her treatment as time went by, and spent more hours awake than at the beginning. She took to coming into a room, taking me by surprise and remarking that, while she was ill and incapacitated, I was taking advantage and not doing the house-work properly.

'You have taken a chair from the rooms into the kitchen!' she shouted 'I have seen the tar marks on the floor! And the kitchen floor hasn't been scrubbed in weeks!' I was afraid to answer, trying to avoid more excitement for her, which, my father had told me – she should be spared at all cost.

My silence irritated her more, and she would go on at me:

'What is the point of dusting, when you haven't swept the floor yet! Sweeping raises clouds of dust!'

Eventually, it was time for lunch. She ate slowly, looking at her plate. I was in a hurry, I had to clear up, take a shower and get ready. I felt my stomach tightening with worry; I dreaded to think what Avi would say if I were late for the appointment with the uncle.

'Stop looking at me like this!' my mother said 'I will finish in a minute and you will be able to go and meet your precious Avi. Nothing matters to you, I may be dying here, and you will still run to your Avi.'

'Mum, it's not fair … I do love Avi, but I don't love you any less … .'

My mother left the kitchen. I cleared up quickly, then took a shower. When I went back in to get dressed, I found my mother walking from one end of the room to the other with long fast strides. Her hands were tearing at each other, her eyes were unfocussed and although she looked ahead, she didn't seem to see the wall when she came to it, crashed against it, then turned back and with the same wild strides crashed into the opposite wall.

I watched on for a short moment, until I realised that my eyes were not deceiving me, then went over to her and tried to stop her.

'Mum …! ' I was shaking with fright. She brushed past me, throwing me off balance, as though I wasn't there, and went straight for the wall.

'Mum, please!' I followed her, making yet another attempt at stopping her. 'What is the matter, please tell me, have I done, or said … '

She reached the wall and began to bang her head against it. Once, twice, three times. I pulled her arm. She was stronger than me. Eventually I managed to pull her away.

'Mum, I won't go, if you don't want me to … . '

'You do everything your own way …, ' she said through clenched teeth, 'always … I don't matter, I don't matter to anybody any longer … ' I succeeded in pulling her towards the bed, where she fell in a heap and as soon as she did, she started to cry. It was so pitiful to see her, shaken by her sobs, limp, helpless on the bed.

'Mum … please, mum, don't cry … things will be all right … you will see … ' I was crying as well. 'Please make an effort to see how … ' She sat up suddenly, the same disconcerting strength in her body again:

'Don't you tell me to make an effort! Only God knows what an effort every day is for me! Can't you understand that I am ILL … ILL … ILL …. '

My father walked in just then. He went over to her immediately.

'What happened my love? What did she do to you? I am here now … don't cry … '

My mother didn't answer him; she had buried her head under the sheet. My father looked up at me for an answer. I shook my head and left. Once outside, I felt my stomach convulsing with nausea; I had barely time enough to run downstairs, 'behind the wall', and be sick. I felt exhausted, but washed my face and ran out – Avi and his uncle were waiting for me. Luckily, just as I was reaching the crossroads, a bus came, and I got on.

I saw Avi pacing up and down. I ran towards him and waved. His face didn't change in recognition. I was out of breath when I reached him. I had never seen his eyes like that. They didn't flare anger, like my father's; they were dark, the blue turned steel and cold. God, how cold they were!

'I am sorry Avi, Mum had a bad day, I couldn't leave earlier, I really am very sorry.'

'How do you expect anyone to want to help us, when you behave in such a manner, this is intolerable! You will remain here now, I will go by myself.'

'But why? We can explain … he will understand, surely … and also, he wanted to meet me, didn't he?'

'Perhaps. I will go first and apologise, then we shall see.'

Avi turned around and left. I watched him walking away for

a while, surprised and hurt, then turned towards the sea and leant on the balustrade. I felt sweaty, I knew my face was shining and my blouse was, no doubt, damp with perspiration. How awful it was to have annoyed Avi in such a way; the uncle mattered to him, and I should have known better than to be late. I felt sick. I looked around and saw no place to hide. The beach beneath was full of bathers, the street – crowded. I tried to breathe deeply and stop the nausea, but it was stronger than me. What was I going to do? Avi would be back any minute to take me to his uncle's hotel!

I vomited . I held the railings and let the pangs take over. Everything around me became a blur; a woman stopped and asked whether I wanted help. I shook my head, then behind her, I saw Avi.

'What's going on?' he asked.

'Nothing ..., ' I said, 'it's the heat, I have been in the sun too long.' My stomach seemed to have settled. 'Thank you very much,' I thanked the woman and she walked away. 'What did he say, was he angry?' The look in Avi's eyes hadn't changed.

'Let's go home.' he said

'But ... aren't we going to ...? '

'No. He is not going to help us. He doesn't approve.'

'But Avi ... why? Just because we were a few minutes late ...? '

'No, silly, he doesn't approve of me, marrying you.'

'But why? He hasn't even met me? And in his letter ... '

'Never mind his letter, you are a Sephardi.'

'What of it?'

'Oh, don't you know anything! The Sephardis are inferior to us Ashkenazis.'

'Inferior? In what way?'

'You are ... oh, stop asking me, I don't know, like Arabs in a way.'

'This is ridiculous, and you know it Avi. I have nothing of an

Arab … and what if I was? Oh, God, what am I saying! Are you affected by his … your uncle's disapproval?'

'He is not going to help us.'

'It doesn't really matter, does it? We will manage on our own.'

'You don't even seem to realise it's three weeks to the wedding!'

'Yes, I am so happy.'

'You are irresponsible. Have you thought of what we are going to wear? How we are going to organise things?'

'Is it important? What we wear, I mean … I don't mind … '

' … and the honeymoon, have you thought about that?'

'I think perhaps we should do without it, we can't really afford … '

'You think … you think nothing! My uncle gave me some money for it, when I told him that my decision to marry you was … irrevocable. So we will go to Haifa for a few days.'

'That's nice of him! Why didn't you say so before?'

'Because you would ask for money for a dress or shoes or some other stupid thing like that.'

'Why do you think such things of me, Avi, have I ever been … have I ever given you reason to think that money mattered so much? that I wanted things? if the money was given to us for … '

'To me!'

'To you … for a honeymoon – that's what we … you will use it for.'

'That's right. I will.'

Avi was in a bad mood. I tried to understand his disappointment, I thought that had it been me, had I relied so much on someone, and I was let down, I would be very hurt. But why was he so aggressive towards me? I had a headache now and felt every bump on the road shaking my whole body. I felt ill, but said nothing. The walk to the village was long and tiring, the evening hot and humid.

As soon as we approached the village I could see movement on the terrace; there was a car parked outside.

'What's going on?' I said, not really expecting Avi to answer me, 'Mum wasn't well at all when I left … '

We found my father pacing nervously, smoking and crying. It was so frightening, to see him crying!

'Dad, dad, what happened, what is it?'

'She swallowed all the tablets … she swallowed them all …. '

'Dad! But why?'

'She tried to kill herself, obviously.' Avi said, 'Is the doctor with her?'

'Yes … '

I didn't hear any more, my mind retained and repeated the words 'kill herself … kill herself … '

'Can I go in?' I asked, 'Can I talk to her?'

'No. She was unconscious, I found her unconscious when I came out of the shower. She had taken them … before … I ran for the doctor … he was still in the village … he made her be sick … he says she has got it all out … she'll be all right …. ' my father sat on the bench.

'My mother tried to kill herself, she wanted to, die … why? What have we done to her?'

'You are as pale as a sheet, sit down and grab hold of yourself.' Avi said, 'these things happen.'

The doctor came out.

'I have pumped her stomach.' he said and the mere words made my stomach come up to my throat. The doctor was talking to my father: 'she is in no danger now, but it doesn't mean that she will not try it again. She is depressive and you mustn't leave her alone. She needs love and care, but you should take her to her specialist. Between you and I, she didn't really mean it. As far as I understand, there wasn't enough there to kill her. She would have slept for a day or so and that's that. But it doesn't mean that she won't succeed next time. Even if she doesn't mean it. These things happen. I also think that she could be quite violent, so take her to her doctor as soon as you can, he might change her treatment.'

'May I go in, Doctor?' I asked.

'Yes. Get her up and don't let her go to sleep for as long as you can.'

I saw my father put his hand in his pocket for his wallet as I walked in. It was very hot and a heavy musty smell hit my nostrils. I went over to her bed and knelt down. Her eyes were closed. There was a basin by the bed, full of what seemed to be dirty water. I took it and went downstairs to dispose of it and rinse the basin.

Avi and my father were still talking to the doctor. My mother hadn't moved. I took her bottle of Cologne from the wardrobe and massaged her temples gently, then her wrists, like Mrs. Stoylova had done in Sofia. Her face remained motionless.

'Mum … ' I whispered, 'Mum … I am so sorry about this afternoon … ' I could see her chest going up and down noiselessly, 'I didn't meet the uncle in the end … ' I went on, hoping for a sign, 'he told Avi that he didn't approve of him marrying a Sephardi … would you believe it …? So you see, I shouldn't have bothered …, ' tears were running abundantly down my cheeks, but I tried not to sob, 'did you know that we … Sephardis are … inferior, inferior to Ashkenazis … isn't it funny, mum?' Her eyelids fluttered. I looked at her intently, awaiting her to say something. I heard the men escort the doctor to his car. 'Shall I make you a cup of tea, mum?'

She now looked at me; a piercing coherent glance which, to my great surprise contained nothing but disgust. I moved back a little, not knowing what to expect.

'You,' she said slowly, her teeth clenched 'you are pregnant!'

Chapter Sixteen

Married

The town was still asleep. The early morning air, although hot already, carried a slight breeze from the sea. The ships in the harbour stood motionless; a few smaller vessels sailed noiselessly between them. They, and a few buses that I could see occasionally between the trees, were the only movements announcing the fact that the town was about to wake up.

I was standing on the small balcony outside our hotel room, midway up the Carmel Mountain. From where I stood I could see the road which led from the harbour to the quarantine camp where, just a few months earlier, I had been a new immigrant. Now, I was back in Haifa, on my honeymoon.

Avi was asleep on his bed. I could hear the hotel waking up too. Crockery and cutlery were being handled and the tables were probably being set for breakfast. The hotel's ballroom had been hired out for a wedding every night of our stay; there had been music and laughter until very late, preventing me from sleep and when I finally did fall asleep, that was cut short by the intense heat and bright light very early every morning. I was tired.

I went back into the room and lay on my bed. I looked at the ceiling; there was a lamp shade in the middle and a fly was flying busily under it. I wondered how such a small creature could produce such a loud noise! It was the last day of our honeymoon. We had been here for five days. In five days we had seen seven films; all Westerns. Avi had had a long siesta every afternoon; as for me, I was fighting nausea most of the time, unable to sleep. At first I had wanted to nestle next to him at night, I wanted to feel his closeness, I wanted to hold him in my arms and I wanted him to hold me.

On the first night, I lay next to him and pressed my cheek against his chest. He was my husband now and I wanted to tell him about my love and how happy I was; Avi pushed me aside, got up and went to the other bed:

'I am not a machine you know!' He turned his back towards me, and even if he hadn't, there was a bedside cabinet between the two beds. I cried, not quite understanding what he had meant, not really wanting to understand. If he had meant what I thought he had, he was so mistaken! But how could I tell him? Couldn't he see for himself? There was no time for talking. He fell asleep so quickly.

And there was my sickness. I fought it as much as I could, but as soon as we sat down at the table, I had to run to the toilet. Avi was annoyed; it spoilt his meals. Together with the nausea, there had been the painful hammering on my left temple, but I hadn't mentioned it.

It was seven o'clock now. Should I wake Avi? He didn't like being woken up; I thought of packing, but I might make noise. I looked at him. He was lying on his stomach, his beautiful profile outlined on the pillow, the mouth slightly open, one arm lying across the bed, the other, hanging down, tucked in a fist in his shoe. He looked like a boy. I smiled, his face was so peaceful, his position so child-like. I went to the bathroom and splashed some water on my face in an effort to freshen up. The water was lukewarm and unpleasant. I looked at the shiny chromium taps, the electric switch. How simple it was. Now, we were going back to the paraffin oil lamps, the tarred floor and the toilet 'behind the wall'.

Avi stirred. But he didn't wake. The sun was scorching on the balcony now and I went back to the bathroom where it was still fairly cool. Avi wasn't a soldier any longer. He was going to a new job next week. This job had been a lucky break for us. One day he had met, totally by chance an old friend of his, Jerome, who promised Avi a job. Jerome worked for civil aviation Company. Avi went for an interview and came back smiling:

'I am sure I've got it! I know how to talk to people, I know how to make them feel important.'

'What kind of a job is it?'

'I will be helping around generally at the beginning, but I will soon be promoted, don't you worry.'

'Do you like the job though?'

'Of course I do.'

'That's the main thing. I wouldn't like you to do something you don't like just because … '

'Don't you worry. I have to earn for three soon … ' he put a hand on my stomach. What a warm feeling that was!

My mouth was dry and I took a sip of water. My stomach reacted immediately, refusing to take it down. With the impact of the nausea, the hammering on my left temple returned. I felt awful. I didn't know how I was going to survive the journey home.

The wedding had gone quite well. The ceremony finished under the canopy erected in Claude and Eve's garden, everybody sat at long tables. My mother wasn't feeling too bad. She sat down, smiling faintly. My father was a little mixed up. Avi perspired so much, he had to change his shirt twice.

Many members of our family hadn't turned up and my mother was deeply offended; I didn't really mind. A young woman in the village had lent me her wedding dress which fitted perfectly and was beautiful. A hairdresser had made efforts to set my hair in a Veronica Lake style, but the heat and the shower I had to take before getting dressed, meant that not much of it was left for the ceremony. Avi's friend, Jerome, was supposed to take pictures, because we couldn't afford a professional photographer, but somehow they never came out; he either exposed the film, or forgot to put it in altogether, so we had no record of the day.

'What the hell are you doing sitting here?' Avi's voice startled me.

'It's cooler here .... '

'Why don't you sleep?'

'I can't. It's too hot.'

'You are mad! come on, let's go down for breakfast. I am hungry.'

Avi ate his breakfast, and I tried not to look. Eventually I had to run to the toilet. When I came back, I was hungry.

'Now that I have finished, you want to eat! I have never heard anything like this before!'

'I am sorry ... '

'Oh, go on. I have seen other pregnant women, but none of them acted as funny! Surely you can control yourself.'

'I try ... but it's difficult.'

I was eating gluttonously. Avi looked on.

'Is it going to stay in?' he asked.

'I have no idea, but I am so hungry, as though I haven't eaten for days.'

Ж

I saw my mother standing on the terrace as we approached the village. We waved and she waved back. I thought I discerned a smile on her face.

'I hope she is better.' I said.

'So do I.'

Avi dropped the suitcase as soon as we got upstairs.

'Oh, my God, this is the hottest August I have known! Hullo mum, is there cold water?'

'Welcome home children,' my mother kissed us, 'come in here, I have a little surprise for you.'

We followed her to the kitchen and we saw a large beautifully decorated gateau on the table. My stomach convulsed at the sight of it and I walked out, my hand over my mouth.

'She has been like this all the time.' I heard Avi say.

'She could make an effort, I have worked so hard in these conditions to make something special for you two.'

When I came back, I sat on the bench, recovering from the run and the sickness. My mother came and sat by me:

'You must control yourself. Everyone can hear you being sick and they will know. I don't want that shame on us, do you understand me?'

I did. I nodded and felt so miserable, realising what it was that worried her. I felt weak and tired and put my face in my hands and cried.

Avi came out, picking his teeth with a broken matchstick.

'Stop the tears and the gossip, I am fed up. I am going to sleep and I want quiet.'

'Go and tell him to take his shoes off! Quickly.' my mother whispered to me. I followed Avi who was already lying on the settee, his feet on the arm-rests.

'Please take your shoes off my love.'

'Why?'

'Well, they would soil the covers .... '

'There is nothing wrong with my shoes, there is no mud,

leave me alone, I will keep my shoes on, and I want to sleep.'

I left him.

'Did he take them off?' my mother asked.

'Yes.' I lied, hoping she wouldn't go in to check.

'What did you do in Haifa?'

'Oh, we went for walks.' I lied again. 'We also saw a few films, very nice.'

'Waste of money. Did you go the theatre?'

'Some films are very informative, historic etc., and there is no propaganda like in the Soviet films.'

'Hmm.' my mother grunted. 'I am going to take a rest.' she said. I went back into our room, made sure the curtain was pulled across, then took Avi's shoes off. He didn't even stir.

My father had bought an ice box from an American who was going back to the States, and life had improved, or rather the quality of life. We could actually keep cooked food in it, also uncooked vegetables which freed us from the tedious daily shopping. You had to remember to empty the drawer where the melted ice collected though; otherwise, it spilled in the night and made a terrible mess.

During the week Avi spent at home, prior to taking up his job, he made quite a few improvements around the house. He fixed a real shower rose at the end of the hose, and we now had a nice soft spray of water, rather than the downpour we had had before; he made some more shelves in the kitchen. My mother praised him endlessly to my father, who according to her 'couldn't put a nail straight in a wall'.

Avi, on the other hand, demanded that our room be ours alone, and not treated as a sitting room during the day. He wanted the settee to be left open, as a bed, for his daily siestas. To this, my mother objected strongly; it wasn't healthy, she said, for a young man to sleep so much. His demands and her objections were voiced through me.

'He can lie down a while on our beds if he wants, but he has to wash before!' my mother would tell me.

'Tell her,' Avi told me in reply to the edited version of my mother's words, 'that I want to sleep in my bed, and that she is not to tell me what to do!'

The constant nausea and the hammering on my temple didn't help. Eventually, it was my mother who had to give in, and the settee was left open.

Chapter Seventeen

Isolation

By mid-September, the days grew shorter and the evenings – cooler once more. This enabled us to go to bed earlier than in the long hot months when it was impossible to breathe inside before midnight or even later. Sometimes, Avi made love to me. He would turn to me impatient and intent, we didn't dare speak for fear of being heard and when he climbed on me, I made sure we were covered by the duvet; I also tried not to move, in order to avoid the squeaking of the bed.

Usually, these embraces didn't last long, Avi's excitement was very quickly exhausted and he slid next to me and almost immediately fell asleep. During our love-making, I hung on to him, trying to feel something, to experience something, but apart from the proximity of his body and the closeness between us that existed in my mind only, I felt nothing.

To my consternation, my mother said to me one morning:

'You mustn't allow him to take advantage of you too often. It takes a lot out of a woman.' and she walked away.

I went quickly after her, to ask her some questions. My mind abounded with unanswered questions on the subject, and since she had spoken first, and I was married now, perhaps the subject wasn't taboo any longer! But when I found her in the kitchen, her face was closed and I knew that she was not prepared to talk. The subject was still taboo.

Eventually my skirt became tight. My mother dug out my old Bulgarian blue dress and gave it to the village seamstress together with an old navy skirt of hers. The seamstress slit my old dress down the front and inserted a navy centrepiece which was folded like a large pleat and held by two hooks. I could hook up the pleat to further notches, as I grew bigger.

I wanted to know all about Avi's work. What he did and what his colleagues were like? How did he find civilian life? At first, I enquired, for the purpose of taking part in his life at work, and perhaps, to make conversation when we sat on the bench during the hot summer nights, with nothing to talk about.

Avi didn't like my questions; he refused to talk about his work and the more he kept silent about it, the more I became curious. At first, just curious and then worried and jealous. I now looked at him as he walked away in the morning, having given me a light kiss, his mind already away, where I couldn't follow him.

I hung on to him, hugging him, wanting a gesture, a word, that all those hours which he spent away from me didn't matter, that he didn't leave me, not really; that when he came back, it was as though he had had me with him all the time, like I had him. I didn't know how to express my feelings, I didn't know the language, I didn't know the formulas, nor did I know any tricks, and when he consistently kept his distance, I suffered; the more he realised I suffered, the more secretive he became.

One night, he announced at the table:

'I have been invited to a cocktail party tomorrow night.' I looked at him, worried, afraid to show my feelings in front of my parents.

'Where?' I asked.

'The General Managers'

'What's the occasion?'

'I don't know. He invited me.'

'Only you?'

'No, no, all employees are invited.' Avi looked at me and stopped eating, 'Yes, wives are invited, but you can't come. Not when you are … like this.' He looked at my protruding stomach, then, probably having seen the pain on my face, he added in a slightly softer tone, 'Perhaps next year?'

'Never mind,' said my father, 'his job comes first. You are expecting a baby and better stay home.'

'What did you think?' said my mother, 'Motherhood means giving, giving from beginning to end. You thought it's child's play, didn't you?'

All I could do was shake my head, fighting tears of humiliation and fear.

'How will you get home?' I asked in the end.

'Jerome will let me have his car.'

I curled up in bed, hugged my large belly, my baby, and cried bitterly. I had visions of a woman, a lot cleverer than me, a lot more experienced than me, scheming and beautiful, seducing Avi, and that I – who loved him so much – would lose him forever, merely because I still was a naive and clumsy girl.

The rains had brought nature back to life. The fields, having absorbed thirstily the first drops, were now saturated and green. Wild flora had once more invaded every inch of earth; blue and yellow wild flowers grew, beautiful and luxuriant everywhere. The pond was once again full and the frogs were back to sing us their nightly serenade. Together with it came the dampness on our walls, the condensation drops, the damp bedclothes every morning and my mother's gloomy moods.

The baby was due soon, around mid-March; I felt enormous with it, and an impression prevailed that whenever I entered a room, there was no room for anybody else. The baby 'sat' low, I was told by the doctor, hence the constant pain in my lower abdomen – it was pressing on my bladder. I was in constant pain and there was hardly any position in which I felt comfortable. To ease the pain, I had to empty my bladder very often which meant frequent visits 'behind the wall' which wasn't very pleasant in the cold, windy winter weather and the crouching becoming almost impossible, but I had began to love the child inside me. My dream of being a mother, of having someone to love and who would love me in return was about to become reality and that was a great comfort which I felt I could not share with anybody. So, I kept it to myself.

In the winter, Avi agreed that our room should be used as a sitting room. Once the settee was closed and the housework finished, my mother and I sat down in the semi-darkness, awaiting the men to come home. I found it difficult to sit for any length of time because of the pain. I endured it, though, for as long as I could and finally got up and paced.

'Sit down!' my mother ordered. I looked at her, hoping that she would understand and allow me to stand up, but her face under the paraffin oil lamp was uncompromising and lugubrious.

'I can't, mum, it hurts me.'

'Sit down or go out to pace, you are driving me crazy! You know I can't stand nervous pacing!'

'I am not nervous, mum, just in pain .... '

'If you don't sit still ... you'll drive me to ... ' her voice from a relatively calm, perhaps just irritated tone, escalated to a high pitched shriek; she got up and began to pace from wall to wall, hitting me, as she passed me by, then hitting the wall with her body.

She frightened me as she had done in the past, I knew that I couldn't wrestle with her now for fear of being hit on my belly. My mother wasn't thin now, she had put on considerable weight and seeing her madly knocking her body against the wall was so painfully grotesque, that I burst into tears.

I took a pace toward her:

'Mum, please, I will not pace any longer, please calm down! I am sorry!'

'Leave me alone! Now that you have done the damage, for which you have considerable talent – go away and leave me alone!'

There was so much hatred in her voice. Why? Why did she hate me so?

'Mum, please, please ..., ' sobs were choking me, 'I will do anything you say ... please ... '

'Leave me alone.' I stood there, clumsy and heavy, and looked at her as she tore at her hands and hit her head.

'Mum, please, let me get you one of your tablets? It will make you feel better, please!'

I went to the kitchen where she kept her tablets. There were so many in the little box! I found the one I knew was the strongest tranquilliser, got a glass of water, and with shaking hands took it back in.

My mother was standing in the middle of the room, she took the tablet and the glass from me and went into their bedroom and pulled the curtain. I stayed where I was, listening. There was no sound coming from beyond the curtain and worried, I parted it slightly. My mother was halving the tablet with quick precise movements. She opened the window and threw what seemed to be one half out, closed the window, put the other half on her tongue and swallowed it. I moved away, stunned. Why did she do that? Distressed as she was, surely she needed all the relief she could get from the tablet? Was this why she complained that the tablets didn't help her?Steps coming up the stairs interrupted my thoughts. It was my father.

'What's wrong?' he asked as soon as he walked in.

'Mum isn't very well .... ' I hesitated to tell him any more.

He went to their room and I heard through the curtain:

'What is it my love? What upset you? I am here now.' I heard my mother's whisper then a few sparse words as my father spoke to her quietly,' ... just a matter of days ... I'll talk to Avi ... '

Despite the pain, I sat down because my legs were giving way under my weight.

Chapter Eighteen

Birth of Raoul – My Son

When the pain woke me up, I wasn't surprised at all. We had, for the last two weeks lowered the wick of the lamp next to me instead of extinguishing it, so that I could, at any time, turn it up and get some light.

I felt the short, strong pain in my groin; looked at the time, it was midnight. Everybody was asleep. I took the watch in my hand, left the wick slightly up, rested back on my pillows – I was, of late, sleeping half propped up, because I couldn't breathe properly if I lay down. In the night, I listened to the frogs in the pond and awaited the pain again. Was it going to come back? Was that it? Was this going to be the beginning of giving life to my child?

The pain came back. It was sudden, short and very strong. It wasn't exactly in the groin, as I had thought before. It was somewhere at the back, I didn't know where. It came again exactly ten minutes after the first one. I got up, took my handbag and extracted from it the long sheet of paper – my admission paper for the Maternity Hospital Dajani, in Jaffa, near to where Aunt Amelia lived. I folded it carefully and put it back in my handbag.

I looked at the long shadows, cast on the walls by the small flame of the paraffin oil lamp. I could see the dark patches on the walls, the dark damp patches along which tiny streams of condensation ran. I heard a dog bark, then the pain came again. 10 minutes.

I didn't want to wake up Avi, in case it was a false alarm. I wanted to be sure. I didn't feel tired at all, and sitting up, checking the frequency of the pain didn't worry me. I thought of my baby. Soon, he would leave my body and become a person, an entity in his own right. What was he going to be like? Was he going to be like the baby in my dream? That dream I had had a few weeks earlier, where I was holding a baby about twelve months old. It was plump, with dimples on his knees – I saw them in my dream, with dark blue eyes, golden hair and fair, peach-like skin. My child! My dream come true!

A pain. It got me by surprise and I sat up, startled by its impact. I waited a moment; it took some time to fade away. Then I relaxed.

It was now three o'clock. The pains had been regular – every ten minutes for three hours. Very short at first and now beginning to lengthen. I had no more doubts. I had to get to the hospital. How? Why had we not thought of this before? How was I going to get to the hospital from where we lived? Miles away from anywhere. The baby was coming ….

'Avi.' I passed a hand over his cheek. I looked at him; when he slept, he was in a world of his own. I put the wick up a little more and called him again:

'Avi.'

He sat up.

'What'?'

'Avi, my love, I think it's the baby. We will have to go … '

'The baby? now?' he rubbed his eyes, as though I was

announcing something totally unexpected. I lent over and kissed him:

'Yes, the baby.'

'But how am I going to get you to the hospital?' He jumped out of bed, 'Are you feeling all right? You are not going to have it here, are you? My God! What am I going to do?'

My father's voice came from behind the curtain:

'Don't scare her, son, may I come in?'

'Yes, dad.'

'Is it the baby?' he asked me as he came in, holding on to his pyjama trousers.

A pain coming up, made me delay my reply; I took a deep breath, waited for it to subside, then nodded.

'Yes.'

'All right, don't worry, we will get you to the hospital. Come, Avi, let's get dressed, see if we can borrow a bicycle from someone, get to the main road. We must stop a passing car.'

'Oh, my God … what am I going to do … why didn't we think of this before … '

'Don't you worry …. ' he said to me, 'You hold on until we get you there …. '

'Avi, I am not worried, there is plenty of time. The first baby takes a long time. Don't you worry, I am sure you will find … ' a pain interrupted me. They all looked at me and waited for me to relax before they talked again. My mother appeared through the curtain. The pain subsided. The men left.

'Can you get up?' my mother asked me, 'You must get dressed.'

'Yes, I can.' I was embarrassed at all this fuss over me. My mother helped me into the dress.

'I am going to make you a hot drink.' she said, 'Do you want tea or hot chocolate?'

'Hot chocolate would be very nice, thank you mum.'

I slid my feet into my shoes and sat by the paraffin heater. I now realised that I was bleeding. 'Probably part of the process,'

I thought and went to get some cotton wool.

My mother returned with the hot drinks.

'Does one bleed before ... long before the actual birth, mum?'

'I don't remember.' she said, then added, 'Why are you bleeding?'

'Only a little.'

We were quiet for a while.

'I wish the men would come back. Why is it taking them so long?'

'Don't worry mum, although the pains are increasing in strength, they are still spaced at ten minutes. And the doctor said that by the end, they get to one minute intervals; there is plenty of time.'

'Aren't you scared?'

'No. Why? Should I be?'

'No, no I was just asking.'

My father came in.

'Avi has gone into his camp, Tel Litvinski. He says that he still knows enough people there and his commanding officer is bound to give him a car.'

'From the Army?', I asked, 'But how?'

'Don't ask me. He says he can do it. There is no alternative. At this time of night – the traffic, even on the main road, is down to zero. And if you ask me, it is crazy, but in this country everything is possible.' He took his coat off and sat down. 'How is she?' he turned to my mother as though I wasn't there.

'I am fine dad.'

He lit a cigarette and began pacing up and down.

'Do you mind the smoke?' he asked me.

All this attention! I was so flattered, touched and embarrassed at the same time!

A pain. I took a deep breath again, felt it come up, then subside, I relaxed and answered my father's question:

'No, dad, not at all.'

'So, finally you're going to drop it, hey?' he said.

I smiled at him. What could I say? I found his words so strange, so unfeeling; here I was, living through what I thought would be the most important personal experience in my life, and he referred to it as ....

A pain. Strong at the centre, expanding, increasing, extracting a slight groan from my throat. I saw their faces. I made an effort to mask the pain, to straighten my face, so it didn't show. What exactly were they worried about, it crossed my mind, the pain that was tearing at me, or the possibility of my giving birth there and then?

I smiled.

'I am OK, really.'

If my father hadn't said that word, the suspicion wouldn't have come to me. The day was breaking outside, and with it, the frogs' nightly serenade stopped. We heard a noise outside, it was that of an engine.

My father peeped out of the window.

'Thank God he is back! And with a car!'

I heard Avi's steps, running. He opened the door:

'Are you ready? Are you all right? Come on, hurry up!'

I stood up to follow him downstairs, but a pain stopped me. I held onto his arm and waited. It spread and grew, then slowly, died out.

My parents kissed me.

'Be courageous,' said my mother, 'the woman's cross is heavy to bear.'

'Don't worry mum I am fine, really.' And then, as it crossed my mind, 'You will be grandparents soon.'

We walked down the stairs, Avi made sure he held me with one hand; that was nice. Aunt Clara, having, no doubt, heard the noise and understood the reason for it, opened the front door and said quickly:

'Good luck!'

A command-car, with its roof off, and a young soldier in the driving seat, stood outside the house. Avi helped me up. I was holding my handbag with my admission paper in it and a small bag, prepared by my mother, with some toiletries in it.

'Take care!' the soldier said. 'Are you all right?'

'Yes, fine.'

I sat next to the soldier, Avi sat behind me, his hands on my shoulders, to prevent me from being ejected from the car, as it meandered through the village lanes. Once on the main road, the soldier put the command-car in top gear and drove fast. Twice, on the way to the hospital, the pain took me and I lifted my hand, in a prayer to him to, slow down, to ease up my pain a little, but he wouldn't hear of it.

'Slow down, you idiot! ' Avi shouted, 'She is in pain!'

'I better get her to the hospital where she can have the baby! I don't want to have to deal with it here!' He didn't conceal his feelings about the whole thing.

Once outside the hospital, he looked at me, a wide smile on his face:

'Here we are! Now you can have your baby! My sister has had three. She screamed the life out of us, but her babies are born within half an hour of her starting to scream. So I wanted to get you here before, see?'

'Thank you very much.'

Avi jumped down and helped me as I tried to tackle the steps with my large body.

'Thanks old man.' he said to the soldier and we headed for 'Reception.' There were a few steps to climb.

'Are you afraid?' asked Avi.

'No, not at all.'

'But it hurts, doesn't it?'

'Yes, it does. But the pain won't last forever, only a few more hours, then we will have our baby, our son.'

'What if it's a girl?'

'Nothing, but I saw him in my dream, it's going to be a boy.'

We headed for the flap doors at the end of a long corridor.

A nurse came out just as we were walking in. She pushed Avi back, her large hand in the middle of his chest:

'No men behind these doors, can't you read?'

We hadn't seen the notice.

A pain.

'Shall I wait here?' Avi asked the nurse who looked at me, saw that I was in no condition to answer her question, and asked Avi:

'Her first?'

'Yes.'

'I see,' she looked at me again. The pain passed.

'Shall I wait?' Avi repeated his question. Did I detect a desire to be released? Freed?

'Sit down, here on this bench, and wait. I'll tell you if we will keep her on not.'

Then she turned to me:

'Come on, you're not the only one today.'

I looked at Avi, with a smile, and followed the nurse through the flap doors. We walked along a narrow corridor, through a small kitchen, then she showed me into a cubicle:

'Take your pants off and lie down.'

She drew the curtain and disappeared. I did as I was told. A woman, wearing a white coat came in, a wide smile on her face:

'Good morning. When did the pains start?'

'At … ' I felt a pain coming, made an effort to talk, but the woman sat down and motioned to me that it was all right, she could wait. I took a breath again, allowed the pain to take over my body, expand, tighten its grip; I felt it peak, then slowly, very slowly, it began to withdraw. I sighed.

'At midnight,' I smiled at her, 'at ten minutes intervals, I think the intervals are still ten minutes, but the pain is a lot stronger.'

The woman went towards the cabinet in the corner, and from one of the drawers took something which proved to be a rolled up rubber 'finger', which she rolled slowly and carefully down her finger.

'Let's examine you now.' she said. 'Fold up your knees.' she helped me do it as she talked, she then took a small jar from the top of the cabinet put the rubber finger inside it; I felt her apply the greasy substance, probably Vaseline, around my anus and just as she was going to proceed with her examination, I felt another pain coming up. I lifted my hand, unable to talk; she understood my sign, looked at her watch and waited patiently. She heard me sigh at the end of the pain and came over. I shut my eyes, embarrassed.

The examination only took a moment; I hardly felt anything. She stood up, rolled off the rubber 'finger' and threw it in the pedal bin.

'You can get up. This is it all right, but the opening is still very small. You can go out and walk around, or sit if you want to, in the garden, for a few more hours. Come back around mid-day, unless, of course, the pains speed up, or you lose your waters – then you must come in immediately. Understood?'

I nodded; I didn't know what 'the waters' meant, but figured out that I would recognise it when I see it. I found Avi where I had left him, on the bench. He got up. What did they say? Isn't it the Baby?'

'Yes, it is, only it's too soon.'

'Too soon for what?'

'To be admitted, I have plenty of time, let's go out and walk in the garden for a few hours.'

'A few hours?'

'Yes, I told you the first baby takes time.'

It was a beautifully landscaped garden, with flower beds, lawns, trees and benches. The benches were still damp from the night mist, but the sun was lighting the sky behind the roofs. At first, its rays passed us by, then as the sun rose in the sky, its rays reached us, warming us up and burning all the remaining dampness from the benches, and the dew droplets on the grass.

There were few people around. A nurse or a doctor would walk quickly from one building to another, a stethoscope hanging loosely from a pocket. Avi walked beside me, and when a pain stopped me, he would stop too, looking intently in my face for a sign of relief. I held his arm as I tried to breathe in and loosen the muscles so as to let the pain take its course, until it was over. Then I felt fine.

'Do you think that mum will get better when she is a grandmother?' I asked.

'How should I know? That's the least of my worries now.'

'You mustn't worry about me. I'll be all right. I so want to do something that will bring mum some joy, some happiness.'

'That's the least of my worries right now, I tell you.' he repeated. 'You are in such pain, I can see … and all those hours!'

'To tell you the truth I didn't know that it took that long either, but I don't regret, I want this baby, we both do! So a few hours of pain don't really matter … '

A pain.

I stopped walking; Avi held my hand and squeezed it. It seemed that the whole middle of me was suddenly rotten and was going to fall to pieces, disintegrate. It held on, I was breathless. It seemed to take ages; then, finally began to go away.

'It's seven minutes now,' Avi said, 'maybe even less.'

'What is the time?'

'Just gone 6am.'

'Do you think the benches are dry enough to sit on them?'

He dried a bench with his handkerchief.

'Come and sit down. Are you comfortable?'

I smiled. I hadn't been comfortable for months.

'Yes,' I said, 'This is fine.'

The sun was right in our faces and we squinted. I felt its

warmth on my skin, it was so vivifying!

'How good it is that the baby will be born in the spring.'

'Yes.' I said, 'Avi, you promise me to buy everything before I come home!'

My mother's superstitions hadn't allowed us to purchase any baby clothes before the baby was born. It was 'bad luck'.

I had been furious at that imposition, but with my mother – one had to obey.

'Don't worry, all I need is a few hours. I'll buy everything.'

'Good.'

A pain.

It seemed to originate somewhere in the middle of my back. I put my hand to it, but then it spread, up and up, and down and it became so sharp I felt blinded by it, and deafened, and numb. I tried a deep breath, but the pain was so sharp, all I managed were a few short gasps.

When it was over, and I relaxed, Avi said:

'I think we better go in. It was five minutes this time.'

'Perhaps we should.'

I was admitted this time, and Avi was told to go. I didn't see him go. The nurse must have told him that I was being kept in.

'Come on,' she said to me, 'we have a lot of work to do before we get you ready.'

We went into a larger cubicle, with more equipment in it.

'Undress!' she ordered, 'everything off!' She left me alone, drawing the curtain as she walked out. I struggled with another pain while undressing.

'Here, put this on.' She timed her return perfectly, 'The opening is at the back.'

I unfolded the thick cotton garment, and as I slid my arms into its sleeves, a pain overtook me again, I sat down, tired, and let it take over. I left it too late to take a breath, now I couldn't; I felt that, if I as much as I tried to breathe, the pain would tear me apart, so I sat there, leaning backwards on my arms, not breathing and the pain was still tightening its grip. Tears came to my eyes, but I held those back; the pain began to withdraw, I felt it untighten, loosen up, go.

I hadn't even noticed the nurse's presence.

'Lie down.' she ordered; I obeyed, and she proceeded to shave my pubic hair. I asked no questions; I was still recovering from the pain.

'Have we finished now?' I asked and she looked at me not understanding what I meant, 'Getting me ready.' I explained.

'No.' she shook her head, 'Now – the enema.'

'Why an enema?'

'Because you have to be clean inside, that's why. To make more room for the baby and not to soil yourself, later, when you push.'

I didn't understand much of what she said, but obeyed. Miraculously, she fitted the enema between two pains. That finished she said, 'You can have a shower now if you wish, then you are going to bed.'

I took a long refreshing shower, soaping my enormous body, passing my hand gently over my belly, not to hurt the baby; I wondered as I looked at it's bulk whether it will ever be as flat as it used to, be. I felt my belly, with my hand stretched over it, thinking that, there it was, my child, with just my skin between him and my hand. I didn't allow the strong jet of water to, fall directly over my belly, in case it would damage him.

'Are you enjoying yourself there?' the nurse shouted, 'Come on! I have work to do!'

I wrapped myself in the large towel she had given me. I felt the bare skin where my pubic hair had been – it felt awful – but I couldn't see it! Then, once more, I slid my arms inside the sleeves of the gown. The nurse fastened the strings at the back, while my body was invaded by a pain. She felt my body stiffen, she waited. When she heard me sigh with relief she said:

'Come on.'

I followed her through more corridors, and as we turned a corner, I heard the screams. No wonder they couldn't be heard from the outer corridor – we must have walked miles inside the bowels of the building! It dawned on me that I had a long way to go yet. A lot stronger pains to come to extract such screams from me.

There were three beds facing the door we had entered through.

She chose the middle one for me; the others were unoccupied. I lay down slowly , manoeuvring my clumsy body, anticipating a pain. On the left there was a set of flap doors: the screams came from behind them.

'Lie here for the time being,' the nurse said, and looking at the flap doors, added, 'you have plenty of time before you go to the delivery room.' She turned on her heels and left.

Along the whole wall, on the right, there was a window, which, through opaque panes , filled the room with strong white light. Above the flap doors there was a round clock; I squinted at it, it was just before 9am.

I felt a pain approaching now and squeezed the small handkerchief I had kept in my hand all the time. I took a deep breath and squeezed hard.

I knew that the pain was going to expand and take over the whole, or so it seemed to me, of my body; I had to let it do it, once more strengthening its grip, holding, holding, until I had no breath left, no vision, no real notion of reality, then slowly it loosened its grip, as I knew it would, I felt grateful to it for that, I relaxed and listened to the screams coming from the other side of the flap doors.

A nurse came in:

'I don't think you feel up to some breakfast, do you? Perhaps you can drink some milk, here you are.' she left a tray on the bedside cabinet.

'Thank you.'

I lifted my heavy body on one elbow, leant towards the cabinet and had a sip of hot milk. Then, I felt the pain come up again. We had developed a relationship, my pains and I, by now. I felt it coming, well in time to prepare myself for it, to take in my breath, to feel it's power over me and without fighting it, let it take me over, nearly to destruction, then having satisfied itself that even though not fighting, I was withstanding it, it would loosen its grip, and slowly very slowly, withdraw.

The woman in the delivery room was screaming. Her screams were horrifying, and as I lay, still, breathless, tired from the last pain, I discerned words being spoken by the screaming woman. Incredulous, I listened. No I wasn't mistaken, she was cursing, in no uncertain terms, her husband, who had inflicted this on her! I then heard another voice, probably another woman having a baby, or perhaps, some of the staff? No, surely not a nurse! She was saying:

'If you hadn't opened your legs it wouldn't have happened'.

'You, bitch!' came a quick reply, 'and why are you here? You didn't keep yours tight together, did you?'

There was no doubt in my mind now who was making the remarks.

'No,' the second voice was saying, 'but at least I am not complaining, like you.'

'Then why the hell don't you shut up!'

'Because it bloody hurts, that's why!'

My own pain was coming up again. My eyes filled with tears as I prepared myself for it. The flap door opened, and in the blur of my pain, I saw a shadow of a man in a white coat. He must have realised that I was in the middle of a pain, because he motioned to me that he could wait.

Finally I sighed, relaxing my body, which by now felt like a heap of rotten flesh.

The doctor removed the covers and said:

'Let's see what progress you have made.'

I looked at him, now my vision and mind clear after the pain, and my heart jumped in recognition. It was my instructor from Maccabi! As I didn't open my legs to enable him to examine me, he looked at me, a slight impatience on his face, but then, he also saw me for the first time since his entrance, and his features changed:

'You! But you are only a kid! What are you doing here?'

'Isn't it obvious?' I laughed.

'Seriously now, you … you were only a kid when I was your instructor at Maccabi … '

'I am eighteen now. I am … '

A pain.

His face, his voice, the room, receded to make everything available for the pain to invade.

'Breathe deeply, breathe deeply … ' I heard his voice in a haze.

'Good, go on, don't stop breathing … now, is that better?'

His face came into focus, the room took back its shape, I smiled:

'That's better.'

'All right, let's examine you now.' he had rolled on one of those rubber fingers and awaited my co-operation. I was embarrassed.

He understood.

'Oh, come on, now. I am a doctor, and I have to do my duty. I am no longer your instructor, besides you don't want anything to happen to your baby do you?' I let him examine me.

'The opening is still quite small, but you are making progress. Do you need anything? Can I get you anything?'

'Yes, please … a book … something to read, anything…'

A pain was coming.

'Do you mean to say that you are actually going to read?'

'I don't know … but I'll give it a try.'

The pain was getting stronger, and I wasn't ready for it …

'I can't listen to ... the screams ... '

He waited for my pain to go, then said:

'All right, I have a few books in my room, I'll send you one.'

I looked at the window, after he left, and the white light . Life was going on outside. Buses were taking people to work, people were walking on the pavements. They had no pain. I looked at the clock 1.15pm. Time had passed. A nurse came in with a tray:

'Try and have some lunch if you can. And the doctor asked me to give you this.' She left the tray on the cabinet. The book was in French and to this day I don't know what it was, but I read it all. I read in between pains, while my body rested from their devastation, and during pains, with my handkerchief between my teeth and tears running down my cheeks and into my ears as I lay on my back. – I read.

The light coming in through the window became softer as day began to turn into twilight. The fluorescent tubes on the ceiling winked a few times before lighting up and filling the room once more, with a white light, that allowed no area of shade. The pains were different now. They didn't give me any warning, they took hold of my body, like a hurricane and tore and gnawed at it, until I felt that there was nothing else in the world but the pain. There wasn't a corner of my body spared. Tears were running down my cheeks generously, and I hardly had time to mop them, before the hurricane swept through me again.

The flap door opened, and I saw a familiar face. My eyes puffed and blurred with tears I didn't recognise her at first. It was my cousin Tina, my father's niece, who, of course, I remembered now, was a doctor. I hadn't seen her since I was a child. I had no idea she worked at this hospital, I only remembered that she was a surgeon.

'Hullo!' she sat on the edge of the bed. 'How are you? Your father telephoned me and told me you were here. It's good, because it's on my regular night duty.' She took my hand as she saw a pain was coming. 'Take a deep breath' she said. I nodded and she went on talking, 'Don't worry, I haven't come specially, it's my regular night duty. I was told your progress was slow, let me see?'

The pain had passed and, unable to speak, I was panting, worrying once more about my cousin, examining me.

'Don't be silly, I have to check the opening. Come on.'

The rubber finger, the insertion into the anus.

'Good, Good.' she said as she was rolling the 'finger' off. 'I'll be back.'

I was getting ready for the next pain. The woman next door was still screaming; her screams were accompanied by juicier curses now, and even in my pains, I couldn't imagine how anyone could feel that way about a child they were going to have. The clock on the wall moved slowly to 7pm.

The flap door opened. It was Tina.

'I haven't heard you. How are you?'

I was in the middle of a pain, squeezing the handkerchief which by now was nothing more than a wet little ball

Why on earth are you crying?' she asked.

'It hurts.' I whispered.

She flung the sheets away from me, quickly rolled a rubber 'finger' on, parted my legs unceremoniously; I didn't even feel the examination. She stood up and walked quickly across to the flap doors; I heard her firm authoritative voice:

'Tanya, Ilana, quick come here, get her ready; I can see the head!'

Two nurses came in almost immediately, took hold of me, as though I was weightless, put me on a narrow trolley and wheeled me into the delivery room. There, once more they transferred me onto a bed, one of them pulled the curtains around me, the other rolled the trolley away.

She now came back, poured a liquid into a basin that stood

on a stand at the foot of my bed and lit it. It went up with a blue flame and died out quickly; she then poured something else into the basin. I was surprised at the long rest the pain was allowing me when the curtain parted and a short plump woman walked in. Tina was behind her.

'Your cousin hey?'

'Yes.'

'Let's see.' She took an old fashioned wooden stethoscope from the pocket of her white coat, bent over my prominent belly, rested the narrow end on it and without pressing, her ear on the other, she listened for a while, then said:

'Have the waters broken yet?'

Tina looked at me for the answer.

'I … don't know … '

'This is … ' Tina said a name which I didn't hear, 'she is the midwife. It is customary that the midwife 'receives' the baby.'

I nodded. The midwife kneaded my belly gently and said:

'It seems in position.'

'Yes.'

She now turned to, me, directly, for the first time:

'Up until now, the baby – your baby – was trying to come into the world on its own. Now, it has come to a stage where it can't do it on its own and you have to help it. And helping means – pushing. Pushing as hard as you can, but only when I tell you, understood?'

'Yes.' I whispered.

'Will someone tell that woman to shut up! I can't hear the baby!' the midwife said impatiently. A nurse walked noiselessly away, behind the screen. The shouting stopped. I had no pain. I felt a strong pressure down, in my pelvis, like the bones wanted to break away from each other.

'Grab hold of the nurse's arms, and push.' the midwife said, 'PUSH.'

I did. It hurt terribly. It was like self induced pain, because when I didn't push, it didn't hurt so much.

'Stop now. Take a deep breath, rest a moment.' she took the stethoscope again, and placed it on my bare belly. The woman had resumed her screams. The midwife stood up, put the stethoscope in her pocket, parted the curtain and walked resolutely away.'Will you shut up!' I heard her authoritarian voice, then a pair of loud slaps.

'I might lose a baby because of your hysteria! You are not due for hours yet! So shut up!'

She came back and said:

'Push, come on, hold on to whatever you want but PUSH!'

I did.

'Now rest.'

With a metal instrument, I saw her pointing towards my vagina, she 'pierced' my 'waters'. I saw a rather horrid yellow jet squirt as far as her white coat.

'I am sorry ... ' I mumbled.

'No time to be sorry now,' she said then ordered: 'PUSH!'

I did. Pain. This time concentrated in the pelvis. Enormous, indescribable pain. I pushed, tears ran from my eyes.

'Give us a good scream,' the midwife said, 'take a deep breath and scream it out, like that one there, come on!'

'I can't scream, I rather ... ' and I felt a push, something from inside me. They were all looking between my legs.

'Here is the head.' said the midwife and turned to Tina: 'Do you want to deliver your cousin's baby, Doctor?'

'If I may.'

I was surprised at this polite display of medical ethics.

Tina took something from the instruments' trolley and moved towards me, in front of the midwife.

'Now you have to give me the biggest push ever, because I am going to have to cut you. You are too narrow, and a clean cut is better than a tear, do you understand?'

'Yes.'

It was then that my Maccabi instructor came in. Tina looked at him.

'Shall I give her a helping hand?' he asked.

'Yes, please.'

He seemed to step on to something high, like a stool, next to me. 'Push hard.' Tina ordered.

I shut my eyes and pushed. There was no natural pain at all, I was inducing it by pushing, and pushing, until I felt that my eyes were going to pop out of their sockets.

The doctor on the stool leant over me, put his two fists at the top of my belly.

'That's all right.' Said Tina slowly. 'Relax a little.'

I saw them exchange a glance, then Tina ordered:

'Push! Now!'

I did. Once more, pain searing through me; then the doctor leant over with all his weight, on his two fists, then I heard a loud 'plop', the doctor withdrew and went quickly over towards Tina who was doing something down on the table, then I saw her lift a small body, all shiny and wet, by the feet, she gave him a little pat on his bottom and I heard the little voice.

'It's a boy! It's a boy!' shouted my Maccabi instructor, then to me: 'Are you pleased?'

'Is he blond?' I asked.

They all burst-out laughing and walked away with the baby.

My parents. Avi. They had completely disappeared from my life during those hours. I had been alone with my baby, with my son. I had a son.

I felt a pressure from inside.

God, another one! I thought

'Tina, nurse!' I called, 'There is another one!'

Tina came up to me, 'Don't worry, it's just the placenta. We can sew now. Your parents and your husband send their love. They are delighted.' I saw her take the thread and needle. I shut my eyes. 'Don't worry, I will give you local anaesthetic, you won't feel a thing.'

The nurses took over afterwards. They washed me – I was soaking in my own blood – changed me, put me on another trolley. My body was without a pain. They turned me around, they lifted me, it didn't hurt. I could see my toes. My belly had completely gone down. They covered me, put some pillows under my head. I was shivering with cold. Some socks were found, and put on my feet. Tina came in, a little bundle in her hands.

'Your son.' she put him next to me. His little hands were making blind gestures in the air. His face was all red. He was a tiny replica of Avi.

'He has fingernails.' I said in amazement.

'Of course."

'He is a complete person, my son!'

Tina took the baby away.

'Now you need rest. He will be brought to you tomorrow for his first feed.' and she walked away.

Eventually I stopped shaking with cold and a nurse brought a tray in.

'Your dinner, I bet you want it now.'

I ate everything.

In the cubicle, behind the curtain, the other woman was still screaming.

'Now, you can go into the ward.' the nurse wheeled me through the swing doors and suddenly Avi was bending over me:

'WE have a son!'

'A boy!' my father said.

'How was it?' my mother asked.

They all kissed me in turn and the nurse wheeled me away.

'It's very beautiful,' I turned back, 'but it's as red as a tomato.'

'Tina will show him to us.' my father said.

'See you tomorrow.' Avi said.

Two nurses lifted me from the trolley onto the other bed – in the ward, where I could see many more beds.

I was asleep before they had pulled the covers over me.

BOOK FOUR

Chapter One

Trying to Keep My Head Above Water

The man was standing behind me. He was holding me firmly by my elbows and was trying to make me look in the mirror. I didn't want to look in the mirror! It was imperative that I didn't look! I tried to free myself from the man's grip – but he was stronger than me. I was crying, struggling, throwing the weight of my body from right to left in an attempt to shake him off and in so doing I caught a glimpse of the mirror a few inches away from my face. My face: how awful it looked, bathed in tears, my eyes puffed, blood shot, my hair half covering it with it's black mass. I pressed my eyelids together. I mustn't look! What right had he to force me? Who was he anyway? I groaned in a renewed effort to fight him when I felt his hands loosen their grip. I was free! I could run away! But my legs refused to obey me; they stayed glued to the ground while perspiration ran freely from all the pores of my body.

I opened my eyes. Reality slowly took shape. The room, the familiar shapes and shades, Avi's breath next to me. I fought to swallow the non existing saliva in my mouth. Slowly I calmed down. It had been a dream. Just a bad dream, a nightmare.

I slipped out of bed, went into the kitchen and poured myself a glass of cold water from the fridge. The day wasn't up yet, but the heat had already replaced the night freshness. I went to the bathroom. The stone tiles felt nice and cool under my bare feet. I splashed water over my face; my eyelids burned.

I turned around, carefully avoiding the mirror, and went back into the kitchen. I put the kettle on and sat down. I was tired. So very tired, and weary. I poured the coffee and, the mug in my hand, I went into the children's room. Raoul was asleep in his bed, and the baby in his cot. The hot coffee burnt my throat. Raoul was five years old now. He had turned out to be the baby in my dream: his eyes as blue as the sky, his hair golden.

I had had a dream during my second pregnancy too. I had seen a little boy on a bicycle, with olive complexion and hair as dark as mine, with blue eyes. He was two years old now. My second son – Rafi. I touched Raoul's cheek, flushed with sleep. He stirred and I withdrew my hand. I mustn't wake them yet. I had a lot of thinking to do. I had to take the plunge and look into that mirror. The stranger had been right, there were a lot of things I had refused to see. But did I have the courage to look at myself, at my life?

The previous day Raoul had broken a vase. This vase was the only beautiful object in the bungalow. Everything else was old, falling to pieces and ugly, Jerome's throwaways. I had a plant growing in the vase, I had decorated it all over and it was the only bright spot in the room. Raoul had knocked it over and broken it. I had lost my temper. I had hit his little hands; I could still see the marks of my fingers on the tender skin. But most of all, I remembered his large blue eyes, looking at me, innocent and uncomprehending. There was surprise in his eyes and perhaps a question, and fear. Fear of such magnitude that I knew I was never going to be able to forget it. I had hugged him and kissed him and held his little body next to me and asked him to forgive me. But, I felt, the damage was done. How would I ever expect him to trust me when I had attacked him so violently, and for what?

I went to the bathroom and looked straight into the mirror. My face was pale, not the romantic paleness of the renaissance painters' models, but the yellow-grey paleness of neglected and undernourished children. The face was too long, much too long, with deep dark circles round the eyes; and the eyes looked back at me without a spark of life in them. Nothing. Blank.

I was twenty-four years old, whatever that meant. People used to say that I was 'very' young'. It meant nothing to me.

I didn't know this stranger in the mirror. Was it the same person who had lost her temper in such a way with the child she loved so much? She didn't look like me, yet it was me. But then, who was I? I wasn't the same girl who lived in Kfar Ana. Oh, yes, Kfar Ana. We had left the village when Raoul was just over a year old. I didn't care to remember the details of that year with the baby and my mother! That had been a real nightmare! Luckily, Jerome was looking for a new flat, and Avi thought he would do the same. We didn't have a penny to our name.

My mother took whatever Avi gave her for the housekeeping, he kept the rest of his wages for his expenses; as for me, well, I didn't really need any money.

Avi found us a room. We had to pay 1,500 key money, and that was 1,500 more than we had.

'Don't worry,' Avi said, 'I will get a bank loan. Jerome will guarantee for me.'

'But how are we going to pay it back?'

'Leave everything to me.'

It was, Avi told me then, a room on a roof, but it had hot and cold water, stone tiled floors, real smooth walls, a real toilet, and electricity. No kitchen, no bathroom. Well, one couldn't have everything at once.

I poured myself another cup of coffee and opened the shutters to let the day in. I sat limply on the chair again, unable to stop the stream of thoughts, yet aware that soon, I will have to get breakfast ready. The room, yes. Our first experience at life on our own.

Ж

Aunt Amelia committed suicide the day we were due to move. My father arrived home – to the village that is – with the news, and we all had to go there. I didn't believe that she was dead. I couldn't believe that I shall never again see the sparkling green eyes, hear her laughter. I remembered the conversation I had overheard, way back, when I was ill, at Aunt Rachel's.

'It would seem that Yani, who is madly in love with his fiancée, had forgotten her birthday.' Mira told me.

'There is only a limited amount of aggravation that any woman can take from a man.' I heard my mother say to my father.

They all cried because they knew that she was dead. I didn't. I had not come to terms with the fact that somebody whom you have known all your life, disappears, suddenly, never to come back. It was like an interrupted dialogue, where there was no chance of a last word! The way little Misho had disappeared, back when I was a child, in Bulgaria. So long ago.

My mother stayed to look after the mourners.

'Should we leave now?' I asked Avi in the evening, 'Aunt Amelia is a big loss to her, she was her lifelong best friend.'

'The woman is dead, and the sooner your mother gets used

to the idea, the better.' said Avi firmly, 'Besides, I have arranged everything with Jerome, he will let me have his car and also, he will give us some of his old furniture.'

I tried to explain to my mother that it was impossible to postpone our moving; she just listened and shrugged.

Life in that room hadn't been too bad, I mean life with Avi. But now, two years later, life had become unbearable and, for the first time I thought that something should be done. I was very unhappy, irritable and didn't like myself at all. How could I be a good mother to my children when I had stopped living? I existed. How could I open their eyes to the world, when I saw it so dark and menacing? How could I explain life to them, when I didn't understand it myself?

The fact that I never had a penny, didn't bother me, not really. When Avi received his monthly wage, he paid the bank. He kept some money for his personal expenses – he smoked, he had to eat in town etc. I used to do all our shopping on account. At the end of each month, he would settle part of that debt; every now and then, he would skip a payment to the bank, settle with the grocer and the green grocer, and then we could start building up the arrears again. I could live with this. After all, it was temporary. Until we paid off the bank loan.

Ж

Last night's row had been about a tomato Avi found in the fridge and which was rotten. I remembered that. Usually I couldn't remember exactly how our rows started, but this time, I had made a point of remembering. It was the tomato.

I had finished my coffee now, but was still thirsty, so I poured yet another cup. I hadn't reacted in the usual way to Avi's attacks on my bad housekeeping last night, because I was too distressed over the incident with Raoul. Avi had shouted, called me the usual selection of names which, as I remembered them now, brought tears to my eyes. And he had gone to the cinema.

The decision came suddenly. I was going to put a stop to this, I was going to leave. I couldn't put up with it any longer; my parents were my only hope. I didn't have a penny to my name, I had nowhere to go but to my parents. I heard the children getting up in their room and went in to get them dressed. Avi came into the kitchen for breakfast, ate without saying a word and left for work.

I packed as many of the children's clothes as I could in two carrier bags, then sat at the kitchen table to write to Avi, to explain. I told him where we were, so that he wouldn't worry. Then, tears flowing down my cheeks and blurring my eyes, I wrote how I loved him, and how I knew I had failed him, but if only he would tell me what it was that I did wrong, what it was that annoyed him so much, I will make all the necessary efforts to change … but as it was … I simply didn't seem to do anything right. In the end, I said that I couldn't live like this any longer. And I stressed that that was final. I had never said anything so … final, so decisive and I hesitated for a moment to erase it, but I left it. It was true.

I took my baby Rafi in my arms, the carrier bags in one hand, and with Raoul holding on to my skirt, we walked over to the bus stop. I must have had some money, for I had to pay the fare.

My parents lived in Jaffa now, in a flat of their own. They left the village about a year after we did. My father's position at the American Embassy was secure, he had been promoted a few times. My mother's health always gave cause for concern.

When the worst of her depressive attacks was over, she remained 'delicate' she took at least four different sorts of tablets every day, and she didn't tolerate any of us opposing her will.

I was prepared to do anything, if they would just help me out. I was full of hope as I climbed the stairs to their second floor flat.

My mother, having heard the children's voices, opened the door before I rang the bell.

'Hullo mum, how are you?' I kissed her.

'No better than usual.'

She kissed the children, showing some pleasure, I thought, in seeing them. Raoul, who knew where to find chocolate, went straight into the kitchen, climbed on a stool and opened the fridge door.

'Raoul! Get off that stool immediately! Don't put your dirty fingers all over the fridge, I have just cleaned it!'

I ran and grabbed him before he had done more damage. In the meantime, Rafi, who loved opening drawers, had gone into the lounge where, on the dresser, there were drawers galore.

'Rafi, stop that! Get out of there! I have polished the furniture.' my mother shouted, then turned to me,'Why can't you control those children! You know I can't stand disorder! He is already emptying a drawer!'

I ran to the lounge and grabbed hold of Rafi.

'Look, it's full of marks!' my mother complained.

I took the children to the kitchen, unpacked their toys and told them to stay there; then I took a duster and went to polish over Rafi's finger marks.

When I got back to the kitchen, my mother was giving the children some chocolate, but she insisted to put it directly into their mouths so they don't get dirty.

'You have brought rather a lot of things.' she said without looking at me. A lump came up to my throat.

'Yes … my marriage … it's not working … I can't take it any longer … I know that I haven't always told you any details about … Avi and I … but … '

'What have you done?' her voice was cold; she was already condemning me. 'What was the row about?'

'It's not a question of just this one row … it's a lot worse than that … he is so rude to me … the way he talks to me, how he treats me … he talks to me … as though I were … dirt.'

'How much patience can a man have with a foolish wife like you? I know, he has told me, you spend, spend, spend. You can't manage. I always told you, you must learn how to budget.'

'But mum … it isn't that at all! He never … ' my tears were choking me, how could I defend myself against such preposterous accusations? Avi has told her, what? And she had believed him! Even if it were true … couldn't my own mother … at least doubt Avi and ask ME?

'Look, I haven't finished my work yet. You know I must have everything done by one o'clock.'

'Let me help you mum, I'll wash the floors … ' I was still sobbing.

'The best you can do, is take the children to the garden. I'll do my own work.'

I did as I was told. I let them free to play in the sandpit with their buckets and spades and sat on a bench. My mind wasn't clear at all, I wanted to think, I wanted to understand, but my mind was in a whirl. I looked at my sons. Rafi was painstakingly constructing a castle, while Raoul was splashing sand over the other children, some of them threw fistfuls back at him, they laughed. How I loved them! My sons!

The moment Raoul was handed to me, the day after his birth, for his first feed, as I held him, a little bundle in a soft blanket, his little hands reaching out for something, for life; sucking avidly his due of food from me, I realised that he wasn't an extension of me, nor an extension of my love for Avi. He was a person in his own right. So very vulnerable, so very dependent on me, but only temporarily, only until he would grow up and take the reins of his own life in his own hands. And it was I who had to teach him how, I who didn't know yet for myself!

'My goodness!' my mother stopped us at the door when we went back. 'They are filthy! Why did you let them get so dirty?'

'Never mind, they have to have a shower anyway, I'll change them. Come on boys, in the bathroom!'

'You will fill everything with sand now!'

'I'll clean it all up mum, I promise.'

I put the two of them in the bathtub and soaped their little bodies, shampooed their hair and rinsed them with the hand-shower. I was aware of every drop that splashed out, making a mental note, to remember and clean it later. I dried them up and put some fresh clothes on them, while they were playfully trying to escape.

'I will leave you to it,' said my mother as I was getting ready to give them their lunch, 'I will have a little rest.'

'OK mum.'

'Where is my gun?' asked Raoul.

'At home. Eat your lunch now, please.'

Rafi was turning his fork into the mashed potatoes, then suddenly he gave it a blow and tiny particles of sticky mashed potatoes flew all over the kitchen.

'Rafi, stop that.'

'I don't want to eat, I don't want to eat.'

'I don't want to eat!' repeated Raoul after him, 'I want my gun.'

'Your gun isn't here. And if you don't eat your food, you will have to go to bed hungry.'

'What on earth is going on here?' my mother appeared at the door.

'We are trying to have lunch.' I said 'But Raoul is going to have to go without it. Since he wants something I can't possibly give him.'

'You should never have become a mother!' my mother's voice startled me, the forgotten hatred and aggression were more than I could take right now. I looked up at her; what did she mean?

'Don't look at me like that!' she went on, 'I sat for hours, yes, for hours, to feed you! Who gives a fork to a two year old? Look at all the mess he has made. You are exasperating, and you want me to plead to your husband!'

'Mum, I'll clean everything … it's that I feel that the child should take part … interest in the food otherwise it will be … '

'Oh, leave me alone!'

The children went to sleep and I cleaned the bathroom and the kitchen. I couldn't wait to finish and join my mother in the lounge, where she was resting on the chaise-longue. But when I got there, she was fast asleep. Her face seemed relaxed, her lips parted and once again, I was surprised. She always complained of insomnia. Was it possible that … no, not my mother. She had fallen asleep and I better keep quiet so she can get some rest.

I went out on the shaded terrace and sat on a deck chair. I felt tired and worried. What was going to happen now? I had taken a step and I needed my parents' support. The mere thought of returning home and facing Avi now seemed an impossibility. I had tried though, I had tried to talk to him; I wanted to tell him what made me unhappy and expected him to tell me what made him unhappy, for I was sure he was unhappy too. But he didn't want to listen. I tried to tell him how I felt something was missing in our sexual relations; he reacted violently, shutting me up and called me a 'slut'. When I asked him why he was calling me that, he said: 'Because you are!'

And I cried. I cried each time he hurt me; I was defenceless, my pain was so great that I was unable to defend myself. Now I knew I had reached the end, I had to be given a chance, I needed to think, to understand.

As soon as my father came home from his office, my mother gave him the brief information about my and the children's presence. He was tired; sat down, lit a cigarette, his brow furrowed. He smoked for a while, not saying a word, then, without looking at me, said in a solemn voice:

'Avi is your husband. You belong with him. A wife has to follow and obey her husband; I have no say in the matter. You can stay the night, if you are sure Avi will not worry, but tomorrow, you must go back to him.'

Ж

When we moved into Bat Yam, it was a quiet suburb, south of Tel Aviv, on the sea-side. It had barely one thousand inhabitants, mainly German and Russian immigrants; they had come to Palestine, after the First World War, and built their houses there. Each house in its own grounds, surrounded by gardens and trees. A beautiful tree-lined avenue ran all along the suburb to the sea . It had a central pedestrian section, with benches and flower beds and sandpits for children to play in. On a side street there was a cinema. It was small and old. It's roof was removed in the hot summer nights to allow the breeze from the sea to refresh the patrons. In order to keep the cinema full, the owner saw to it that the films changed frequently, up to three per week. He kept the prices down, and that ensured him an excellent attendance from the otherwise bored inhabitants of Bat Yam.

This is where Avi went to on the nights when we had a row, or when I did something to displease him, or because he simply felt like it. This behaviour began when we still lived in the room on the roof, and only had Raoul.

At that time, my days began at 6 am, when Raoul woke up asking for his breakfast. When that was done, Avi woke up, and I had to prepare his breakfast. By the time he left for his office, I was getting ready to wash Raoul's clothes. I was in a hurry to hang them and get them dry because I didn't have enough clothes for him. Raoul would play with his toys while I did the day-to-day housework around the room. Some days were more difficult than others. Some days, I cleaned the room more thoroughly; on others, I had a pile of Avi's shirts to wash and iron – and that had to be quite immaculately done, because Avi had had yet another promotion, and he had to wear a uniform with a starched collar shirt.

Round about midday, Raoul had his bath. We had a metal one (plastic wasn't around yet) which I positioned on two chairs, in the middle of the room, near the table where I could put him after the bath, and dry him and put his clothes on. The water for the bath, had of course to be heated on the paraffin oil burner, out on the landing, poured in, brought to the right temperature.

His cheeks shiny, and his clothes clean, Raoul had his lunch, then I put him in his cot for his afternoon nap. Now, I could empty the heavy bath, clean the floor which had taken no little punishment from Raoul's exuberance, tidy up and, once the child was asleep, I would slip out to do the shopping.

I hurried back to cook our dinner before Raoul got up, managed to collect the clothes from the line and iron them before he woke up. I gave him his tea, then put him, in the push chair, which Jerome had given us when his son grew out of it, and took him out.

He had to have the benefit of a few hours in the fresh sea air. I pushed his chair up the avenue, near the sea, by a sandpit and joined my little boy in building castles and making shapes out of sand. We played and splashed and laughed. When the weather permitted I went down the steps to the beach played and bathed with him. Then we returned home, sand sticking to our skin and in our clothes and shoes. It was fund getting cleaned up and putting on fresh, clean clothes. Sometimes, tired, I didn't join him for very long, but sat looking at the sea, shimmering at my feet. Large, ink-blue, all powerful and all beautiful. The poems of my early days very rarely came to my mind then. I felt sad, a heavy painful feeling of solitude and an impression of an impasse. Even the wide blue expanse of the Mediterranean didn't help.

When Avi got his second promotion, he was allowed a longer lunch hour. He came home at about two o'clock and left by four. That meant that he arrived home when Raoul got up from his nap. Avi insisted on having his nap then and as I couldn't keep the child quiet – and there wasn't another room – I had to go out with him during those two hours, when the heat of the sun was at its cruellest. I hurried to the shade, but it wasn't much help; the heat, even there, was suffocating. My temples were pulsating and painful, luckily, Raoul didn't seem to suffer too much, his fair skin was a little flushed, but I gave him a lot of cool tea to drink, and moistened his plump little body with a flannel. I pleaded with Avi to let us stay home, but he insisted that the breadwinner must be made comfortable and needed rest.

I didn't mention anything to my parents about this, but Avi had obviously complained to them, and they had agreed with him.

Many times, when he arrived home from his office in the evening, I had fallen asleep. Having finished with Raoul's dinner, I would have mine, then leave Avi's on a low flame over the paraffin oil burner, and fall asleep. I was very tired, my temples were painful. It was no later than seven o'clock, perhaps just after.

After an hour or so, I would wake up, a little refreshed from the sleep. From the empty plate, I would realise that Avi had returned home, but that he wasn't home now. At first I didn't understand, I worried, panicked: where was he?

'What do you expect?' he answered, when I enquired upon his return, 'what was I supposed to do? Watch you sleep? I went to the cinema. Frankly, I don't understand what you do all day … why should you be as tired as you say you are.'

'I am not so tired any longer … I have rested a little now.' I would try and change the conversation, 'Let's go to bed … or perhaps you want to go for a walk? Yes, let's! It's so beautiful by the sea. Raoul won't wake up, just for a little while, what do you say?'

Avi would look at me with that cold light in his eyes:

'You would … wouldn't you,' he would say, 'You would always come out with some preposterous idea or other. Why can't you be like all the other wives? Why can't you behave like any normal housewife? You always have to have these … indecent thoughts, these dirty ideas in your head!'

'But, there is nothing dirty … all I want is … to hug you … you are my husband and I love you, is that dirty?'

I would get near him, and hug him; I felt the need for his caresses, for his nearness. Sometimes he would ask me to leave him alone; at others, he would turn towards me, and I would feel his penis pressing against me; I would want to stop him for a while, wanting his caress, his desire of me, but he held my hands down when I touched him, and proceeded with the act. I can't call it anything else, because that's what it was. An act that he performed. It didn't take very long before he had his little final tremor. I took no part in it.

When he was asleep, not long afterwards, I lay awake, staring in the dark. And as the months and years passed by, and I felt more and more agitated, and the cramp in my loins became more and more painful, I began to think that something was wrong, very wrong.

Ж

When Avi took me home with the children on the afternoon after the night at my parents I knew I was very close to losing him, to losing grip on my life, and if there were any doubt, Avi, in his own peculiar way, made sure there was no mistake.

'We are invited to a party at Jerome's on Saturday night.' he said.

'That is very nice!' I hadn't been out in months and the very thought of going to a party was so attractive I forgot the situation I was in.

'What's the occasion?'

'Don't get so excited! It's just a normal Saturday night gathering. He had asked me before, but I don't like parties.'

'Oh, but Avi, I do! I want to go out … so much! And a party … doesn't involve spending money! Why have you refused before?'

'For the very same reason that I am sorry I haven't refused this time as well – your stupid excitability, besides, you can't have everything you want.'

'I have so little … '

'Oh, my God! You are pathetic!'

'I didn't mean 'things', clothes etc., I mean … there is so little between us … did you read my note?'

'Some of it. You do go on. You think you are so clever, so bloody articulate, let me tell you your big words didn't impress me.'

'Avi, I wasn't trying to impress you. I want us to … I want our lives to be … I want you to understand me … and I … '

'Understand you? Who can understand you? You are a hopeless waste of time, leave me alone, I am tired.'

In the morning, before he left for work, he threw a bunch of bank-notes on the table:

'Here, buy yourself a dress.' and he left. I looked at the money, bewildered. I had thought that we were penniless!

A neighbour minded the children while I went to buy a dress. It was such a thrill to try on all the beautiful party dresses; but I had never spent such an amount of money on myself and I couldn't make my mind up to buy the dress. I walked out of the shop, feeling the disdainful glance the shop assistant gave me, walked around looked at another shop, but my heart was with that lovely dark halter neck which looked so glamorous on me. I went back and bought it.

I put it on, put the high heeled shoes on and felt like a film star. Sophia Loren was the star of the day. Every young woman wanted to look like her and Brigitte Bardot, of course. Well, I thought my figure left a lot to be desired, but still the dress fitted tightly round my hips and stressed my narrow waist, the high heels made me seem taller, I was quite pleased with myself. Avi looked at me for a while.

'I've always said that you have the best legs I have seen, apart from that, you look like a slut.'

'Do you want me to change then?'

He shrugged. I didn't know what to do. I was ready to go in my every day skirt, if this would make him happy. I told him so.

'Do as you please.'

I wore the dress.

I hadn't seen Jerome since our wedding, when he was supposed to be taking the photos. He greeted us now and immediately put his arm round my shoulders.

'I see you every day old man,' he said to Avi, 'but your lovely wife is very seldom around. I can see why. What would you like my dear? Cognac? Vermouth?'

The man standing by the bar turned to Jerome:

'Who is this ravishing creature? I bet you it's Avi's wife!'

'Yes. This is Alex my dear, beware of him, he has a way with women.' Alex handed me a glass.

'Chin-chin.' he said.

'Chin-chin.' I searched the room for Avi, but he had disappeared.

'Let's dance!' Jerome took me in his arms and held me tightly. Behind his back, I saw Avi appear at the door, a glass in his hand. He seemed to have been in the kitchen. He looked on at the dancing couples, very much at ease. I didn't think he was searching the room for me. Alex appeared from nowhere and took me away from Jerome's arms.

'She is mine for this dance.' he said.

'Hey! You!' Avi shouted from across the room 'Keep your paws off!'

Alex made a face at him and I felt pleased that Avi had intervened for me, that he had noticed, that he cared.

Suddenly, someone switched the light off; Alex's powerful arm held me tightly to him while his hand went all over me, my hips, my back my breasts, and he was kissing my neck, my shoulders. I felt an intense heat as if my blood were boiling, my whole body vibrated, I responded, our mouths met in a passionate kiss – the kind of kiss I had experienced with Vlady, but had not returned, not in this way; then I came to, I moved away, pleading with him, still kissing him. I was so ashamed of myself!

He loosened his grip.

'What a volcano you are my love! I so want to taste you, the whole of you … when shall we meet?' Someone switched the light on. I had more or less regained my composure. 'I'll be in touch,' said Alex as the music stopped and I moved away from him.

'You'll do nothing of the sort.' I said but he had already disappeared into the crowd.

A young woman came up to me:

'My name is Irene. I am Jerome's wife. Avi has told me a lot about you.'she said to me in a tone which was pleasant and at the same time, I detected, a little condescending, 'Come and meet the others. This is Alice – Alex's wife, and her sister, she is married to that chap over there.'

'Very pleased to meet you.' I shook hands with them.

Alice withdrew her hand from mine and turned to her sister:

'Isn't it nice the way she wears her hair, loose and free, looks so young, don't you think?'

'Yes, rather.'

I looked at their bleached hair, with elaborate hair-dos' and stiff with hair lacquer, which was now the rage, and which, even if I could afford, I didn't like. Jerome came to my rescue:

'Come on, let's dance.'

'Where is Avi?' I asked him.

'What do you care? Let's enjoy ourselves now. You will have him at the end of the evening.'

While we were dancing, Avi and Irene appeared at the door. They had obviously been together. I left Jerome, and went to Avi:

'Avi, let's dance, please?'

'You are enjoying yourself, aren't you?' he said, not moving from where he was, and Irene listened and looked on. I blushed. I put my arms on his shoulders:

'Come on.' We hadn't danced together since the very first time we met at Claude's.

'Where were you Avi?' I asked, mortified with jealousy.

'I went to see the children.'

'Are they all right?'

'Yes. Fine.'

'You were gone for such a long time … ' I said, already regretting my audacity.

'What of it?'

'Were you alone?' I pushed my luck.

'This is none of your bloody business.' he said, smiling, enjoying my disarray. 'You exasperate me, your questions exasperate me.'

I had some more vermouth and danced with Alex. I felt light headed because I wasn't used to drinking. At the back of my mind I had the conviction that I had lost Avi, and this I didn't know how to live with.

Later, when we got home, in my half drunken state I hugged him, I wanted to feel the excitement Alex had made me feel, I wanted to experience the kiss that had aroused me, I wanted it from Avi.

'Go away!' he hissed and his coldness sobered me up like a slap in the face.

'You are always ready for it, aren't you?' he went on, 'You slut!'

Chapter Two

The Lower Depths

The doctor is a middle-aged man. I can see his blue eyes behind his glasses. I can feel his penetrating glance. But he is smiling. At least I think he is smiling. I try to do the same, but I am not sure that I succeed. I can feel perspiration running down the middle of my back, I know my face looks awful and shiny and I wonder whether there are damp patches around my armpits.

'Your name?' he is looking down now, at his pad.

'Age?'

'Married?'

'Any children?'

My answers are coming out with ease, because he is not looking at me any longer. I give a deep sigh of relief.

'Ages?'

'Normal births?'

He puts his pen down and looks up at me again. Slowly he

puts his elbows on the desk, the tips of his fingers touch each other as though for a prayer, but not quite. He rests his chin on them. I meet his eyes.

'What seems to be the trouble?'

I take a deep breath. Now I have to speak. I have to tell him. I must make sense. My pause has made him slightly impatient I think, because he leans forward as though to remind me that he is waiting.

'I ... I seem to be ... highly strung, tense, doctor. I ... lose my temper ... very easily ... I shout at the children, and they are good children; it's me, I am sure .... '

I feel the lump, the awful lump blocking my throat, and I know I won't be able to say another word without crying. What a performance! It isn't often that I talk about myself to anybody. Anybody who listens, that is, but I had promised myself I will behave ... normally ... that I would not cry! What an idiot I am!

'You are very young,' his voice interrupts my thoughts. He is looking down at his notes, 'to have two children of those ages. It is a trying task. It is natural to be tired and impatient sometimes. Do you have any help?'

I don't know exactly what he means, but the lump goes away and I look up at him.

'Your husband, tell me about him.'

I don't know what to say. Does he help me? I think but say nothing.

'Does he take part in the home, say, with the children? Does he, from time to time, take over, to give you a break?'

'Oh, no, he can't! You see, he has a very important job. He owes himself to it – it is our sole income and ... '

I swallow with difficulty.

'Yes. Of course. I understand. But how about Saturdays? He doesn't work on Saturdays, does he?'

I shake my head.

'So? Does he take part in the children's education generally?

Or help you with anything around the house? On weekdays, does he, for instance, do your shopping, sometimes?'

I look at him sheepishly. What should I say now? He … used to, sometimes … but now he is … too busy … too important … or …

'My husband is very nice.' I say finally. 'We love each other very much and I must make it possible for him to do his job. He started at the very bottom and became assistant manager, within only a few years, so you see … '

'What does he do?' he interrupts me.

'He works for an airline.'

The Doctor looks at his hands for a moment. I take advantage that he is not looking at me to wipe my forehead and nose. I could feel them shiny with perspiration.

'Do you go out?' he finally asks, his hands back under his chin, his eyes on mine.

'Not very much … I mean, we do, but not very often … '

'Do you have any help, for the house?'

'Oh, no we can't afford that … we … '

'You do have your parents, don't you? I mean they are alive?' He sounds just a little impatient.

'Oh yes, they are.' I answer quickly.

My hands grab hold of the strap of my handbag. His question worries me. What has all this to do with my parents? I have been enough of a nuisance to them as it is. I should not have come here! I wish I hadn't.

'Come here.' he says, 'Stand up. Lift your arms so, straight ahead, level with your shoulders, that's it.' he is guiding my arms and I let him. 'Now shut your eyes.'

I obey.

'Walk straight ahead, slowly, that's right. Don't open your eyes! Now, stop, bend your knees and go down, now up, keep the arms straight! Down, up! Don't open your eyes!'

I do my best but I lose balance and nearly fall over. I open my eyes, despite his instructions and hold onto the desk, just in time.

'Sit down.' he says and goes back behind the desk.

Time seems to have stopped. We are facing each other again, but I have my balance. Physical and mental. I am calmer. I look at him but then, as our eyes meet, something in him worries me again. Again I wish I hadn't come here. Can I get up and go? Can I just say: 'I want to go now.' and walk out?

'How is your sex life?'

The bomb has dropped. This is what I feared, I recognise it now. *Now* I have to get out of it, somehow.

'OK.' I say, looking above his head, at the picture on the wall. I feel his glance though. He doesn't say a word, yet I feel that he knows. He knows that I have lied. My question is, will I get away with it?

My head is suddenly invaded by an unfamiliar roar. A dark curtain falls in front of my eyes. The curtain is opaque, black. Then it turns grey with black crevasses and they start to spin round and round, I am part of them, I turn round and round and I begin to fall.

I fight against it, I try to hold on to something solid, to stop this fall, then I feel a pair of arms; strong and vigorous. They get hold of me, they steady me, but I don't want them; I know them and I don't want them. I fight again, I struggle. I want to scream but no sound comes from my dry throat I hear him whisper:

'Stop fighting, that's enough now … ' the voice is velvety, caressing, 'you know and I know that you want it, let yourself go … let yourself go now … to me …. '

I struggle.

His voice becomes impatient:

'We both know how much you want to fuck, why all this pretence?'

His voice becomes distant, as though reaching me through a thick fog. I am fighting him, and I am thinking: 'what right has he to speak to me like that? I don't want him, I want my Avi. It's him, I want. Surely there must be somebody to take my defence? Against this man … somebody … please … how was I going to tell Avi? He would never believe me! He thinks I am a liar anyway …. Why should he believe that I thought him to be a friend? How would he believe that I was to polite to slam the door in the face of your husband's friend?

A hot wave invades my body. I don't want to … I don't want to … what? Ah, yes, I don't want to be unfaithful! Or is it that I don't want 'that' from him? I want 'it' from my Avi! I fight, I scream, I cry. His face fades away. I continue to fall. I fall … fall … like the time when … when Avi … what? I panic, I don't remember! I have to remember! it's important that I remember …

I hear the Doctor's voice, loud and clear:

'And your sex life? Is it normal? Satisfactory?'

My eyes try to focus, but it seems that there is a flimsy sheet of film between him and me.

'It's OK.'

Through the film I can see the doubt in his eyes. I look down.

'What exactly do you mean by that.' he persists.

'We love each other … very much. Isn't that enough?'

'Yes, that is fine. Tell me, how many times per week, say, do you make love? Or let's put it another way, how many times do you reach a climax? Do you reach a climax every time? Every other time?'

I am defeated. I feel my shoulders drop. I have lost, I have to confess.

'You mustn't be embarrassed about this, my child, it's only normal. We all experience sex, come on, tell me.

'It's that I don't know … what 'a climax' is.'

Now that I have said it, now that I have confessed, I lean back, I feel better. I dare take a deep breath. I hadn't before. I was holding my breath, in case he thought that I was ill at ease.

He sighs. He looks at his notes.

'You have been married … what? over six years?'

'Yes.'

'I expect you haven't had any sexual experience before? With another boyfriend?'

'No.' I whisper.

'And you have never had a climax.'

He doesn't ask me; he tells me. And the way he pronounces the 'never' makes me shrug my shoulders apologetically.

'Have you discussed it with your mother?'

My mother? What is he talking about! … but he doesn't know my mother.

'No,' I try to be as natural about it as I possibly can, 'we don't … ' here I give myself away, I know it because my voice is shaky … ' we don't talk about … such things.'

I await his reply to erase the echo of my words still hanging in the air, but he keeps quiet. I look down at my handbag. I can feel his glance piercing me from behind the heavy rimmed glasses. He unlocks his fingers, places his arms along the desk, picks up the pen and starts running his fingers up and down it, turning it over each time. That makes a soft rhythmic noise.

'And you are surprised at being tense?'

I shrug.

'When you do make love, does he caress you, does he kiss you?'

His voice is softer than before. I look up at him, not knowing what to say.

'Doesn't he caress you?'

The questions amplifies in my head, repeats itself like an echo. I shake my head in order to give a reply. It's impolite not to reply. I shake my head and the light becomes white, white and bright and it hurts my eyes though my eye lids which are shut. I bring my knees up to my chin. I am embarrassed.

I pull the sheets to cover my nudity. I am aware of Avi, standing by the bed. He undresses slowly, not saying a word. His hand removes the sheet from my grip then, from over my body. I resist a while, but he is stronger. He stands awhile, looking down at my body. I want the earth to open and swallow me there and then, but of course, it doesn't.

Avi's hand comes towards me instead, touches my breast, then my legs, then my stomach. Just touches them with his fingertips. His face, when I take a furtive glance at it, is solemn, unmoved. His hand uncrosses my tightly crossed legs, puts them neatly down, alongside each other, looks at them. He looks at my body with that solemn, serious expression on his face. He hasn't once looked at me. My body feels cold. Cold inside. I look for his eyes, I want him to set me alight. I find his lips and I want to find passion. It's cold. I am looking for passion. He freezes me. He lies on me, having parted my legs. I can feel him penetrating me. I feel a brief tremor. I want to respond but, his hands on my shoulders, he doesn't allow it. He immobilises me. My tremor disappears. He moves in and out, his breath even. A few seconds, a minute perhaps. He quivers, I can feel his body quiver. Then, he withdraws, lies down and goes to sleep.

I look at the ceiling. I have an insipid taste in my mouth. The light is burning my closed eyelids. The ceiling begins to turn round and round. I make an effort to open my eyes. Things seem to get more stable around me. The ceiling first. I look at the room and realise that for the first time I can make out some of the contours. It's still a little vague, but it's a room. Oh, yes! I know! It's a hospital room!

My eyes notice my hand on the covers. It is my hand and I can move it's fingers. I see them move, but I can't feel them. Isn't that strange? I try to get my other hand out from under the covers and pinch it. I feel perspiration running down my temples. How can I feel the pinch and not the hand?

Suddenly a bomb explodes right next to my bed and I turn my head slowly towards it, very slowly, trying to prevent the room from collapsing, and I see a white cloud. It's a nurse, and she is talking to me.

'We are awake are we?' She takes my hand and I can see her looking at her watch. She puts my hand back where it was.

'Good. Now we shall be a very good girl and drink some coffee.' Her hand lifts my head and the ceiling moves away again. I can feel the pressure of the cup against my mouth, as though it were pressed through a sheet of foam, 'from afar'. I try to swallow and feel that the liquid is hot. Some of it is dripping down my chin.

I want to apologise for being so messy.

'Thank you.'

But I hear a strange roar instead of the words.

'Pardon?' says the nurse.

'an … oo.' I try to enunciate.

'It's all right my dear. Are we feeling better now?'

Why is she talking to me like one talks to children? Still, I want to thank her, and as I can't say the words, I attempt a nod, and the whole room capsizes taking me with it. I want to smile at her and thank her, but everything keeps spinning.

' … mustn't cry … you mustn't cry any more!'

I try to open my eyes. The white light is so strong! I blink towards the white cloud which I take to be the nurse, trying to steady myself.

'Ah?' I say, trying again, to gain time, to compose myself.

'You mustn't cry any more!' she repeats.

I understand her and I try to smile.

'You did understand me, didn't you? You mustn't cry any more!'

No, no, what I understood was that I would get nowhere by crying, that's what I understood; but how can I tell her? I make an effort:

'I … I …' I can see the white shadow walk away I try to think now. I must think, it is important. I can't afford to lose … to lose what? I panic; what … is it that I mustn't …? oh, yes, the thread. The thread of my thoughts. Now that I am alive, I mustn't lose the thread of my thoughts. Now that I am alive … I must make something out of my life. That's it! I made it to the end of the thought! I must think further though. Now that I am alive … I mustn't fail my life, like …? like what? like I failed my death?

'Nobody can take your decisions for you my child.' the doctor had said from behind his glasses. Now I understand what he was trying to tell me; I must tell him I understand, as soon as I can. I understand now that all my decisions were always taken for me, by other people. Even those who profess to love you most, the doctor had said, are still 'other people', now I understood, and what is more, I believed him.

The doctor is looking at me again. His chin on his hands:

'Yet, you are a very attractive young woman. I am sure that offers are numerous … '

I am crying again. I can feel the tears, hot and salty flowing down from my aching eyes.

He gets up; he is tall, formidable. He comes to me round the desk, takes my face, in his hands. I can feel their warmth.

'Don't cry … and don't worry. I will be able to help you, I hope.' he turns away and asks, his back turned to me, 'Have you had another man?'

What is he talking about? Doesn't he know by now that I love my husband? He goes back to his seat, facing me.

'You haven't had the courage, I bet. It's your upbringing, probably, but it's not important. I will talk to your husband, he sounds like a reasonable man. He is reasonable, isn't he?'

I can't swallow. I try but I can't.

'He is.' I mumble.

'Have you ever thought that you might have to get a divorce?'

'Never!' my reply's sharpness takes me by surprise.

'My God, how frightened you are! What a defence you put up? Why are you so frightened? Who frightens you so much, my child?'

My mother's voice, from long since forgotten depths of a long since forgotten childhood, or was it youth, emerges: '… loose woman … she is a loose woman … ' I mustn't be a loose woman! My mother would strongly disapprove of me! And again, I am crying; desperately, pitifully.

'I love my husband … I love my children … I don't want to destroy their home … '

'Or perhaps you are afraid to destroy your illusion of a home?' He is quiet for a while; I have nothing to say.

'One thing is certain,' he adds, 'you can't go on like this.'

Yes. I agree. I had thought about it myself once. I must have nodded.

'So, you agree. I am pleased, because you see, the older you get, the more you feel the need for … ' he has seen my face, he knows that he is going to hurt me and he checks himself. I realise that he feels sorry for me.

'You know nothing about it, do you … well, I can't tell you everything in one go; you are not ready. How did you manage to grow up in this world, so sheltered, so protected; for all the good it's done you!'

I shrug.

'I must tell you this: you must not be stoical, you must not make a martyr of yourself. The mental hospitals are full of women, not old women but middle aged women, early forties even, whose nerves are destroyed through lack of understanding of their own needs … puritanical upbringing … and unfeeling husbands … and this is how it starts … nervousness, agitation … But stop crying for God's sake and listen to me.'

His voice gets further and further away, the last words echo in my head painfully; the echo flies from wall to wall, inside my head, gaining momentum, hurting me. Then the noise stops and I hear a clear voice:

'You can try now.'

I can see a shadow standing by the bed. Someone is talking to me. I try to focus my eyes, it's a blue cloud this time. A policeman. He utters my name.

'Do you understand me?' he asks.

I do 'yes' with my eyelids.

'I know that you are not feeling very grand at the moment …, ' he says, 'but in cases of suicide, we have to get the details as soon as possible … ' A case of suicide. I am a case of suicide. I feel very sorry for myself; I try not to cry. I blink, my eyelids are sore.

'Do you hold anyone responsible?' he asks. 'Did anyone make you take the tablets?'

I try to say 'no' quickly, but all that comes out of my throat is a groan; I do 'no' with my eye lids.

'Not your husband?'

I shake my head, but the room gets unsteady.

'Somebody else?'

'No.'

'Something must have happened though, because the dose you took was … fatal, the doctor said. What I am trying to say is: you didn't just mean to attract attention, like some do, or to scare somebody. From what I can ascertain of the details, you would not have been found until morning had you not taken the lot in the bathroom and … well, you fell there and then, didn't you?'

What is he talking about? Whom could I scare? No one cares enough … whose attention would I draw and what for? I failed with words, pleading, crying … how could I achieve anything when I was going to be dead!

'Is he unfaithful?'

I say quickly:

'No!'

'Does he hit you?'

'No' again.

The policeman is holding a little pad, yes it is a pad, and he is writing continually in it. I take a deep breath and make an effort to put my thoughts into words:

'There … is … no one … to blame … . It's me.'

He nods and goes on writing.

So, I had fallen down in the bathroom! I am crying again, but an order comes quickly from somewhere inside my brain: YOU MUSTN'T CRY ANY LONGER. A strong hand lifts my head.

'Here, have some more coffee. That's a girl … you'll be all right in no time. My, oh my, aren't we skinny! No wonder you have no resistance!'

She puts my head down on the pillow and immediately I feel that I am falling down the pit and I hear a voice, a strong authoritarian voice:

'Let's hope this is the last for the night. I am exhausted. Why do people always do their stupidities at night, and always when I am on duty. Do your best not to wake me up again nurse.'

I understand what he means and I think: he doesn't give a damn. He doesn't care one tiny bit about me and then there is an echo in my head: but neither does anyone else, not really. This is painful, oh so painful!

I cast it aside, and it has come back now. The pain-thought expands in ever increasing circles. Becomes larger than life.

' … it's up to you … if you want to become a martyr, but in the name of what, is beyond me.' my doctor shrugs.

'If this is your decision, so be it, but don't expect your husband to be faithful to you, because he won't be! and I'll tell you why. Because you, with your glowing femininity will always be there to remind him of his failure, his lack of virility, yet men like to think that they are virile. And you, you poor child, you won't even know how to feign! So, he will have affairs. If he doesn't already.'

His words hurt so. Because I knew them to be true.

'But why does he hurt me so much doctor? Why?' I say, not knowing why I say it, feeling already ashamed that I have made the admission.

'How do you mean?'

'He … tells me that I lie to him … but I don't … he says that I am a … slut. But I am not. He is cruel to me … when I am upset … he teases and teases … '

I can feel his eyes on me; I look up. His eyes are good, patient and so is his voice but I am afraid of what he is going to say, I want to go away, get up and go, but our eyes meet; I can see his goodness, his kindness and nothing else matters, there are just his eyes behind his glasses and his kind voice:

'I am talking to you like a father …, '

What is he saying? Whose father? Not mine. Doesn't he know that some fathers just don't 'talk like a father', here I found something he didn't know! Some fathers go as far as denying the very existence of things to 'talk' about!

' ... there is no harm done to the marriage ..., ' he is saying, 'many marriages survive only thanks to 'the other man', or 'the other woman' so you see ... '

I have a sudden thought, and I interrupt him:

'Doctor, doctor, couldn't you give me something ... something that will make me ... not ... need ... it.' I lower my voice to utter the word 'it', but then I go on, 'some tablets or something, then everything will be ... '

The doctor gets up again and laughs. His laughter takes me by surprise. He takes his glasses off while he is laughing and walking around the room.

'Excuse me.' He puts his glasses on and his face becomes serious. He is standing by me, looking down at me, angry, 'You want to give up your femininity, you want to give up your sexuality, but you can't, you see, this is the most precious gift nature has given you?' His voice expands, gets louder, 'Give up and waste the most beautiful thing you have.'

'But I don't want it – this sexuality!' It's I who is shouting now. I am angry. 'It may be beautiful, but since I have no use for it, since it is hidden somewhere inside me, where even I can't find it, since I don't even know it, what good is it to me?'

'Hidden? You must be blind! It isn't hidden inside you, it's all over you! In the texture of your skin, in the curve of your hips, your legs, your neck! It's crying out. It isn't your sexuality that's hiding from you – it's you who is hiding from your sexuality, you even refuse to acknowledge it's very existence!'

It's the man who is shouting now, not the doctor. He goes slowly back to his seat.

'If you have chosen yourself a husband who has less sexual drive than you, who, as I understand it, is intimidated by your sexuality, do you think you should deny yourself the realisation of your very essence as a woman?'

There is a long silence. I have nothing to say. I feel terribly embarrassed and dare not look at him. His voice rises again; I am looking down, my sight blurred by tears:

'I am sorry. I shan't distress you any more. I have opened up enough, shall we say, closed doors for you today.'

There is a pause, but I still don't look up and he probably thinks that I haven't understood him.

'I have given you enough problems to think over.'

I nod and steal a glance at him. He is writing in his notepad.

'There is not much I can do for your low blood pressure. Lie down with your feet higher than your head for a few minutes, when you feel dizzy. Also, take three of these every day, try to feed yourself a little better, you are very underweight. I want to see you back here in three weeks. The tablets will help you calm down; you will find it easier to deal with your children, and also, think things over.'

He escorts me to the front door.

'It's easy for you doctor' I mumble 'you know all the answers ... I don't even know the right questions .... '

He taps my shoulder gently and I step out. I step out and ... I fall ... I am falling again, down the dark pit, I try to stop myself, hold on to something, but I continue to fall and spin down the pit. I panic, I open my eyes and I realise that my bed is being wheeled. I hear voices. I calm down. Oh, good, I wasn't falling down a pit, it's just that my bed is being wheeled away. This is nice. I know what is going on. I feel secure. Now I have to go on thinking.

They are in the process of ... I lose the thread for a moment.

That was a nice beginning of a thought, I must think on. Someone was … oh, yes, I was going to die … I was dying and someone was …. The piercing sound of the ambulance siren I remember hearing it. It was good that I remember something for sure, now I must put some kind of order in all these thoughts; I mustn't hurry, there is time. There is plenty of time. Someone had said that? Who? I don't remember, but it seems very long ago.

A voice interrupts my thoughts. I know it's a doctor's voice, I can't see him, although I am trying to. I know it's not my good doctor … no, no, it is my good doctor, I can discern the kindness in his voice. Has anyone spoken to you with kindness? It's so, good, so reassuring, to be spoken to with kindness.

'You mustn't worry, my child … you will find yourself. One fine morning you will wake up, and you will KNOW. You will see yourself in your true light. There will be no more clouds, everything will be clear and bright, and then, no one would be able to hurt you any longer, because you will know yourself. Not the girl you have been told you are – by your parents, husband, friends, people in general – but the true, real you, the one no one knows yet, not even you. Dry your eyes, child, such nice eyes …. '

I feel something wiping my face; a flannel probably, which I feel on my skin 'from afar'; a hand lifts my head.

'Here love, drink some of this. It's coffee, don't be afraid. It's good for you.'

I feel blinding light in my eyes, I squint, it hurts. I am aware of people standing around my bed. I can't see their faces, they are all wrapped in a cloud. I feel again 'from afar' that the covers have been lifted.

I feel a prick in my thigh. A voice says:

'It's just an injection. Don't worry.'

I want to tell them that I am not worried, that I trust them, but I feel a hand on my body. A cold examining hand. First on my sides, then my abdomen, then something smaller, a stethoscope, and colder; at the same time, something is being wrapped round my arm, I realise they are taking my blood pressure. I try to keep still because I am afraid that if I move, the room will capsize again, and I will feel that I am falling in the pit. I know there is no pit, I know it's just a feeling I have, but I don't want to feel it. So I keep still.

'I think she is going to make it.' someone says.

'Do you think there might be some brain damage?' someone else asks and I can't hear the answer, though I wanted to.

Brain damage? No! I can't allow that! If I am going to live, I will have to make use of my brain … if I have any …. Avi thought I didn't …. Yes, this is what happened, I meant to finish it all, I couldn't go on like this. I failed even that … I tried to make sure I am not found until morning. I took them all just as Avi had left for the cinema and … oh, I lost the thread again … what happened then … I must think! Oh, yes there it is, yes, he was going to come back and go to bed. He wouldn't have found it unusual for me to be asleep; he would not have realised until … the morning and by then …

'She is reacting to light.' someone said.

Like a KGB investigation. I thought. I found the thought humorous. I was very proud that I could think of something funny. I wanted to tell them about it and make them laugh, then the doctor, who was angry that they had woken him up because of me, in the night, might forgive me ….

'Take it easy, lie back and rest … ' somebody seems to bend over me.

'Pull the curtain …, ' a voice says, 'this light is too much for her.'

So, it's the sunlight, not an inquisitor's lamp! Ah, well, so much for my witticism.

'Your husband will pick you up later.' the voice said.

Avi? I feel a cold sweat all over my body. I mustn't think

about Avi now! The perspiration is oozing out, like water from a tap. I can't see him now! Not before I have put some order in my thoughts! I have to be in charge, in control, but Avi's voice, cold and disdainful imposes itself on my tired mind:

' ... I don't want you to come with me ... can't you understand that? You should consider yourself lucky that I talk to you every now and then. You liar. You slut! I know all about you ... don't think that I don't .... '

The words are not unfamiliar; they come from the back, they echo louder and louder in the labyrinth of my mind, hitting me harder and harder with each syllable until I can't take it any more.

And then, he had gone. He had gone to the cinema; he hadn't wanted me to go with him, nor had he wanted to speak to me. I wasn't worth bothering with. My parents thought the same, only they didn't use the same words to say it, but I knew.

There was nothing left. Nothing at all. All the people I cared for, I loved and needed, didn't love or need me. Nothing left for me to do but to end it all.

The children? Oh, I love my children! but what did they want with a person like me for a mother?

I went to the bathroom. I still remembered the pace, slow but there had been no hesitation. The decision had been taken and was going to be carried out. Of course, my parents would be upset. They always were when I did something without consulting them. Avi will be free of me; any woman with a little sense would love and appreciate those children. I was sure of it, I wasn't just a soppy mother. They are exceptional children; golden creatures who had not asked me to bring them to this world. Someone else might make this world a better place for them. I was inadequate. I could not imagine that my boys might miss me.

The tablets slid down three at a time. I stood on the bathroom floor, barefoot with the intention of going to bed as soon as I would have taken them all. Avi was sure not to suspect anything until morning, because we slept so far apart.

I remembered now how quickly I felt dizzy. On the third or fourth lot. It was incredible. I hurried to take them all, because otherwise it wouldn't work; and I hurried because I didn't want my children to wake up and find me ... they would be so frightened, and I didn't want them to be frightened.

The crystal clear thought faded away and I lost my thread again, I am in a state again, perhaps even crying; what was I thinking? Where was I? Suddenly I hear the siren, piercing the silence, the picture gets blurred, then I see my doctor's eyes and I hear his voice:

'It's a clear case of transfer of guilt. In psychiatry; when someone does something against his conscience, something he can't cope with, he transfers the guilt. In this case, the guilt is transferred to you ... lets face it, you are quite weak .... '

I blink, I try to understand.

'If he thinks those things are not right, why is he doing them?' I ask.

'Logic. There is no logic in some people's psyche. It's very complex. He is lying to you, he calls you a liar because he lies; he calls you a slut, because he thinks you are as easy as his affairs. And let's face it, to him, you are, aren't you?'

Oh, doctor ... I think ... oh, please spare one little corner of my mind, my soul, my pride! Must you hurt it all, lacerate it all?

He goes on, carefully:

'You love him too much, that's your problem ... '

'But why? Why? I am the only person in the world who loves him, he had no one, what is it that makes him hurt me so, me of all people?'

'You see, your love makes you vulnerable … and I am afraid, there definitely is a sadistic streak in him … and you provide an ideal outlet for this streak. I know I am hurting you, child, but this outlet, is more necessary to him than … your love.'

He has stopped talking. The last word was whispered, so as to hurt me less. It doesn't succeed. My heart feels swollen inside my chest and heavy. So heavy: my eyes are puffed and dry.

I think of Avi's steel cold eyes, of the smile forming slowly on his face when he has made me cry. On the 'bad days in the month', when he teases me. He teases and teases until I can't take it any longer, I cry, I plead then, irrationally, I scream and shout, and he follows me around the kitchen, the rooms, teasing, teasing. Then he says:

'You see, it's you who is mad. I don't need a headshrinker! It's you!' and he goes to the cinema.

Could I now put all this in cool, plausible order? Could I remember the actual words, in order to understand? Was it important? I feel my mind clear and lucid.

'You have been seen on Thursday of last week, at three o'clock in the afternoon on Allenby Street. Where were you going? What were you doing? Meeting someone?'

It's three o'clock in the morning, Avi has shaken me out of my sleep to tell me this. My heart begins to race now that I conjure up those thoughts. No, no, this is behind me now, it should stay there, I must concentrate on … I don't know, I have once more lost the thread and I am falling again, spinning, suddenly Avi's face bends over mine. I can see every muscle of his face twitch, like when he has a fit.

'What have you told him then? What have you told your doctor?'

He scares me, his voice is cold, his eyes freeze the blood in my veins.

'Nothing … '

'It can't be nothing, since he wants to talk to me! Why me? You scum, you dirty whore, what have you gone and told him?'

'I only … nothing bad … I wanted to find some help for … '

I take a pace back, and he advances towards me.

'I'll teach you nothing … ' his hand hits me before I have seen it rise.

I hear a loud buzzing sound and fall back. I don't seem to reach the ground, I fall … and fall … I try to stop myself, desperately …

'She seems to be responding better.' I hear a voice and stop falling. Good. I open my eyes and the room gets steady again. I feel a pain in my foot.

'It hurts.' I say but they don't understand my groan. 'It … hurts … ' I try to enunciate.

'Good! That's the idea,' a voice says, 'here, have some soup now, it will do you good.'

I can nearly see the nurse's features.

'You … are … very … kind.' I say slowly.

She feeds the soup to my mouth with fast precise gestures. I can feel it. I swallow the tasteless liquid with difficulty. My throat aches, and this reminds me of the tube that they stuck down it to wash out my stomach. I remember the tube, the suffocation, the cramp, the pain.

'Don't worry,' the nurse says, 'you won't be sick. You just feel you might be, but you won't.'

I feel tired.

'No! You mustn't sleep!' she slaps my cheeks. 'Come on, drink, I have other patients to see to. You must help me to help you. No one will help you if you don't help yourself.' I keep swallowing for a while, then she says, 'Your husband will come later for you. You have such a handsome husband, and you cause such trouble, you ought to be ashamed of yourself!'

Yes. I had forgotten that Avi was handsome. But beauty doesn't replace goodness. I know that now, I know it only too well, but why do people associate beauty with goodness so readily? Didn't they know that beauty can be very ugly? Oh, how ugly Avi was!

I feel my legs stuck together with perspiration. I dare not shut my eyes for fear of dizziness. I can focus more or less now. Through the window I see a little white cloud, lovely and free, playing a game with the wind up there, in the sky. My mother's voice emerges:

'... you are frivolous; what did you imagine marriage to be? Going out every night and dancing, and wearing fancy clothes? and did you not think when you wanted children that there were no responsibilities involved? That Avi will sit with you all day long, holding your hand?'

The little cloud, has sailed away from the piece of sky framed by the window.

'Another injection, I am afraid.' says the nurse. I can see her now, I can even help remove the bedclothes. The injection hurts. 'You felt that, didn't you?'

'Yes, I did.'

'Good, and I can understand better what you are saying. You are a strong girl, you must get hold of yourself, you have everything to live for.'

I smile. I feel tired from this conversation, but I realise the progress and I am pleased. Because now I have taken another decision: I wasn't going to fail my life. Not any longer; I had my children to live for. It was I who was going to open up the world for them, I and nobody else; just as soon as I have put my thoughts in order and understood the mess my life has been so far, after that, it would be easy to hold the reins. The nurse had said that I was a strong girl. She hadn't meant it that way, but I knew I was, and that I was going to make it. I had to, for myself and my children.

Chapter Three

Hard Facts

I don't know how long I stayed at the hospital. I counted two days. Had there been any during my unconsciousness? I didn't know. Avi came to pick me up. I was dressed and ready, sitting on my bed, waiting for him. I felt weak and still a little dizzy. Avi picked up my coat from the bed and took me by the thick of the arm to get me on my feet. He didn't say a word and his eyes avoided mine. Was he a little weary of me?

It was a pleasant, warm, evening. Avi had the Company car.

'Where are we going?' I asked when I realised he wasn't heading for home.

'To your parents!'

'How are the children?'

'They are fine.'

'Who is looking after them?'

'We found a woman. She is with them all day long, until I come home. Back at our place.'

'Why are we going to my parents' now?'

'You need looking after for a while.'

Avi looked straight ahead, as he drove, and I could observe him freely. I could see the curve round the mouth that made it sag, the occasional pressing of the jaws and the play of the muscles where the two jaws joined, the distant, cold eyes. Was this the man I had loved so, much?

I was breathless when we arrived at my parents'; climbing the two flights of stairs was too much for me. My father opened the door.

'Here, come in my love.' he led me by the arm, as Avi had done, towards the lounge. 'We have prepared your old bed in the lounge, your old settee. You can go straight to bed, if you want.'

As he spoke to me, I looked at him, trying to find some reaction to what had happened, but his eyes carefully avoided mine.

'Thank you, I will go to bed.' I said.

'Your night-dress is under the pillow,' shouted my mother from the kitchen, 'I am bringing your supper in.'

'I want to get undressed.' I said to the men in the room.

'Yes, sure!' My father went towards the door as though relieved to get away, 'Avi will help you.'

'I don't want any help, thank you. I can manage.' I stood by the bed waiting for them to leave. Avi followed my father and closed the door quietly behind him as they left.

I undressed slowly. Changing my position from vertical to horizontal made me feel dizzy again. I kept my eyes wide open to prevent the 'falling down the pit' feeling.

My mother came in with a tray. I hadn't seen her yet. I don't know whether I really expected something special from her, some expression of warmth, or compassion, I looked at her only to find that, she too, avoided looking me in the eyes.

'Here,' she said, 'eat it all. We will have you plumped up in no time.' She deposited the tray on my knees and left the room.

My diaphragm, felt tender and so did my stomach. My temples throbbing but no longer as painful as they had been. I ate as much as I could, then leant over to put the tray on the floor.

I lost balance, and nearly fell off the bed. They must have been just outside the room, because Avi was by my side before I had fallen, and straightened me up. I freed myself from his grip. He didn't react.

'Do you want to go to sleep now?'

'Yes, please.'

I was left alone.

For two weeks, trays were brought in to me and taken away. I was left 'to rest' and seldom did anybody stay in the room more than a few moments. Avi came to 'visit' me, a few times; he didn't stay long either. He went home, or to the cinema, or, somewhere. I only asked him about the children.

For two weeks, I saw my parents in slow motion; my mother – a plump ageing woman, preoccupied with her ailments; my father – a guilty husband, eager to please my mother. Did they know what had happened? If Avi hadn't told them, had they enquired? Had they asked him what was the matter with me? If they had, if they knew – they didn't mention anything to me during my stay there. They didn't ask me what had happened, they didn't ask me why it had happened.

Slowly, the dizziness disappeared; the pain in my diaphragm and stomach disappeared too, my appetite became healthier.

I could get up and lie down without falling 'into the pit' any longer and my mother was very tired of looking after me. I was told that I was well enough to go home and lucid as I had become in this short period of time, the truth became clear to me and hurt. It hurt more than the doctor's tube down my throat, more than anything else. My parents wanted me out of their patch again. Once more – someone else's responsibility.

Raoul and Rafi were a little shy of me at first; they ran to their room as I came in. I found the house clean. The woman was there, waiting for me to arrive. She had put flowers in the middle of the table in the kitchen to greet me and welcome me home; there was food in the fridge.

'Thank you for everything, specially for looking after my children.' I said.

'Don't mention it love, they are wonderful children, so well behaved. I have seen some children, I can tell you! God has blessed you with them. Are you well enough now? Can you look after them?'

'Oh, yes, I am.'

The woman left. I went into the children's room.

'Come on, give mummy a kiss!'

They remained shy, Raoul looked at his fingernails.

I was alive and another woman had looked after my children! Had I died, she would have stayed on, until Avi had brought home a real new mum.

I had thought that it wouldn't make much difference to them. Now I knew I had been wrong. They needed me, and I had a lot to give them. I was about to find it all in me, I knew it was there, and I would share it with them alone. There was nothing of me that I could share with Avi; not any longer.

I looked around and sighed. How drab everything was. A collection of Jerome's cast-offs. I will have to see to that.

I sat on the floor with the children where there were some cubes.

'What shall we build?' I asked.

'I built a bridge yesterday!'

'Can you do it again?'

'I think so.'

'Mummy, where have you been all this time?' asked Rafi.

'I was ill, not very ill, just a little, but I am a lot better now and I will never be ill again.'

'And never go away again?'

'No my darling, I will never go away again.' I took him in my arms and kissed him. Raoul was busy with the cubes. I noticed on the inside of the box a picture of the Walt Disney's Snow White and the seven Dwarfs with instructions to enlarge it and transfer it on a wall.

'Hey, look! I said, 'wouldn't this look nice on the wall?'

'Snow White and the seven Dwarfs?'

'Yes, how about it, shall we do it?'

'Can we?'

'Of course we can.'

We went out to buy gouaches and brushes, I also bought a newspaper; I wanted to look for a job.

Avi came home unusually early that day, went into the lounge/bedroom, stretched on the settee/double bed and read his paper. The children and I were busy tracing the squares on the wall, following the instructions. I noticed that I was involved with what we were doing and although I was aware of his presence next door, the urge which had tortured me all those years, to run to him hug him and kiss him, please him in some way or other, wasn't there. I felt relieved.

Eventually he came into the children's room.

'How about supper, I am hungry.' He then realised what we were doing. 'Your mother is the only woman I know, crazy enough to think of mucking about and spoiling a perfectly nice, clean wall!' and to me: 'You'll never come to your senses, you are hopeless!'

I didn't react to, his words.

'Come on children, let's wash our hands and have supper. We will continue tomorrow.

It was during this meal that I realised that Avi was the children's father, that I had no right to spoil or interfere with their love for him and least of all, I had no right to take him away from them.

'Where do you think you are going?' Avi shouted when he saw me dressed and ready to go out in the morning. The children had already gone to school.

'I have a few appointments for jobs.'

'I don't want you to go to work, do you hear? I forbid you!'

his finger pointed at me, his eyes flaring, angry and cold, left me unmoved.

'Don't expect me to help you in any way!' he went on when he didn't get a reply.

'I won't lift a finger to help you, you'll have to do everything, on your own.'

'I always have done.'

At night, I lay awake and proceeded with my thinking things out. More often than not, Avi wasn't there. He went to the cinema. I thought about my parents. My mother, forever ill, forever complaining, always my critic and judge. My father, obedient, the accommodating husband, jumping up to fulfil her command, shouted at like a deficient boy, guilty, pathetic. They claimed they did everything for me out of love, yet when I now thought and analysed my life and their influence in it, I found very few or none of their actions which I could safely classify as love-motivated.

It was all so complex. But I was sure of my feelings now. I had stopped fighting for my mother's love, for her approval. I had lost that desperate need for my father to 'talk' to me. I stopped loving Avi. I realised that I had loved an illusion. I had, for a long time, pretended that the illusion was there for me to love. It was time to face up to facts.

Raoul and I worked for a few days at the painting, Rafi made his contribution, since I insisted it was going to be the work of all three of us. Raoul, was an accomplished artist. He was imaginative and his paintings and drawings were a subject of much pride for me. The instructions on the box were easy to follow, the squares very clearly defined, but somehow, where I put my hand to it, it didn't come out right. I had often tried to paint, but for some reason, I never succeeded. No matter how much I tried, it never came out the way I saw it in my mind's eye. This time, it was the same, it simply didn't look right . Rafi, smaller but no less artistic, holding the brush in his left hand covered the design very adroitly. I looked at him, I knew he was left-handed because ever since he was a baby, he always reached with his left hand. I let him be. I was proud of my talented sons. So, not so much thanks to me, in the end, there was a lively mural on the wall of the children's room. We all loved the results of our labour.

Chapter Four

Head Against the Wind

I found a job. It was the only way to stay safe. I found a woman to do my work at home, get the children their lunch when they came home from school and wait for me until I came home from work. Half of my wages went to pay her, but it didn't matter. I informed Avi about it.

'If you go out to work, I am leaving this house.' he shouted.

I didn't answer.

'I am talking to you! Can't you hear, you scum!'

'You are shouting.'

'What do you expect? Whispers? I am leaving this place and that's that!' He was suffocating with anger.

I looked at him. How I would have worried a few weeks ago! How I would try to explain, to justify myself, how I would cry. Now, I didn't care, not any longer. I could look at him, and not worry. It was his turn to get worked up.

'Besides,' he went on, 'do your parents know about this? Have you told them?'

'Not yet, I haven't seen them.'

'I'll see what your mother will say when I tell her.'

'Avi, leave them out of it. I have taken a decision, and I am going to carry it out, no matter what anybody says. I will see to it that your meals are ready for you, that your shirts are ironed and that your suits are taken to the cleaners. Does this satisfy you?'

He was lost for words, but only for a moment.

'You slut! You call yourself a mother! You want to go and do as you please and leave the children in the street: I am leaving this house!'

I didn't answer.

'Did you hear me! I am leaving!' he was struggling for breath. 'But before I leave, I'll have to see what your father will say about it!'

He left, slamming the door. I went into the children's room. They were in their beds.

'I will go to work next week, children.' I sat on Raoul's bed. They had obviously heard the shouting and their ears were pricked up, their little faces worried. It pained me to see them, so young and already burdened with the unhappiness of the adults' world.

'There will be a lady, you will meet her soon, who will come here and clean, and cook, and do everything instead of me. You will like her, and you must promise to be nice to her, as she will be nice to you, and when I come home from work, I will be free and spend all the time with you! We will have games, and look at the homework, and I won't be busy all the time.'

'Why is daddy so angry?'

'Because he thinks it's wrong that I should go out to work.'

'Is it wrong, mummy?'

'It may be wrong, I don't know. Nothing is really right; it all depends who is looking at it, and how. For instance, do you remember last week, Raoul when you wanted to climb that tree in the park? And I told you, you might fall?'

'Yes.'

'You see, it seemed wrong to me, but you didn't think it was wrong and you wanted to climb it. It's more or less the same with me going to work. I get bored at home, all alone all day. Who knows, I might find work boring too, after a while, but I have to find out for myself, can you understand that?'

I heard the front door open. I kissed the children and left their room. I saw Avi walk in, followed by my father. I anticipated this. It was trouble of a kind I had experienced many times before. I was going to be put on trial. Avi was my prosecutor as usual, and my father – his and my mother's advocate. I was going to stand up to them. I had learned.

My father sat on the arm chair. I sat in the middle of the settee which felt like 'the dock'. Avi was pacing up and down, smoking nervously; the twitches on his face were a bad omen.

'Now,' he said, 'tell your daughter, if she wants to stay with me, if she wants to be my wife, she will have to do as she is told, you tell her!' My father looked ill at ease. He wasn't an old man then, but somehow, the way he sat, the way he held himself was that of an old, tired man. He wasn't looking into my eyes when he spoke to me:

'Is it true?' he asked. 'What Avi says, is it true?'

'Yes.'

'Why? Why my child? You were well brought up … we gave you a good education, we cared for you … as much as we could … why …? ' there were tears in his voice, but he wasn't crying. Something seemed wrong.

The doctor's words came back to me, a suspicion crept into my mind.

'What has he told you dad?'

'That you … that you have been … unfaithful …. ' I could see how the very uttering of the word hurt him, how his shoulders became narrower, how his wide forehead became moist.

And there hadn't been a shadow of a doubt in his poor mind that Avi was telling the truth! And he was my father! I felt sorry for him.

If one day one of my sons is accused of robbery or murder and he denies it, I will believe him, trust him no matter what anybody says.

A new thought came to my mind painful like a stab in the back. The thought had also been triggered by what the doctor had said: what if Avi wants a confession? Just one confession. To his subconscious, it would be, if I were to trust the doctor's judgement, like his own confession to me. And if I give him, a chance to forgive me it would be as though I had forgiven him. And that he had forgiven himself. Would that be it? Shall I risk it?

'Yes, dad.' the thoughts were lucid and clear, but I was crying again. The pain was almost unbearable.

Avi's finger was pointed at me, his hand slightly shaking:

'You see, you see, I told you!'

'I was very neglected … or at least I felt … ' I was crying desperately now, like I used to, like I had decided never to, again. But it was so difficult; it wasn't as clear cut as I had wanted it. ' … but,' I went on, ' … it was a long time ago … I will never do it again … ' I mopped my eyes, sobbed and sat there, determined not to say any more.

'So, you see,' Avi said to my father, victory in his voice, 'if she wants to be my wife, if she wants me to stay here – no pretence! She will have to do as she is told. I want this understood, here and now.'

'He is your husband …. ' my father said to me, looking awkwardly above my head, 'You have to, obey him, he is your husband, I have no say in the matter … '

I went over to him.

'Yes dad.'

I had thought it was going to be about my wanting to go out

to work. I wasn't crying any longer.

'I will, don't worry about me, I understand.'

I saw him to the door, went straight to the bathroom and got undressed there. I felt tired and went to my corner of the bed.

'So it's true.' Avi said in the darkness.

'What?'

'Your little escapade?'

'Did you really think there was one?'

'You didn't deny it, though, did you?

I realised that Avi was talking to me. He hadn't actually talked to me in years! How I would have been happy, only a few months ago, if he had addressed me in those terms, even on this painful subject!

It didn't matter now.

'I didn't deny it, because I knew that you didn't want me to deny it, in any case, it doesn't matter any longer.'

'It does matter! I am not going to put up with .... '

'Don't. In any case, I was under the impression that the whole problem tonight was about my going to work.'

He didn't answer. I wondered for a while whether the doctor had been right about him; I also wondered, whether at this stage, if he suddenly changed, if life became liveable, would I still want him? Would I accept him?

Chapter Five

Learning the Rules of the Game

The routine of going to work, mixing with the busy crowds in the morning, and coming back home in the afternoon, soon became a habit. The myth about office life that Avi had so successfully created for me, was soon dissipated. I was ready now to find out more. I rang Alex. I hadn't forgotten the night of the party, the electric impulses his kisses had sent all over me, now I wanted to experience the whole process.

'You! At last you made your mind up!' his breath became short as soon as I had said my name.

'Yes.'

'When? You say when, and leave the rest to me; it has to be in middle of the day.'

'Tomorrow at three in the afternoon?'

'Yes. I'll pick you up at your office.'

'How do you know where I work?'

'I made it my business to know. I was going to ring you if you hadn't. See you tomorrow.'

'See you.'

'Uuummmmmuuuuhhhh...' he made a noise in the telephone, resembling that of a man who hasn't eaten for three days and who has just seen his favourite dish on the table. I put the receiver down, feeling a slight distaste for the whole thing, but my curiosity was greater; I was going to go through with it.

I asked my boss for two hours to go to the dentist. He agreed. It was so easy. Alex's large American car sailed round the corner at precisely three o'clock. I didn't know his car, and it wasn't until the door opened and I saw him through the windscreen, that I realised it was him. He was leaning over, holding the passenger door open for me to get in.

'Hullo baby! Get in, let's get going before anyone sees us!'

I sat on the soft leather seat. It was very luxurious. Alex took my hand and fondled it, handling the steering wheel with one hand. There was no electricity passing between us, his grip hurt my fingers rather than exciting me.

'Can you drive?' he asked 'Do you want me to teach you?'

'I'd love to learn yes, but not now.'

'OK baby , I'll teach you. I'll teach you many things!'

'Where are we going?' I noticed that we were heading out of town.

'A motel. I have booked a bungalow.'

So, I thought, this is how these things are done.

'Impressed?' he asked. He was looking for appreciation, for recognition; I knew the feeling too well.

'Yes, very!' I put as much enthusiasm into my words as I could muster.

'We will be comfortable there. It's very luxurious and expensive, but it's worth it.'

'Do you want me to participate in the exp … '

'Of course not! What an idea: I didn't mean it that way, you little chick! In any case, women usually want money, they don't give it! No, we will enjoy ourselves … I long for you … oh, you have been in my dreams, in my mind all the time … ,' he was squeezing my hand, 'I have been so jealous of Avi! You … that he should have you, you have a figure … the way you move … you drive me mad!'

'You are flattering me … ' I said carefully, thinking that his outburst was rather distasteful, also I had to admit that it seemed that he was following a set pattern of behaviour, and that, perhaps, the same was expected of me. I wasn't familiar with it, I felt that I should call the whole thing off. I wasn't in love with him … how could I pretend? I remembered his wife.

'Surely, your wife is a good looking woman?'

'But,' he looked at me sideways, 'she is my wife.'

I tried to ascertain from his expression whether or not he was serious and he was! Surely … I was Avi's wife … he could see that? Then, looking at his tense features, I realised that he didn't.

'Isn't it lovely,' I changed the subject, 'I love the spring.'

'Yes. It's the time of year when everything wakes up, comes to life; the beast in me wakes up too!' He squeezed my hand again, 'That's what you want, don't you, the beast in me!'

I freed my hand and massaged my fingers. He must have noticed.

'Sorry baby, did I hurt you? I get carried away … you see … you drive me mad …. '

He was working himself up into a state verging on the farcical.

'Here we are at last! Ooohh, I can't wait.' He flew out of the car and through the swing doors into the office from where he emerged a few seconds later, a set of keys in his hand. He drove on and stopped outside one of the bungalows. He came round to open my door, locked the car and, his brief case in his hand, let us into the bungalow.

I found myself in the semi-darkness of a large air-conditioned room. The curtains were drawn and the blinds shut. It was decorated in blue-green. There was an enormous bed. To the left along the wall was a rosewood chest above which was a long mirror. Alongside the bed, also in rosewood, there were built in cupboards. Alex opened one of them. It was a small fridge! He took a bottle of Martini out of his brief case, ice cubes from the fridge and poured out the drinks. He even had a lemon in his brief case; he sliced that, and put a slice in each of the glasses. It was done quickly, efficiently. He seemed to have done this many times before.

'Cheers!' I said, 'You are very well organised.'

He took a sip and sighed, put his glass down and before I knew what was happening I was on the bed; Alex was on top of me panting, his fast, hot breath, tinged with the smell of pickled herrings, straight in my face. I struggled for breath as he kissed me;

'Oh … oh … you … you … your curves have been haunting … me … ' he was talking in between the kisses, his hands tearing at the buttons of my blouse, fondling my breasts.

I felt nothing. I made one attempt to try and stop him, and tell him to 'take me in', but I soon gave up, it seemed that he wasn't aware of my presence! He just carried on, transfixed by his own passion. He unbuttoned his trousers, then pulled and tore wildly at my skirt, pushed himself against me once, twice then had a few tremors and fell like a huge, mortally wounded animal, on me. I was totally immobilised under him. I was lucky I could breathe.

'Oh … ' he sighed 'you are too beautiful … '

I pushed him away. He reached for a cigarette:

'I am sorry I was so quick baby, but just you wait, the second time will be for you … I will give you such pleasure … '

I got up.

'I have to go now.'

'No! So soon?'

Did I detect a slight relief in his voice?

'Yes, it's time for me to go.'

'As you wish baby.'

He got up rather more readily than his words had suggested he would. The doctor's words came to my mind: ' … the failure of the one night stands are easier to explain … '

'Have another drink before we go.' Alex offered.

'No thank you, let's go.'

He squeezed the cigarette into the ashtray and buttoned up his trousers. I adjusted my clothes, combed my hair. He hadn't even taken my pants off.

'I can't take you home love, it's too dangerous. We mustn't be seen together.'

'That's all right, I'll get on a bus.'

He dropped me near my office.

It was still early; I could get on a bus and be home before the rush hour. Instead, I took a walk, down towards the sea-front. I felt awful. I felt cheated, and I felt a cheat, myself Not that it mattered any longer, but the feeling was still there I knew that 'thing' existed somewhere inside me. The 'thing' the doctor had called my sexuality. I had experienced bits of it on occasions. Now I knew Avi couldn't help me find it, I also knew it was impossible to get to know it, all by myself.

The sea was indigo-blue and calm, so calm! There was hardly a ripple. The waves crept quietly one after the other, barely furrowing the surface. The question was: was I a 'loose' woman, merely because I thought about it? I wanted to find it? to experience *it*? Would it be the right thing to do if I tried to forget about it, to ignore it? Something that my mother would approve of. Or should I listen to the doctor? Was he right? Should I search for it, and 'realise' it? would that make me happier? more complete? But how many more trials would I have to make before I found it? Was there a way of knowing, before, to avoid this awful feeling of waste, of emptiness, of loneliness I experienced today?

Chapter Six

Private Experience

I went home. I played with the children, a little absent-minded. I looked at Avi over dinner. Was this what he felt each time he lied to me? I knew I couldn't do it before, when it mattered, when Avi mattered, and now, now that he didn't matter any more, I still felt so guilty. Did that mean that I hadn't mattered to him, not for a long time? And that, that was why he could do it? How awful. How pitiful I must have seemed to him, loving him as I did. So overtly, so totally, so submissively so abjectly. And he had a life of his own all the while, in which I played no role, in which I didn't matter. How awful! How humiliating!

In my corner of the bed again. I curled up, trying to put as much distance between us as I could. Then, Avi made a gesture. He put his hand out and rested it on my shoulder. For a moment, a very brief moment, I felt a little cramp in my groin. I checked myself. I didn't move. If he wanted me, now, he had to make more than one gesture. He had to talk to me. Avi pulled me a little towards himself. I didn't resist but I didn't help either. I so wanted him to say something, a word of endearment, a word of regret. I was praying that he should slide his hand down my back and that I would feel wanted, desired, that I would experience it, finally! I felt lit up, my insides pulsating. But he didn't move. He was used to my immediate response, and I could not do it. I could not go through another failure with him. Not ever.

He withdrew his hand from my shoulder without a word. He turned away and soon I heard his even breath. He was asleep. I stretched out now and lay on my back feeling sorry for myself. Tears of frustration ran down my cheeks and because of the way I was lying they filled my ears and then spilled onto the pillow. It felt uncomfortable; I dried my ears, reminding myself that I had promised never to cry again.

Then, I fell asleep.

Ж

I felt him penetrate me. I felt his hand gently parting my legs, I felt his hand caress my cheek, his mouth kiss my shoulder. He was doing everything slowly, very slowly. He wasn't heavy on me; I hugged him, and kissed him and I felt his whole body, his whole being, wanting me. I heard his whispers in my ear, but I couldn't tell what he was saying. I felt the pulsating waves invading my whole being. Nothing else existed, nothing else mattered, but our two beings, our motion inside each other, our hands touching, our lips – kissing.

Then came the explosion. Everything blew up – inside me, around me. I hung onto him as I felt the climax coming up, he moved once more and again, and I felt, for a moment, that I was going to lose consciousness. Slowly, then, I relaxed, fell back, catching my breath, coming back to reality from the magic world of orgasm.

I woke up. I was bathing in my own perspiration. Avi was peacefully asleep next to me. There was no one there. I got up; my legs hardly bore the weight of my body. I was shaking from the experience. I poured myself some water and slowly drank it. Who was it? I thought I hadn't seen the man's face! I didn't know who it was! And slowly, as I calmed down I realised that it didn't really matter, not now, not this time. But I knew now what it was. I had experienced it, somehow. I went back to bed; my limbs felt heavy but an unfamiliar peace had invaded the whole of my being. And again, I cried. I cried because I had found out something about myself I hadn't known existed, I cried because of the way I had found it out, I cried because I knew now that it wasn't imaginary – that it was there, that it had always been there, and no matter what anybody said: it wasn't bad – and for that alone, it had been worth finding out about it the way I had.

In the morning, I woke up refreshed from a deep sleep. My body felt happy, and my mind preoccupied with the night's experience.

At work, I was light-headed; my boss had to address me a few times before he got an answer and all the while, I didn't know whether I was utterly happy, or utterly miserable and lonely.

Chapter Seven

My Life in My Hands

I came out of this state of semi-torpor when I arrived home to find that Rebecca hadn't come at all, that the children had let themselves in and were fighting in their room; there were no telephones in those days. The beds were not made and the children hadn't had their tea. I prepared a light meal for them with what I found in the fridge and went out to do some shopping for dinner.

Avi found me in the kitchen, cooking.

'What's going on here?' he asked me but the children ran towards him to greet him and ask for their kiss.

'Daddy, daddy! Rebecca didn't come today and mummy made us our tea!' Avi sent the children to their room and turned to me again:

'What happened?'

'You can see what has happened. Rebecca hasn't been here. I don't know why. Dinner will be ready in time.'

'Do you mean to say that you left home before Rebecca arrived? That the children came to an empty home and were on their own, hungry?'

'Come on, Avi it's the first time; I am sure it's for a good reason. She is a responsible person; besides the children were alone for just one hour.'

'Just one hour! What kind of a mother are you! Wait until I tell your mother, see what she'll have to say to this!'

He stopped to catch his breath, 'You are not going to work any longer, do you understand? Or I am leaving!'

I looked at him. His face was flushed, twitching. I felt nothing.

'Did you hear me! I am talking to you, or have you gone deaf?'

'I heard you.'

'Well?'

'Well, what?'

'Are you or are you not going to stop working?'

'I am not.'

Avi's breath became shorter.

'I … I am leaving this place! Yes … I am leaving! You … you are … '

I stopped doing whatever it was that I had been doing throughout, and looked at him again. I felt nothing for him. How easy it was, I thought, when you didn't care. Was this why he had had the power to drive me out of my mind? Because he hadn't cared? How awful if this were true. That I should have loved him so much, cared so much, while he hadn't. And, I admitted to myself, I had persisted in believing that despite his aggression, his irrational accusations, in a strange way, in his own way, he had loved me.

'All right, Avi.' I said calmly 'if that's what you want.'

“What … what do you mean?'

'I am not going to stop working. I am even going to look for a more satisfying, better paid job. If you disapprove … '

'I am leaving! And I will tell your mother! She won't tolerate the way you neglect the children! She loves them, she cares for them! She might talk some sense into your stupid head.'

'I am sorry you disagree with me. Stupid or not, it is my head, and you are perfectly right, you don't have to put up with it. Let's go to the Rabbinate tomorrow and register for a divorce.'

'Yes! that's what we will do, tomorrow!' Avi shouted, as though sorry he hadn't said it before me.

There was a job advertised in the paper, where no typing or shorthand were involved; the applicant had to 'have a pleasant personality and speak at least three European languages'. I applied and received a letter summoning me for an interview within a few days. I was confident of my French and Russian, I spoke some Spanish and I had spent my free time learning English. I thought I might stand a chance.

Avi arrived at the Rabbinate punctually at eleven. We went into the office and applied for a divorce by mutual consent. We were given three months at the end of which, if a reconciliation hadn't occurred a date would be fixed for a hearing. At that hearing, we had to convince the judges that cohabitation was impossible and that our plan for the future of the children satisfied them. A divorce would be granted there and then.

'Would you like to have a cup of coffee?' Avi asked me when we left the Rabbinate. He hadn't addressed me like that for years.

'Yes.'

He held the door for me as we walked into a nearby coffee shop. He ordered two cappuccinos and some cakes.

'Are you hungry? Perhaps you prefer a sandwich?'

Tears pushed their way out and I blinked to conceal them. Why? Why now? He had never, not in years asked me how I was, or how I felt, or was I tired, happy or unhappy, hungry or otherwise … why this tone now? I nearly spoke; I nearly expressed a hope, but something stopped me. Was it my pride which had been knocked too much for too long?

'No, thank you. I've got to get back to the office.'

'As you wish.'

The Company car was parked outside.

'I'll give you a lift to your office.' Avi said.

I sat on the passenger seat and thought: 'oh, Avi, if only our nightmare of a life together could turn into ... this ... that's all it would take ... just this tone, just this little bit of care ... of attention ... ' I was hoping that he was noticing the change too; that perhaps he would say something. I had tried so many times; I had failed so miserably.

'See you later.' Avi said as I got off.

'Yes, see you.'

I popped in to see my parents on my way home. My mother opened the door:

'Well, well, you remember us! Your bus passes outside our door, outside! and you pass by not even thinking of coming in to see whether we are dead or alive!'

'I am sorry mum, but I have to take over from Rebecca. She has a home to go to as well.' I kissed her cheek rather reluctantly, 'How are you?'

'Do you really care?'

'Oh, mum, please! You know I do.'

'No you don't. Other women's daughters can't spend a day without seeing their mothers, but not my daughter. All she is interested in, is that stupid job, and Avi tells me that what you earn is not even enough to pay Rebecca!'

I didn't tell my parents about our visit to the Rabbinate and I asked Avi not to tell them. To my great surprise he didn't. That was, once again, inconsistent. Before, he would have done it, if only to spite me.

The days passed quickly, and with each passing day, I became more and more certain of my feelings. I was less afraid of the future. I felt I could tackle it. The divorce was irrevocable.

I went for the job interview. It was late afternoon, and I asked Rebecca to make arrangements to stay until I came back.

Ж

The man sitting behind a huge semi-circular desk was the proprietor of a well known chain of book shops. He had a round face, pink cheeks, and sparkling blue eyes. He was probably well over sixty, but his eyes were petulant and his smile cheeky.

'Sit down,' he motioned to a chair facing him, across the desk, 'let me tell you about the job. We sell books. Do you like books? I need somebody who likes books, who is prepared to work hard and learn the trade. I don't want any previous experience because I want you to learn how I conduct my empire .... This,' and he made a wide sweeping gesture with his arm, 'is my empire. We sell books, mainly in English, but we have a large French section, as well as Spanish and German. We have the best selection of Art books. Do you like Art? And we sell Law books. Our main shop is in Tel Aviv; this is where the heart of the empire beats, this is where you would be learning about it. This will take, I estimate, three months. If I find you suitable, at the end of three months, I have plans for you, which I will tell you about later. Now, who are you?'

He had spoken in one breath. He hadn't stopped to allow me to answer any of the questions his speech contained, but I made a mental note and was going to answer them all. Whilst speaking, his eyes were scrutinising me and his thoughts were split between his speech and a thorough appraisal of my person. He didn't give any indication as to what the result of his appraisal was.

'I was born In Bulgaria. I went to a French school, therefore my French is very good ... '

'Only very good?' he interrupted.

'No; excellent.'

'Don't be unnecessarily modest. It doesn't pay. Go on.'

'I have an extensive knowledge of European literature; I am fluent, apart from French and of course Bulgarian, in Russian, Spanish and English. I have two children aged ten and seven. I have a very reliable lady working for me and therefore I am not likely to miss work because I am a mother, except of course, if there is something very seriously wrong. I love books. I love Art and I would very much like to work with books.'

'Do you have a job now?'

'Yes.'

'Why are you looking for another job then?'

'I need a more satisfying job than the one I have now, both financially and intellectually.' In my hurry to answer, I hadn't noticed that he had addressed me in Russian.

'But you speak Russian.' I said to him.

'I was born in Moscow. I graduated at Moscow university before the Revolution, my little one!'

The Russian language lends itself very well to endearments, and it was very pleasant to hear his informal address.

'How lovely! I love Russian, but I haven't spoken for a long time, it's a little rusty.'

'You speak quite a few languages, don't you? Tell me,' he went on before I could answer 'why do you want a better paid job?'

'Because I am in the process of divorcing, and I don't want my children to want for anything.'

'Divorcing? This is quite a step to take, with two little children. Surely your husband will have to support you.'

'I don't want him to support me. Perhaps he would help out with the children: clothes, etc., but not me.'

He looked at me. A short penetrating glance.

'Do you know which book is top on the best sellers' list this month?'

I didn't have a clue. I looked around; the desk was littered with books, piles and piles; some tied with a string, some still in brown paper. A large hard-cover book seemed to be predominant among the others. I glimpsed at the title.

'Isn't it Michener's ... '

'The Source, that's right. Good. Well, my girl, if you are as good as I think you are, I will make you the manageress of a small bookshop I am opening in one of the large new Tel Aviv hotels; how does this strike you?'

'It would be wonderful!'

'It also is hard work.'

'I am not afraid of hard work.'

'How soon can you start?'

'I have to give notice ... I can't leave my present boss in the lurch .... '

'Good, I like that. You are loyal. Are you loyal?'

'Yes, I am.'

'Good. I will see you on the first day of next month, at 8.30 am, at my main shop in town.'

'Yes, thank you.'

'Good bye now.'

'Good bye, sir.'

I walked quickly out. I wanted to get home and free Rebecca.

A warm breeze met me in the Street. Dusk was already falling over the roofs. I sped towards the bus stop when a shop window attracted my attention. I stopped and looked. It had mirrors. Mirrors everywhere. They were positioned in such a way, that no matter where I looked, I saw my face from all possible angles. I looked at each and every one of them, taking my time. When I looked at the one showing me my face, full on, I pulled my tongue at the reflection. It wasn't such a bad face after all. The eyes were smiling and the cheeks had a pink roundness I hadn't realised they had. Yes, not such a bad face after all. 'Yes, my dear Bambo' I thought to myself, 'you will become someone else's responsibility, and not before time too – your own!'

And I sped home.